ELEMENTS OF HYPERSONIC AERODYNAMICS

Flow past a blunted cone of 30° total angle at $M_1 = 10 \cdot 4$, $\mathrm{Re}_d = 2 \cdot 6 \times 10^5$

ELEMENTS OF HYPERSONIC AERODYNAMICS

R. N. COX
Ph.D., M.A., B.Sc.

*Royal Armament Research and Development Establishment,
Fort Halstead*

L. F. CRABTREE
Ph.D., B.Sc., D.I.C., A.F.R.Ae.S.

*Royal Aircraft Establishment,
Farnborough*

1965

ACADEMIC PRESS · NEW YORK · LONDON

Academic Press Inc.
111 Fifth Avenue
New York, New York 10003

Library of Congress Catalog
Card Number: 64—8218

Printed in Great Britain

ERRATA

Page 10   *Fig. 9 Legend:* 300,000 should read 200,000

Page 13   *Table 2, $\rho/\rho_{s.l.}$:* 10^{-1}, 10^{-2}, 10^{-5}, 10^{-7} should read 10^{-2}, 10^{-4}, 10^{-6}, 10^{-9}

Page 23   *Fig. 1.2:* Mach numbers 2, 3, 4 and 5 on lower axis should read 5, 10, 15 and 20

On second curve M_2 should read M_{n_2}

Page 40   *Equation (2.10c):* $\dfrac{2}{\gamma + 1}$ should read $\dfrac{2}{\gamma + 1} \sin^2 \beta$

Equation (2.10d): $\dfrac{2}{\gamma + 1} \tan \beta$ should read $\dfrac{\sin 2\beta}{\gamma + 1}$

Page 46   *Equation (2.13):* should read

$$\frac{\partial}{\partial \tilde{x}} \left(\frac{\tilde{p}}{\tilde{\rho}^\gamma} \right) + \tilde{v} \frac{\partial}{\partial \tilde{y}} \left(\frac{\tilde{p}}{\tilde{\rho}^\gamma} \right) + \tilde{w} \frac{\partial}{\partial \tilde{z}} \left(\frac{\tilde{p}}{\tilde{\rho}^\gamma} \right) = 0$$

Equation (2.15d): should read

$$v = \frac{2}{\gamma + 1} \left\{ \left(\frac{d\tilde{r}}{d\tilde{x}} \right)^2 - \frac{1}{M_1{}^2 \tau^2} \right\} \left(\frac{d\tilde{r}}{d\tilde{x}} \right)^{-1}$$

Page 46   *Line 14:* $d\tilde{r}/dx$ should read $d\tilde{r}/d\tilde{x}$

Page 48   *2.3.2. Line 4:* $\tilde{x} = \tilde{x} - \tilde{\imath}$ should read $\tilde{\tilde{x}} = \tilde{x} - \tilde{\imath}$

Page 49   *2.3.3. Line 2:* $\gtrsim$ should read $\geq$

Insert 'low' between 'at' and 'supersonic'

Line 4: τ should read τ^2

Page 54   *Line 15:* p should read $\tilde{\tilde{p}}$

Page 71   *Equation (3.4):*

$$\left(\frac{\gamma + 1}{2} M_1{}^2 \right)^{\frac{1}{\gamma - 1}} \text{ should read } \left(\frac{\gamma + 1}{2} M_1{}^2 \right)^{\frac{\gamma}{\gamma - 1}}$$

Line 7: 2.50 should read 2.33

Equations (3.5) and (3.6):

$\dfrac{\sin \theta}{2}$ should read $\sin \theta$

Page 92   *Line 5:* delete s/v

Page 107 *Fig. 4.15:* lower axis $\dfrac{C_p}{\delta^2}$ should read $\dfrac{C_D}{\delta^2}$

Page 111 *Line 10:* 'the flow was' should read 'the flare was'

Page 112 *Line 14:* yy' should read yy''

Line 16: rr' should read rr''

Page 113 *Equation (4.32b):* p should read $\tilde{p}$

Page 115 *Equation (4.35c):* r should read $\tilde{r}$

Page 116 *Line 9:* $\dfrac{\partial f(\eta)}{\partial r}$ should read $\dfrac{\partial f(\eta)}{\partial \tilde{r}}$

Page 124 *Table: for $m = \frac{4}{7}$:* (x/l) should read $(x/l)^{\frac{6}{7}}$

Page 129 *Equation (5.3a):* should read

$$y_s = 2^{\frac{1}{5}} f_1(\gamma) \left(\frac{\bar{E}}{\rho_1} \right)^{\frac{1}{5}} t^{\frac{2}{5}}$$

Page 129   *Equation (5.3b) :* should read

$$r_s = \left(\frac{8}{\pi}\right)^{\frac{1}{4}} f_2(\gamma) \left(\frac{\bar{E}}{\rho_1}\right)^{\frac{1}{4}} t^{\frac{1}{2}}$$

Equation (5.4a) : Delete $2^{\frac{1}{2}}$

Equation (5.4b) : Delete $2^{\frac{1}{4}}$

Equation (5.5a) : should read

$$C_{D_N} = \frac{D_N}{\frac{1}{2}\gamma M_1{}^2 d_N p_1}$$

Page 130   *Equation (5.5b) :* should read

$$C_{D_N} = \frac{D_N}{\frac{1}{2}\gamma M_1{}^2 \frac{\pi}{4} d_N{}^2 p_1}$$

Page 142   *Line 1 :* $_e\bar{v}$ should read $\bar{v}_e$

          Line 13 : V should read V_1

          Equation (5.29) :

$$\int_v \frac{p_0}{\gamma - 1} \, dv \text{ should read } \int_{v_s} \frac{p_1}{\gamma - 1} \, dv$$

Page 143   *Equation (5.30) :*

$$\int_{v - v_0} \text{ should read } \int_{v_s - v_0}$$

          Line 7 : 'surface area of the piston' should read 'effective surface area of the shock layer'

Page 143   *Line 13 :* $v = y_s$ should read $v_s = y_s$

          Equation (5.35) :

$$\tfrac{1}{2}\rho_1 y \left(\frac{2}{\gamma + 1} y_s\right)^2 \text{ should read } \tfrac{1}{2}\rho_1 y_s \left(\frac{2}{\gamma + 1} \dot{y}_s\right)^2$$

Page 144   *Figure 5.9 :*

$$\frac{2}{C_{D_N}} \theta_w{}^2 \left(\frac{x}{d_N}\right) \text{ should read } \frac{2}{C_{D_N}} \theta_w{}^3 \left(\frac{x}{d_N}\right)$$

Page 145   *Line 8 :* delete $E \to 0$

          Equation (5.42) : should read

$$\frac{C p_w}{\theta_w{}^2} = \frac{p_w}{\frac{1}{2}\rho_1 V_1{}^2} = \frac{4}{\gamma + 1} \frac{d}{dt} (\bar{y}_s \cdot \dot{\bar{y}}_s)$$

Page 148   *Equation (5.45) :* should read

$$\frac{D_N}{2} = \int_{y_b}^{y_s} \left\{ \left(\frac{p}{\gamma - 1}\right) + \frac{\rho v^2}{2} \right\} dy - \frac{p_1}{\gamma - 1} y_s - \int_0^x p_b y'{}_b \, dx \simeq \frac{p_e}{\gamma - 1} (y_e - y_b)$$

          Equation (5.46) : delete $D_N = \dfrac{1}{\gamma - 1}$

Page 149   *Fig. 5.12a :*

$$\frac{\theta_w}{\epsilon C_{D_N}} \left(\frac{y_s}{d_N}\right) \text{ should read } \frac{\theta_w{}^2}{\epsilon C_{D_N}} \left(\frac{y_s}{d_N}\right)$$

Page 168   *Equation (7.2) :* should read

$$\text{Pé} = \frac{\rho C_p l U_1}{K}$$

Page 201   *Line 22 :* 5.46 should read 5.45

          Line 23 : delete (5.47)

PREFACE

In recent years there has been a considerable emphasis on the aerodynamics of vehicles flying at speeds which are many times the speed of sound. Although the subject is still developing, it nevertheless seemed to the authors that sufficient progress had been made to be able to attempt to view the field of hypersonic aerodynamics as a whole, and to discuss the relative importance of the different theoretical principles and methods which have been developed. Existing works on hypersonic aerodynamics already include two classics—*Hypersonic Flow Theory* by W. D. Hayes and R. F. Probstein, and the Russian volume by G. G. Chernyi (translated by R. F. Probstein) *Introduction to Hypersonic Flow*. In view of these it might appear presumptuous to add yet another account of the subject. It was felt, however, that sufficient new work had appeared since they were published— particularly on the nature of the flows past blunt-nosed slender bodies —to be able to give a more complete and balanced account of the hypersonic flow past bodies of practical interest than was possible a few years ago.

The present volume, which is intended as an introduction to the subject of hypersonic aerodynamics for, say, a post-graduate course, is divided for convenience into two parts, of which the first deals with inviscid perfect gas flows, and the second with real gas effects, with the hypersonic boundary layer, and with low density flows. Although the separate treatment of inviscid flows implies the separation of the flow field into an outer inviscid flow and an inner region where viscous effects become important (the thin boundary layer concept of Prandtl), it must be noted that in hypersonic flow the shock is closer to the body than in supersonic flow, the boundary layer is thicker, and, at the same time, the shock is often curved so that vorticity is present in the external flow. Thus the division into viscous and inviscid flow regions can no longer be taken for granted, and the important subject of the interaction between the boundary layer and the outer flow, and the effect of the external vorticity are considered in Part II.

In Part I an attempt has been made to distinguish between general similarity principles and simplified flow models such as Newtonian flow, and the actual theoretical methods which may be employed to calculate the flow field round given forms of body. At the same time comparison has been made with the relatively small number of experiments which are available—a state of affairs which reflects the difficulties of obtaining high-Mach, high-Reynolds-number flows in the laboratory.

Part II deals with those fields in which developments are taking place most rapidly and an enormous amount of research is in progress at the present time. Rather than attempting to provide a definitive treatment of these subjects, therefore, we have tried to give an up-to-date and coherent survey with a large number of references. However, since the book was effectively written in 1962–63 there are inevitably some aspects in which the treatment is already outdated to some extent.

It is regretted that limitations of space made it necessary to exclude discussions of experimental hypersonic facilities and magnetohydro-dynamics. Several surveys of both these topics are available in the literature, and the proceedings of regular conferences such as the Denver Symposia on Hypervelocity Techniques and the Symposia on Engineering Aspects of Magnetohydrodynamics (the 5th Symposium was held at M.I.T. in April, 1964) give the latest information.

The division of the volume into two parts also corresponds to a division of labour on the part of the authors and, although every attempt has been made to achieve uniformity, this accounts for some differences of style and treatment in the two parts. Thus, the first author undertook to write the inviscid flow chapters, and the second author the remaining chapters; it must, however, be emphasised that many joint discussions took place both between the authors and with their colleagues at R.A.R.D.E. and R.A.E. and that the complete volume is a joint responsibility.

The writing of such a text makes a considerable demand on the time of the authors, and we wish to acknowledge the support given by the Ministry of Aviation and the War Office. At the same time the authors wish to thank their colleagues for their willingness to discuss the many points raised, and for reading the manuscript. In particular we wish to record the help given by Dr. J. W. Maccoll, D. S. Butler, F. E. Mauger, and F. Smith at R.A.R.D.E., and by K. W. Mangler and B. A. Woods among many others at R.A.E. N. B. Wood of R.A.R.D.E. played a special part in correcting the manuscript of Part I, and to him special thanks are due. The first part of the book has served also as a basis for a course of lectures which the first author gave at the Faculté des Sciences of Marseille University in the summer of 1963, and he wishes to acknowledge the many helpful comments made by Prof. J. Valensi of the Institut de Mécanique des Fluides.

The authors wish, too, to acknowledge the permission given by various authors, organisations and journals to include previously published material. In particular, permission has been received from the Controller, H.M. Stationery Office to reproduce Figures 3.5 (b), 4.18 (c), 6.2, 7.2, 7.4, and 8.3, which are Crown copyright reserved.

CONTENTS

CHAPTER 8
BOUNDARY LAYER INTERACTION WITH THE EXTERNAL FLOW

CHAPTER 9
LOW DENSITY EFFECTS

LIST OF SYMBOLS

a speed of sound

A area, or area ratio

Æ   aspect ratio

b wing span

B bluntness parameter (equation 3.7)

C constant in linear viscosity-temperature relationship (equation 7.23)

c_p specific heat at constant pressure

c_v specific heat at constant volume

c_f skin friction coefficient (equation 7.30)

C_D drag coefficient

C_{D_N} nose-drag coefficient

C_L lift coefficient

C_M pitching-moment coefficient

C_N normal force coefficient

C_p pressure coefficient

d, D body diameter

d_N nose diameter

D_{12} binary diffusion coefficient (Section 7.6)

D drag

D_N nose drag

$\bar{E}$ energy density due to passage of blunt nose (Section 5.2)

f, g, h non-dimensional radial velocity, pressure and density (Chapter 4.6)

f number of active degrees of freedom (Chapter 6)

f reduced stream function (equation 7.26)

g reduced total enthalpy (equation 7.27)

h specific enthalpy

H total enthalpy (equation 7.13)

$\bar{I}$ transverse impulse per unit width or angle due to normal force (Section 5.2)

k thermal conductivity

K_1 $M_1 \sin \alpha$, similarity parameter (Section 2.3.6)

K_2 $\dfrac{d}{l} \cot \alpha$, similarity parameter (Section 2.3.6)

Kn   Knudsen number, λ/l

l characteristic length

l_x, l_y, l_z direction cosines of normal to body surface

L lift

Le	Lewis number (equation 7.36)
m	index of power-law body shape
M	Mach number
N	normal force
N	Newtonian flow parameter (Section 4.5)
p	pressure
Pe	Péclet number (equation 7.2)
Pr	Prandtl number (equation 7.1)
q	dynamic pressure, $\frac{1}{2}\rho U^2$
q	heat transfer rate (equation 7.17)
r, R	radius
R	gas constant
Re	Reynolds number
$\mathfrak{R}_s, \mathfrak{R}_v$	shock and shear layer reflection coefficients (Section 4.2)
s	specific entropy
S	surface area
Sc	Schmidt number (equation 7.37)
St	Stanton number (equation 7.29)
St_0	Stanton number for zero mass transfer (equation 7.59)
t	time
t	leading-edge thickness (Chapter 8)
T	temperature
U_1	free stream velocity
(u, v, w)	velocity perturbations in (x, y, z)-directions
(x, y, z)	cartesian coordinate system
Z	compressibility factor, $p/\rho RT$
α	angle of incidence
α	dissociation fraction (Chapter 6)
β	shock angle
β	viscous hypersonic similarity factor, $M_1^\omega/\sqrt{Re}$ (Section 7.5)
γ	ratio of specific heats, c_p/c_v
δ	boundary-layer thickness (Chapter 8)
$\delta^\star$	boundary-layer displacement thickness
δ_e	thickness of entropy layer (equation 5.20)
Δ_s	shock stand-off distance
ε	density ratio across strong normal shock, $(\gamma-1)/(\gamma+1)$
ζ	vorticity
(η, ξ)	curvilinear orthogonal coordinate system (equation 3.8)
(ξ, η)	transformed boundary layer coordinates (Section 7.5)
θ	body angle
η	wall catalytic efficiency (equation 7.55)
λ	mean free path
Λ	angle of yaw
μ	coefficient of viscosity

xii

LIST OF SYMBOLS

ν kinematic viscosity

ρ density

σ index indicating plane ($\sigma = 0$) or axisymmetric ($\sigma = 1$) flow

τ thickness-chord ratio

τ shear stress (equation 7.18)

ϕ velocity potential

Φ dissociation rate parameter (Chapter 6)

χ hypersonic viscous interaction parameter, $M^3\sqrt{C}/\sqrt{\mathrm{Re}}$ (equation 7.35)

ψ stream function

ω exponent in viscosity-temperature relationship, $\mu \alpha T^\omega$ (Section 7.5)

Subscripts

0   stagnation

1   free stream

2   downstream of shock wave

b body

c cone

c coolant

d characteristic values for dissociation

e outer edge of entropy layer

f flare

i relating to i-th chemical species

r recovery

s shock wave

w wedge, wall

δ outer edge of boundary layer

Superscript

*   sonic throat conditions

INTRODUCTION

1. General Remarks

Hypersonics is still a comparatively young subject. Although there were a few isolated early papers dealing with flows at high Mach numbers, most of the theoretical and experimental developments in the subject have taken place since the end of the second World War. The major impetus to the subject was undoubtedly given by the very rapid advances in rocket technology, starting with the German work on the V.2 rocket, which made possible the attainment by 1958 of the flight velocities of more than 26,000 feet/second needed to launch an earth satellite into orbit. This, together with the parallel development of long range ballistic missiles and of hypersonic glide vehicles made it necessary to study the problems of flight at high velocity in the earth's atmosphere, and the result has been the growth of a new branch of aerodynamics, namely hypersonics. It is the purpose of the present volume to discuss the fluid dynamic effects which occur in flight at high Mach numbers, and to consider some of the theoretical techniques which are available for handling them.

2. Definition of Hypersonic Flow

The term 'hypersonic' was first used in a paper by Tsien (1946), and implies that the flight velocity is very much greater than the ambient speed of sound. The term 'hypervelocity' is also employed. No precise definition may be given of the velocity at which a supersonic flow becomes a hypersonic flow because the onset of those effects characteristic of hypersonic flow is in fact gradual, and varies with the geometry of the vehicle and with the nature of the surrounding atmosphere as well as with the flight velocity. Nevertheless, an approximate classification of the flow regimes of aerodynamics may be based on the value of the Mach number M, that is to say on the ratio of the flow velocity relative to the vehicle to the ambient speed of sound, and is given in Table 1.

It may be noted here that in the hypervelocity flight of a typical blunt-nosed vehicle, there will be parts of the flow field round the body in which the flow has become decelerated and in which subsonic, transonic, or supersonic flow may exist. Thus the study of the hypersonic flow past such a body may involve a knowledge of the aerodynamics of all the above flight regimes. The types of problem which arise in these local regions of subsonic or supersonic flow may, however, be different from those which are normally considered for flight at lower velocities; for instance, curved shock waves are often present in

TABLE 1

Flow Regime	Mach Number Range
Subsonic	0–0·8
Transonic	0·8–1·2
Supersonic	1·2–5
Hypersonic	> 5

hypersonic flow and it is necessary to consider the influence on the flow field of the vorticity generated at the shock.

There are, broadly speaking, two main effects associated with hypersonic flows—the purely fluid dynamic effects arising from the high Mach number, and the physico-chemical or 'real-gas' effects due to the high temperature developed in the flow. At the same time hypersonic flight often takes place at high altitudes where the atmospheric density is so low that the mean free path may become comparable with a characteristic dimension of the flow field; under these conditions continuum flow no longer exists and the methods of rarefied gas-dynamics must be used.

3. Types of Hypervelocity Vehicle

The attainment of velocities up to the orbital value means that extremely long ranges—of the order of thousands of miles—become

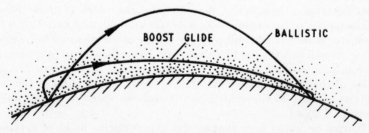

FIG. 1.—Ballistic and boost-glide vehicle trajectories.

possible for travel between points on the earth. We may distinguish two basic types of trajectory for this purpose, the ballistic and the boost-glide. These are illustrated in figure 1.

In the ballistic trajectory the rocket thrust is maintained for several minutes so that the vehicle rises at a steep angle and for long ranges does not attain its maximum velocity until it is out of the dense part of the atmosphere. After separation of the rocket booster, the payload reaches a height of several hundred miles with an approximately parabolic trajectory, and then re-enters the atmosphere at a very high velocity. Although the actual passage through the dense part of the atmosphere may last only a quarter of a minute or so, it is during this period that very large deceleration forces and heating rates occur and, if the vehicle is to survive without being burnt up, the nose shape must be so chosen that the heating is minimised. For long range trajectories, the heat input is so high that the surface temperature will become higher than the melting point of any existing materials, and, unless some form of cooling is provided, it is necessary to provide a heat-shield which is allowed to ablate during re-entry.

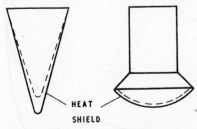

(a) Low Drag   (b) High Drag

FIG. 2.—Typical low and high drag re-entry heads for ballistic vehicles.

The heat input to a re-entry body depends on the conversion of part of its kinetic and potential energy to heat and this is governed mainly by the velocity in the re-entry part of the trajectory. In general there are two extreme types of ballistic re-entry head, the low-drag and the high-drag head; typical examples are illustrated in figure 2.

Velocity–altitude trajectories for the two types of head are shown in figure 3 for re-entry from the orbital velocity of 26,000 feet/second.

The high-drag head (upper curve) decelerates at a higher altitude than the low-drag head (lower curve). Because of the lower velocities, the total heat input to a high-drag head is somewhat less than to a low-drag head; since it also has a lower velocity in the final part of the trajectory, the high-drag shape was chosen for manned re-entry in the Project Mercury. The low-drag head, because of its high terminal velocity, gives greater accuracy (less influenced by winds) and is likely to be more suitable for a long range missile warhead and the Jupiter nose-cone, which was successfully recovered after re-entry, was of this type.

A typical study of the motion and heating of ballistic vehicles was made by Allen and Eggers (1953).

The boost-glide type of trajectory, in which the payload is first boosted by a rocket to the required speed and altitude, and then glides back to the earth's surface, was proposed by Sänger as long ago as 1933. The glide type of trajectory can also apply to re-entry of a satellite vehicle from orbit, and, for manned flight, has the advantage over the ballistic trajectory that accelerations are smaller, and that the vehicle is more readily manoeuvred. The way in which the range of a glide vehicle varies with its velocity after boost and with the lift to drag ratio L/D is shown in figure 4.

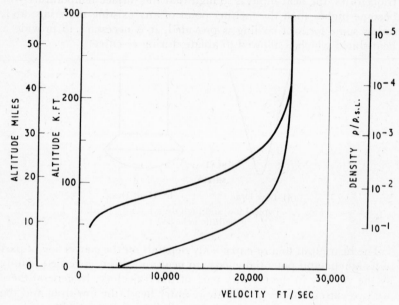

Fig. 3.—Velocity-altitude trajectories for re-entry of high and low drag heads.

For ranges up to about a quarter of the earth's circumference, a high lift to drag ratio can lead to an appreciable reduction in the boost velocity required and hence on the ratio of payload to take-off weight, but the effect of the L/D ratio becomes less at the longest ranges because more and more of the lift arises from the centrifugal force.

The heating problem must also be considered for glide vehicles, and, although the effects of heating are less severe than for a ballistic trajectory, the flight time in the atmosphere will be much longer, and unless a large amount of refrigeration or coolant is to be carried, the trajectory must be so chosen that the temperature reached by the skin does not become too high. (An equilibrium temperature is attained when the heat radiated from the surface balances the heat input from aerodynamic heating.)

For ranges up to about a quarter of the earth's circumference, the *L/D* ratio also has a large influence on the heating rates—largely because, for a given range, the boost velocities are smaller for high *L/D* ratio (figure 4). For longer ranges this siuation may be reversed and the heat input for high *L/D* can become greater than for a low *L/D* vehicle (which flies at a greater altitude for a given range). To obtain an acceptable value for the deceleration and reasonable manoeuvrability,

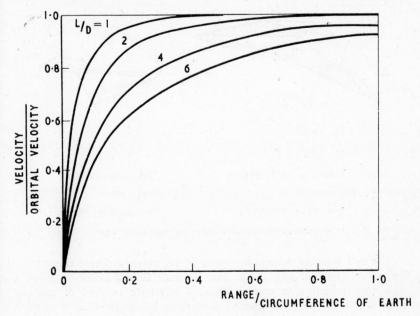

FIG. 4.—Variation of range with velocity after boost and with lift/drag ratio (Eggers, 1959).

a value of *L/D* of about unity is suggested by Eggers (1959) for a global range vehicle. Vehicle shapes for the two ranges are shown in figure 5.

In the wing-body design on the left use is made of the so-called favourable wing-body interference principle—that is to say the wings are designed to extend out to the body shock so that the pressure behind the shock acts on the wings, which are shaped so that momentum is directed downward as shown.

The low *L/D* vehicle, re-entering at near orbital velocities is fairly blunt so that the heating rates are reduced; lift is provided by removing the top half of the blunt body of revolution, and some degree of stability and control is provided by adding small blunted delta wings.

Altitude-velocity curves for the re-entry phase of the two types of glide vehicle are shown in figure 6. (The chain-dotted curve shows a ballistic trajectory for comparison.)

Two limiting boundaries are shown on the figure, an upper one above which the lift is inadequate for horizontal flight, and a lower curve·below which the structural heating becomes too severe. Between these curves is the so-called 'flight corridor' within which glide vehicle trajectories must fall if manned flight over long distances is to be possible.

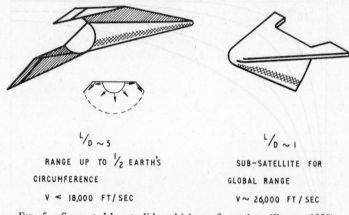

$$L/D \sim 5$$

RANGE UP TO $1/2$ EARTH'S
CIRCUMFERENCE

V < 18,000 FT/SEC

$$L/D \sim 1$$

SUB-SATELLITE FOR
GLOBAL RANGE

V ~ 26,000 FT/SEC

FIG. 5.—Suggested boost-glide vehicle configurations (Eggers, 1959).

The two types of vehicle discussed by no means exhaust the possibilities for hypervelocity flight. For instance it is possible to have a trajectory which is a combination of alternate periods of ballistic trajectory into the atmosphere followed by longer periods of upward glide trajectories during which heat can be radiated away: this is known as a 'skip' trajectory (Eggers, 1957). Another type of satellite re-entry involves a drag-brake giving some control over the deceleration (Detra et al., 1959), and, of course, there are designs based on the use of retro-rockets.

For all the designs discussed, some form of directional and roll control must be provided and their stability must be considered. It must also not be forgotten that any vehicle which is required to make a normal landing must be capable of being flown at transonic and subsonic velocities, so that departures from conventional aircraft shapes should preferably not be too great.

Enough has probably been said for the reader to realise that there are likely to be serious aerodynamic problems associated with the design of hypersonic vehicles. We may, for instance, list two typical groups of fluid dynamic problems which are considered further in the present volume as:

(1) the prediction of shock shapes, flow fields and pressure distributions for high velocities and Mach numbers for non-lifting and lifting bodies, including the effect of nose and leading edge blunting, and

(2) the determination of heat transfer and boundary layer flow, together with the effects of ablation and methods of surface cooling.

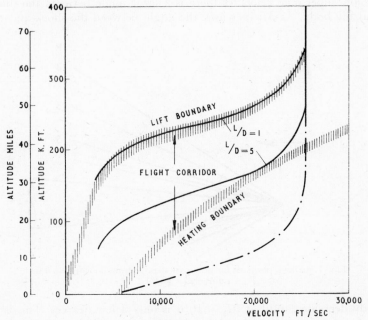

Fig. 6.—Altitude-velocity trajectories for glide and ballistic vehicles (wing loading 50 lb/ft²).

4. The Effect of High Mach Number

We now consider some of the aerodynamic phenomena associated with hypersonic flight, emphasising particularly the way in which they differ from those occurring in flight at lower speeds.

Probably the most striking difference between flow at subsonic and at supersonic speeds is the formation of a shock ahead of bodies and wings when the flight velocity is above the ambient sonic velocity. Upstream of such a shock the flow is completely undisturbed, and it is only downstream of the shock that the influence of the body is felt. The shock may be either attached, as in the case of a slender pointed body or a wing with a sharp leading edge, or detached, i.e. standing off from the surface, if the nose of the body or the wing leading edge is blunt. The behaviour of the shock for the flow past a body of revolution as the Mach number, M_1, increases from supersonic to hypersonic values may be illustrated by considering the flow of a perfect gas past two different body shapes—a slender cone and a sphere. (The term 'perfect' gas is used to mean an inviscid gas obeying the law $p/\rho = RT$, and for which the ratio of specific heats, γ, has a constant value.)

Figure 7 shows the position of the attached shock at different values of the Mach number for the flow about a slender cone with $\gamma = 1\cdot4$. At low supersonic velocities there is a large angle between the shock and the body. As M_1 increases, the angle between the shock and the

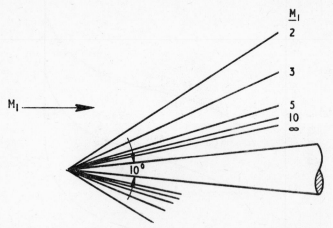

Fig. 7.—Shock positions for flow past slender cones at different Mach numbers ($\gamma = 1\cdot4$).

body decreases, until at $M_1 = 10$ it is only a few degrees. This is of some consequence to the theoretical treatment of hypersonic flows because one of the main approximations used in linearised supersonic theory is based on the shock angle being large relative to the body angle, and this is evidently no longer true at high Mach numbers. It should also be noted that a limiting shock position is reached as $M_1 \to \infty$, and that from $M_1 = 10$ to $M_1 = \infty$, there is very little further change in shock position with increasing Mach number. It will be shown later that this limiting shock position is a consequence of the density ratio across the shock having reached a limiting value with increasing Mach number.

The variation of the bow shock with Mach number for the flow past a sphere is shown in figure 8. The shock stands off from the body by an amount which decreases as the Mach number increases, and again limiting position is reached as $M \to \infty$. The limiting shock lies fairly close to the surface of the sphere (it is very nearly concentric with it over most of the front of the sphere) and the region between the shock and the surface is referred to as the 'shock layer.' Just behind the front part of the shock the flow has been brought nearly to rest and is subsonic; as it passes round the sphere it accelerates, passes through the local velocity of sound at the sonic line and then becomes supersonic. In contrast to the flow past the sharp cone, the shock is highly curved;

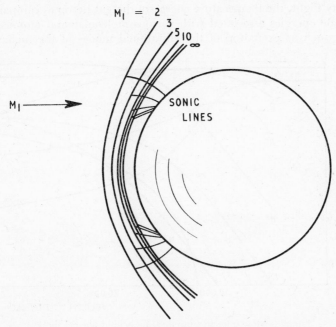

Fig. 8.—Shock shapes for flow past sphere at different Mach numbers ($\gamma = 1\cdot4$).

this means that there are large transverse gradients of the flow quantities and these gradients play an important part in determining the flow field.

For the corresponding plane flows past a wedge and a cylinder the shock behaves in a similar manner. Such differences as there are will be discussed in subsequent chapters.

The slender pointed cone and the sphere represent two extremes of aerodynamic shape. A practical hypervelocity vehicle is likely to have a slender afterbody (to reduce drag) but a nose which is blunted to reduce the heat transfer in the stagnation region. Such a body is often referred to as a 'blunt-nosed slender body'. The two-dimensional equivalent is a slender wing section having a rounded leading edge, and this may in addition be swept back to further reduce the heat transfer. At hypersonic Mach numbers such leading edge or nose blunting can result in a substantial increase in pressure over the whole of the afterbody, whereas for supersonic flow only the region near the nose is affected by the blunting. The effects of nose blunting are discussed in Chapter 5.

5. Real Gas Effects

At the high temperatures which exist behind the shock for hypervelocity flight, the temperature energy of the gas becomes comparable with the energies associated with various molecular and atomic processes, such as excitation of the vibrational modes of the molecules,

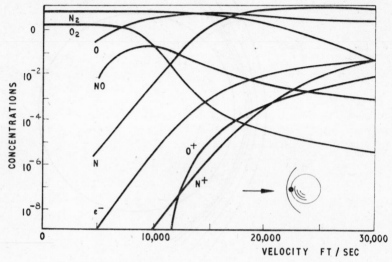

Fig. 9.—Mole fraction concentration behind normal shock
(300,000 ft altitude).

dissociation and ionisation. Under these conditions the gas no longer behaves as a perfect gas having a constant value of the ratio of specific heats, and the energy which is involved in these processes must be taken into account when calculating the flow field.

Figure 9 shows how the chemical composition of air behind a normal shock wave varies with the flight velocity for flight at 200,000 feet altitude. Oxygen starts to dissociate for velocities above about 5,000 feet/second, and Nitrogen above 12,000 feet/second. The number of free electrons produced becomes appreciable when the velocity exceeds 18,000 feet/second. The electrical conductivity of the gas may exceed 1 mho/cm, and this makes attractive the possibility of controlling the flow field by electric or magnetic fields; in addition the presence of free electrons surrounding the body alters the dielectric properties of the medium, and can have a large effect on radio communications to and from a vehicle.

As a result of these real gas effects, the effective specific heat ratio, γ, behind the shock wave can change significantly from the normal value of 1·4 for air (Chapter 6). As the velocity increases γ first decreases from 1·4 as vibrational modes are excited and then decreases further as dissociation and ionisation take place. Many of the approximate analytical approaches to hypersonic flow are based on having a small value of $(\gamma - 1)$—an approximation which because of real gas effects can hold for a wide range of hypersonic flight conditions.

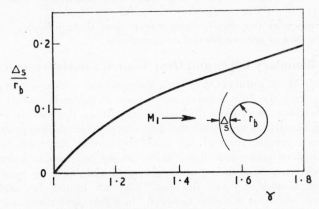

Fig. 10.—Variation of shock stand-off distance with γ for flow past sphere ($M_1 = \infty$).

A change in γ can have a significant effect on the flow field. For instance the variation with γ of the shock stand-off distance for the flow past a sphere at $M = \infty$ is plotted in figure 10 (it is assumed that γ is constant between the shock and the body). We see that the stand-off distance depends quite markedly on the value of γ, and, since the stand-off distance is relatively easy to measure experimentally, it gives a good indication of the influence of the real gas effects on the flow field.

Another feature of the high temperature layer of gas surrounding a body is that radiation from the gas into the body, or to the atmosphere can become important at hypervelocities. The light emitted from the nose region of such a body can become quite intense and is readily observable in experiments in high enthalpy wind tunnels.

6. Non-equilibrium Effects

Thus far in the discussion of real-gas effects, the assumption has been made that the gas is in thermodynamic equilibrium at all points in the flow field. However, the transfer of energy to vibrational modes, and the processes of dissociation and ionisation, together with the recombination which occurs in regions where the temperature is falling, all require a finite time, the 'relaxation time', before equilibrium is reached.

The rate processes are functions of density, pressure and temperature, and if in a given region of the flow these quantities are varying rapidly there may not be time for thermodynamic equilibrium to become established. In this event it is necessary to solve the equations for the chemical kinetic rate processes and the flow equations simultaneously when calculating the flow field round the body and in the wake behind the body.

Real gas and non-equilibrium effects and their influence on the flow over bodies are considered in Chapter 6.

7. The Boundary Layer and Heat Transfer in Hypersonic Flow

At high Mach numbers very high temperatures will be developed in regions where the flow is decelerated, such as in the boundary layers close to surfaces. Because of the high temperatures, the viscosity is high, and the density is low, and the boundary layer thickness may be very much greater than at the same free-stream Reynolds number in subsonic or supersonic flow. Since, as we have seen in section 4 the shock wave will lie relatively close to the body in hypersonic flow, the boundary layer thickness may no longer be negligible compared with the distance between the body and the shock. The additional displacement effect of this boundary layer can result in an appreciable modification of the whole flow-field—an example of viscous interaction. Thus the pressure along a flat plate with even a very sharp leading edge can differ significantly from the free stream value because of the effective blunting caused by the thick boundary layer. This interaction is considered in Chapter 8.

Separation effects, too, may become important in hypersonic flows, because of the prevalence of thick laminar boundary layers which do not readily withstand adverse pressure gradients.

Another feature of hypersonic boundary layers not normally present in the types of body used at supersonic velocities is the vorticity interaction arising from the presence of curved shock waves. If a boundary layer is formed on a surface which is supporting a curved shock, the vorticity gradient behind the shock influences the rate of growth of the boundary layer.

The process of heat transfer through boundary layers in hypersonic flows does not differ in principle from that in supersonic flows, although certain extra simplifying assumptions become possible in hypersonic boundary layers with cooled walls because the density in the hot outer part of the layer may be much less than that near the wall. The main differences between supersonic and hypersonic heat transfer are that very much greater temperature differences between the stream and the wall may have to be considered, and that because of the high temperature gradients, there will be large changes in the viscosity and thermal conductivity across boundary layers.

In addition real-gas and non-equilibrium effects can have a large influence on the boundary layer growth and on heat transfer rates, and it is necessary to consider the influence of the diffusion and convection of the various species produced by dissociation and ionisation through the boundary layer. The nature of the wall can play an important part in determining the local recombination rates as it can act as a third body for recombination processes. The boundary layer problem is further complicated for bodies during atmospheric re-entry if the heating rates are so high that melting or sublimation of the surface takes place. The effect of the injection of some form of coolant into the boundary layer must also be considered. Boundary layers in hypersonic flow are dealt with in Chapter 7.

8. Low Density Effects

At normal altitudes and velocities the air flowing past a vehicle can be treated as if it were a continuum. At high altitudes, the air becomes less dense, and the motion of the individual gas particles becomes important. The parameter which determines the onset of low density effects is the Knudsen number, Kn, which is the ratio of the ambient mean free path to a typical body dimension. Continuum flow starts to break down when Kn is of the order unity.

As the density is reduced, the main effect is that the shock ahead of a body becomes merged with the flow close to the body. At very low densities (Kn $\sim$ 10–100) free molecular flow conditions are approached in which the individual air particles reflect from the surface, but do not undergo collisions with other particles until they are outside the region

TABLE 2

(A.R.D.C. MODEL ATMOSPHERE 1959)

Altitude (ft)	Mean Free path (ft)	Density ($\rho/\rho_{s.l.}$)
0	$2 \cdot 18 \times 10^{-7}$	1
100,000	$1 \cdot 61 \times 10^{-5}$	$1 \cdot 35 \times 10^{-1}$
200,000	$8 \cdot 45 \times 10^{-4}$	$2 \cdot 57 \times 10^{-2}$
300,000	$1 \cdot 25 \times 10^{-1}$	$1 \cdot 75 \times 10^{-5}$
400,000	$2 \cdot 18 \times 10^{1}$	$9 \cdot 90 \times 10^{-7}$
500,000	$1 \cdot 65 \times 10^{2}$	$1 \cdot 28 \times 10^{-9}$

of influence of the body. The variation of the atmospheric mean free
path with altitude is given in Table 2.

It is only for altitudes above 200,000 feet that low density effects
must be taken into account for typical hypersonic vehicles. Rarefied
gas flows will be considered in more detail in Chapter 9.

60 - 96 Km

CONTINUUM FLOW OF AN INVISCID, NON-HEAT-CONDUCTING PERFECT GAS

In the chapters of Part 1 the continuum flow of an inviscid, non-heat-conducting perfect gas is discussed.

A 'perfect gas' is a gas which is assumed to satisfy the ideal equation of state $p/\rho = RT$, where the gas constant, R, is a characteristic constant for the gas considered; in addition, we will take the term perfect gas as including the concept that the gas is calorically perfect, i.e. having a constant value of the ratio of specific heats, $c_p/c_v = \gamma$. The effects of departures from the ideal equation of state, and of a variable γ due to the influence of intermolecular forces (van der Waal forces) and of real gas effects such as the excitation of molecular vibrational modes, and dissociation, will be considered later in Part II.

By an 'inviscid non-heat-conducting' gas is meant a gas in which the effects of viscosity and thermal conductivity are negligibly small. In fact, of course, all gases are viscous and heat-conducting; however, the entropy production terms in one-dimensional flows have the form

$$\frac{\mu}{T}\left(\frac{\partial u}{\partial x}\right)^2 \qquad \text{and} \qquad \frac{1}{T}\frac{\partial}{\partial x}\left(\frac{k\partial T}{\partial x}\right)$$

where μ is the viscosity and k is the thermal conductivity and it is only in regions where the velocity and temperature gradients are large that these terms become important. At high values of the Reynolds number, Re (based on free stream conditions and on the body diameter), such regions occur in the interior of shock waves, and in the boundary layers next to surfaces. On the other hand when the Reynolds number, Re, becomes small (of order 10) the effects of viscosity and of heat conduction can become important over the whole field.

For flows at hypersonic Mach numbers, it happens that such low Reynolds numbers are also those associated with the onset of low density effects. Thus the Knudsen number, Kn, which is the ratio of the mean free path to the body diameter can be expressed in terms of the Reynolds number and Mach number.

$$\text{Kn} = \frac{\lambda}{d} = 1\cdot26\sqrt{\gamma}\cdot\frac{M_1}{\text{Re}}$$

Departures from continuum flow will occur when Kn $\sim$ 1 and for, say, Mach numbers from 5–30, the corresponding Reynolds number will vary from about 3–20. This means that the effects of viscosity and of heat conduction become important over the whole flow field at about the same values of M_1 and Re as those for which departures from continuum flow conditions are taking place. (A fuller discussion of this is given in Chapter 9.)

Thus, by restricting our attention to relatively high values of the Reynolds number, continuum flow conditions are ensured. It can then be shown, that although, because of high local temperatures and low densities the boundary layer thickness may be greater than in supersonic flow, the boundary layer may nevertheless still be distinguished as a relatively narrow region next to the surface. It will here be assumed that the body shape, plus the boundary layer displacement thickness together form an effective body about which the flow field can be calculated without having to include the effects of viscosity and heat conduction. This does not, of course, exclude the possibility of interaction between the outer flow field and the boundary layer; a discussion of such 'shock-boundary-layer' interaction will be left to Chapter 8 of Part II.

Furthermore, it can be shown (see Chapter 9) that so long as a narrow boundary layer can be distinguished, the shock front can be considered to be negligibly thin, and, in this part of the book, the shock will be treated as a mathematical discontinuity.

Since curved shock waves are often present in hypersonic flow the effect on the flow field of the vorticity generated at the shock front must also be considered and in hypersonic aerodynamics it is normal to use a form of the governing equations which allows the rotational nature of the inviscid part of the flow field to be taken into account. The presence of vorticity in the external flow field can also influence the boundary layer growth—a subject which is dealt with in Chapters 8 and 9 of Part II.

CHAPTER 1

GENERAL FLOW RELATIONSHIPS

In this chapter hypersonic flow through normal and oblique shocks and through expansions, and about simple bodies such as wedges and cones will be considered. Because of the simple geometry of these flows, exact solutions of the equations of motion may be obtained and it is possible to examine the effects of high Mach number and to deduce relationships which will be of importance for studying the flow past more complicated bodies.

1.1. One-dimensional Steady Isentropic Flow

1.1.1. Energy Equation

For the adiabatic flow of a perfect inviscid, non-heat-conducting gas along a streamtube, we commence with the adiabatic energy equation in the form

$$h + \frac{U^2}{2} = \text{const} = H_0 \qquad (1.1)$$

This expresses the fact that per unit mass of a flowing gas the sum of the static enthalpy h, and the velocity energy, $U^2/2$, is a constant and is equal to the total enthalpy, H_0. This holds for all adiabatic flows whether isentropic or not. If the gas obeys the gas law $p/\rho = RT$ where $R = c_p - c_v$ and c_p and c_v are constant, (1.1) may be also written in the alternative forms:

$$c_p T + \frac{U^2}{2} = c_p T_0 \qquad (1.2)$$

or

$$\frac{\gamma}{\gamma - 1} \frac{p}{\rho} + \frac{U^2}{2} = \frac{\gamma}{\gamma - 1} \frac{p_0}{\rho_0} \qquad (1.3)$$

or

$$\frac{a^2}{\gamma - 1} + \frac{U^2}{2} = \frac{a_0^2}{\gamma - 1} \qquad (1.4)$$

where a, the speed of sound, is given by $a^2 = \gamma R T$ and $\gamma = c_p/c_v$. The energy equation may also be written in terms of the Mach number, $M = U/a$. Thus, since the ratio of the velocity energy per unit mass to the enthalpy per unit mass is given by

$$\frac{U^2/2}{a^2/(\gamma - 1)} = \frac{\gamma - 1}{2} M^2$$

the energy equation becomes

$$H_0 = \frac{U^2}{2}\left(1 + \frac{2}{(\gamma - 1)M^2}\right) \tag{1.5}$$

As the Mach number becomes large, this expression becomes

$$H_0 \to \frac{U^2}{2} \tag{1.5a}$$

(The symbol $\to$ will normally be taken to mean "tends to as $M \to \infty$".)

1.1.2. Bernoulli Equation

If the flow is isentropic

$$\frac{p}{\rho^\gamma} = \text{const} = \frac{p_0}{\rho_0{}^\gamma}$$

and this, combined with equation (1.3), yields the integrated form of the Bernoulli equation for compressible flow:

$$\frac{\gamma}{\gamma - 1}\frac{p_0}{\rho_0}\left(\frac{p}{p_0}\right)^{\frac{\gamma-1}{\gamma}} + \frac{U^2}{2} = \frac{\gamma}{\gamma - 1}\frac{p_0}{\rho_\bullet} \tag{1.6}$$

1.1.3. Dynamic Pressure and Pressure Coefficient

A useful relationship for the dynamic pressure q, in terms of the Mach number is

$$q = \tfrac{1}{2}\rho U^2 = \tfrac{1}{2}\gamma p M^2$$

This may then be used to express the pressure coefficient, C_p, in terms of reference conditions p_1 and M_1 as:

$$C_p = \frac{p - p_1}{\tfrac{1}{2}\rho_1 U_1{}^2} = \frac{p - p_1}{\tfrac{1}{2}\gamma p_1 M_1{}^2} = \frac{2}{\gamma M_1{}^2}\left(\frac{p}{p_1} - 1\right) \tag{1.7}$$

1.1.4. Isentropic Expansion from Reservoir or Stagnation Region

By using the energy equation in the form (1.4), we may express the velocity after a one-dimensional isentropic expansion from a reservoir (or round the body from the stagnation region for the flow past a body) to a given Mach number M as

$$\frac{U^2}{a_0{}^2} = M^2\left(1 + \frac{\gamma - 1}{2}M^2\right)^{-1} \tag{1.8}$$

For high Mach number

$$U \to \sqrt{\frac{2}{\gamma - 1}} \cdot a_0 \tag{1.8a}$$

Hence the velocity after expansion reaches a limiting value equal, for $\gamma = 1\cdot4$, to $2\cdot3$ times the speed of sound in the reservoir.

Other quantities, however, such as the temperature, density and pressure, all decrease with Mach number as follows:

$$\left(\frac{a}{a_0}\right)^2 = \frac{T}{T_0} = \left(1 + \frac{\gamma-1}{2}M^2\right)^{-1} \to \left(\frac{\gamma-1}{2}M^2\right)^{-1} \qquad (1.9)$$

$$\frac{\rho}{\rho_0} = \left(1 + \frac{\gamma-1}{2}M^2\right)^{-\frac{1}{\gamma-1}} \to \left(\frac{\gamma-1}{2}M^2\right)^{-\frac{1}{\gamma-1}} \qquad (1.10)$$

$$\frac{p}{p_0} = \left(1 + \frac{\gamma-1}{2}M^2\right)^{-\frac{\gamma}{\gamma-1}} \to \left(\frac{\gamma-1}{2}M^2\right)^{-\frac{\gamma}{\gamma-1}} \qquad (1.11)$$

As the Mach number becomes high, the static value of the quantities after expansion reach very low values. A consequence of the rapid fall of temperature with Mach number is that if air is expanded from a reservoir at room temperature it is only possible to reach $M \simeq 5$ before the static temperature is so low that liquefaction of oxygen takes place. This means that to obtain hypersonic Mach numbers using air as a working gas the supply chamber must be heated.

The way in which the various quantities vary with the Mach number for $\gamma = 1\cdot4$ are given in figure 1.1.

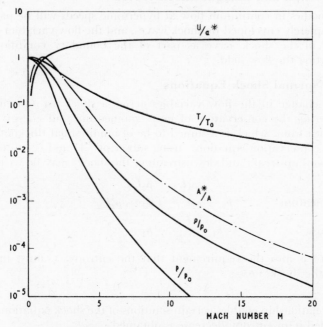

Fig. 1.1.—Variation of flow variables with Mach number for isentropic expansion ($\gamma = 1\cdot4$).

1.1.5. Area Ratio

The one-dimensional isentropic flow equations may also be used to determine the relationship between the change of area of a stream tube or channel with the Mach number so long as the expansion of the stream tube takes place slowly enough for conditions to be considered uniform across each section.

In addition to the energy equation we require the equation of continuity

$$\rho U A = \rho^* U^* A^* \tag{1.12}$$

where the superscript (*) refers to sonic or throat conditions.

The ratios between the flow variables at a section having area A and those at the throat may be obtained from equations (1.9) and (1.10) (putting $M = 1$ to obtain the throat conditions), and, after some manipulation, the area ratio is found to be given by

$$\frac{A}{A^*} = \frac{1}{M} \left\{ \frac{2}{\gamma + 1} \left(1 + \frac{\gamma - 1}{2} M^2 \right) \right\}^{\frac{\gamma+1}{2(\gamma-1)}} \rightarrow \left(\frac{\gamma - 1}{\gamma + 1} \right)^{\frac{\gamma+1}{2(\gamma-1)}} M^{\frac{2}{\gamma-1}}$$

$$\tag{1.13}$$

The variation of A/A^* with M is given in figure 1.1.

1.2. Normal and Oblique Shock Waves

All bodies in continuum flow at hypersonic speeds will be partially or completely enveloped by shock waves, and the flow variables downstream of the shock serve as part of the boundary conditions for calculating the flow field.

1.2.1. Normal Shock Equations

The change in the flow variables across a shock are obtained by considering the conservation of mass, momentum and energy across the shock front, which is assumed to be of infinitesimal thickness.

The conservation equations (using subscripts (1) and (2) to refer to conditions upstream and downstream of the shock) may be written

Mass $\qquad\qquad\qquad \rho_1 U_1 = \rho_2 U_2 \tag{1.14}$

Momentum $\qquad\quad p_1 + \rho_1 U_1^2 = p_2 + \rho_2 U_2^2 \tag{1.15}$

Energy $\qquad\qquad h_1 + \dfrac{U_1^2}{2} = h_2 + \dfrac{U_2^2}{2} \tag{1.16}$

There is also the requirement that the entropy, s, must increase across the shock, i.e.

$$\Delta s = s_2 - s_1 > 0 \tag{1.17}$$

(This relationship enables certain solutions of the shock equations to be discarded if an entropy decrease is obtained.)

By combining equations (1.14) to (1.16) the following expressions relating the variables across a shock to the initial Mach number, M_1, may be obtained:

Temperature ratio

$$\frac{T_2}{T_1} = \left(\frac{a_2}{a_1}\right)^2$$
$$= \frac{[2\gamma M_1{}^2 - (\gamma - 1)][(\gamma - 1)M_1{}^2 + 2]}{(\gamma + 1)^2 M_1{}^2} \rightarrow \frac{2\gamma(\gamma - 1)M_1{}^2}{(\gamma + 1)^2} \quad (1.18)$$

Pressure ratio

$$\frac{p_2}{p_1} = 1 + \frac{2\gamma}{\gamma + 1}(M_1{}^2 - 1) \rightarrow \frac{2\gamma}{\gamma + 1}M_1{}^2 \quad (1.19)$$

Density, Velocity and Dynamic Head ratios

$$\frac{\rho_2}{\rho_1} = \frac{U_1}{U_2} = \frac{q_1}{q_2} = \frac{\gamma + 1}{(\gamma - 1) + 2/M_1{}^2} \rightarrow \frac{\gamma + 1}{\gamma - 1} \quad (1.20)$$

Mach number behind shock

$$M_2 = \frac{U_2}{a_2} = \left\{\frac{(\gamma - 1)M_1{}^2 + 2}{2\gamma M_1{}^2 - (\gamma - 1)}\right\}^{\frac{1}{2}} \rightarrow \sqrt{\frac{\gamma - 1}{2\gamma}} \quad (1.21)$$

and the pressure coefficient

$$C_p = \frac{p_2 - p_1}{\frac{1}{2}\rho_1 U_1{}^2} = \frac{4}{\gamma + 1}\left\{1 - \frac{1}{M_1{}^2}\right\} \rightarrow \frac{4}{\gamma + 1} \quad (1.22)$$

It is to be noted that whereas the temperature and pressure ratios across a normal shock both increase (with $M_1{}^2$) the density, the velocity, and the dynamic head ratios, the Mach number behind the shock, and the pressure coefficient reach limiting values for large M_1.

1.2.2. Oblique Shock Relationships

For an oblique shock, we have the requirement that the tangential component of velocity is unaltered, whereas the normal component obeys the relationship for a normal shock.

The change of temperature, density and pressure across an oblique shock may be simply obtained from equations (1.18)–(1.20) by replacing M_1 by $M_1 \sin \beta$, where β is the shock angle.

The relationships are then

$$\frac{T_2}{T_1} = \frac{[2\gamma M_1{}^2 \sin^2 \beta - (\gamma - 1)][(\gamma - 1)M_1{}^2 \sin^2 \beta + 2]}{(\gamma + 1)^2 M_1{}^2 \sin^2 \beta}$$
$$\rightarrow \frac{2\gamma(\gamma - 1)M_1{}^2 \sin^2 \beta}{(\gamma + 1)^2} \quad (1.23)$$

2

$$\frac{\rho_2}{\rho_1} = \frac{(\gamma + 1)M_1^2 \sin^2 \beta}{(\gamma - 1)M_1^2 \sin^2 \beta + 2} \rightarrow \frac{\gamma + 1}{\gamma - 1} \qquad (1.24)$$

$$\frac{p_2}{p_1} = 1 + \frac{2\gamma}{(\gamma + 1)} (M_1^2 \sin^2 \beta - 1) \rightarrow \frac{2\gamma}{\gamma + 1} M_1^2 \sin^2 \beta$$

$$(1.25)$$

The Mach number behind the shock is given by

$$M_2^2 = \left(\frac{U_2}{a_2}\right)^2$$

$$= \frac{(\gamma + 1)^2 M_1^4 \sin^2 \beta - 4(M_1^2 \sin^2 \beta - 1)(\gamma M_1^2 \sin^2 \beta + 1)}{[2\gamma M_1^2 \sin^2 \beta - (\gamma - 1)][(\gamma - 1)M_1^2 \sin^2 \beta + 2]}$$

$$(1.26)$$

and the pressure coefficient

$$C_p = \frac{p_2 - p_1}{\frac{1}{2}\rho_1 U_1^2} = \frac{4}{\gamma + 1} \left\{ \sin^2 \beta - \frac{1}{M_1^2} \right\} \rightarrow \frac{4}{\gamma + 1} \sin^2 \beta \qquad (1.27)$$

In addition the velocity components u_2 and v_2 behind the shock are given by

$$\frac{u_2}{U_1} = 1 - \frac{2(M_1^2 \sin^2 \beta - 1)}{(\gamma + 1)M_1^2} \rightarrow 1 - \frac{2 \sin^2 \beta}{\gamma + 1} \qquad (1.28)$$

$$\frac{v_2}{U_1} = \frac{2(M_1^2 \sin^2 \beta - 1) \cot \beta}{(\gamma + 1)M_1^2} \rightarrow \frac{\sin 2\beta}{\gamma + 1} \qquad (1.29)$$

As in the case of the normal shock, the temperature and pressure ratios for the oblique shock increase, for large Mach numbers, with the square of the Mach number (more precisely, with $M_1^2 \sin^2 \beta$) whereas the other ratios reach limiting values which are independent of Mach number and are a function either of γ only, or of γ and the shock angle β. $M_1 \sin \beta$ is, of course, the normal component, M_n of the incident Mach number M_1, and the way in which the various parameters vary with M_n for $\gamma = 1\cdot4$ is shown in figure 1.2.

1.2.3. Shock Relationships in Terms of Deflection Angle

In the last section the variation of the flow properties through an oblique shock were given in terms of the shock inclination angle β. It is however, more convenient when discussing the flow past general bodies to consider parameters in terms of the flow deflection angle θ. Unfortunately, there are no convenient explicit functions for the variation of the flow parameters across a shock in terms of θ, although certain simple approximate relationships may be obtained for small flow deflection angles.

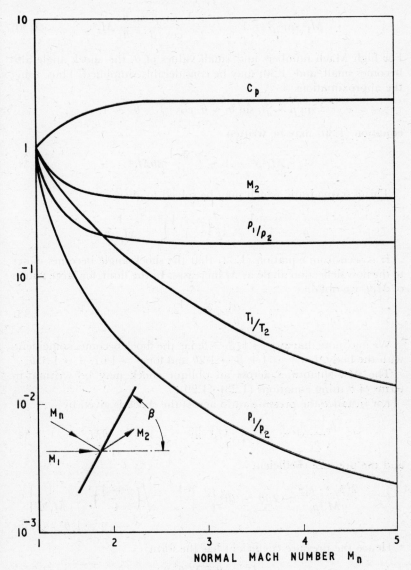

FIG. 1.2.—Variation of flow parameters behind oblique shock with
normal Mach number ($\gamma = 1.4$).

The general relationship between β and θ is

$$M_1{}^2 \sin^2 \beta - 1 = \frac{\gamma + 1}{2} \frac{\sin \beta \sin \theta}{\cos (\beta - \theta)} M_1{}^2 \qquad (1.30)$$

For high Mach numbers and small values of θ, the shock angle also becomes small, and (1.30) may be considerably simplified. Thus, using the approximations

$$\sin \beta \sim \beta, \sin \theta \sim \theta, \cos (\beta - \theta) \sim 1,$$

equation (1.30) may be written

$$M_1{}^2\beta^2 - 1 \simeq \frac{\gamma + 1}{2} \beta\theta M_1{}^2 \qquad (1.31)$$

This is a quadratic which may be solved to give

$$\frac{\beta}{\theta} = \frac{\gamma + 1}{4} + \sqrt{\left(\frac{\gamma + 1}{4}\right)^2 + \frac{1}{M_1{}^2\theta^2}} \qquad (1.32)$$

It is seen from equation (1.32) that the shock angle becomes closer to the flow deflection angle as M increases. In the limit, for large values of $M_1\theta$, we obtain

$$\frac{\beta}{\theta} \to \frac{\gamma + 1}{2} \qquad (1.33)$$

We may note that as $\gamma \to 1$, $\beta \to \theta$, i.e. the shock becomes coincident with the body. For $\gamma = 1\cdot4$, $\beta \to 1\cdot2\theta$ and for $\gamma = 1\cdot67$, $\beta \to 1\cdot33\theta$.

The flow quantities across an oblique shock may be written in terms of θ using equations (1.23)–(1.29).

For instance the pressure ratio across the shock is given by

$$\frac{p_2 - p_1}{p_1} = \frac{2\gamma}{\gamma + 1} (M_1{}^2 \sin^2 \beta - 1) \to \gamma\beta\theta M_1{}^2 \qquad (1.34)$$

and the pressure coefficient

$$C_p = \frac{2(p_2 - p_1)}{\gamma M_1{}^2 p_1} \simeq 2\beta\theta \simeq 2\theta^2 \left\{\frac{\gamma + 1}{4} + \sqrt{\left(\frac{\gamma + 1}{4}\right)^2 + \frac{1}{M_1{}^2\theta^2}}\right\}$$
$$\to (\gamma + 1)\theta^2 \quad (1.35)$$

Hence the pressure coefficient has the form

$$C_p = \theta^2 f(M_1\theta, \gamma) \qquad (1.35a)$$

The parameter $M_1\theta$ is called the 'hypersonic similarity parameter'; and it is shown in Chapter II, by considering approximations to the full equations of motion valid for small disturbances, that for high values of M_1, $M_1\theta$ becomes the governing parameter for a general hypersonic flow past a body whose surfaces have a small inclination to the flow direction.

It is also of interest to consider the expressions for the velocities, Mach angle and Mach number behind the shock which are valid for small flow deflections.

The expressions for the change of velocity across the shock are given from (1.28, 1.29 and 1.33) for β small by

$$\frac{\Delta u}{U_1} = \frac{U_1 - u}{U_1} \simeq -\frac{2}{\gamma + 1}\beta^2\left(1 - \frac{1}{M_1^2\beta^2}\right) \to \frac{\gamma + 1}{2}\theta^2 \quad (1.36)$$

and

$$\frac{\Delta v}{U_1} = \frac{v_2}{U_1} \simeq \frac{2}{\gamma + 1}\beta\left(1 - \frac{1}{M_1^2\beta^2}\right) \to \theta \quad (1.37)$$

The perturbation of the 'u' velocity, is seen for M_1 large to be of order (θ^2) and that in 'v' of order (θ); the effect of a body inclined to the flow is thus to produce gradients of the flow parameters which are much greater in a direction normal to the flow than those parallel to the flow. If, then, we consider a slab of air initially at rest, and a slender body passes through it, the main effect is for the body to push the disturbed air sideways; this concept leads to the 'equivalence principle' which relates the steady flow of gas past a body to the unsteady flow in a plane at right angles to the direction of motion, and which will be discussed in more detail in subsequent chapters.

The Mach number, M_2, behind the shock may be written, for small inclinations;

$$M_2^2 \simeq \frac{(\gamma + 1)^2 M_1^4\beta^2 - 4(M_1^2\beta^2 - 1)(\gamma M_1^2\beta^2 + 1)}{[2\gamma M_1^2\beta^2 - (\gamma - 1)][(\gamma - 1)M_1^2\beta^2 + 2]} \quad (1.38)$$

For a strong shock with $(\gamma - 1)M_1^2\beta^2 \gg 1$ this becomes

$$M_2 \to \frac{1}{\theta}\frac{2}{\sqrt{2\gamma(\gamma - 1)}} \quad (1.38a)$$

Evidently for small deflection angles the Mach number behind an oblique shock becomes large. This may be contrasted with the Mach number behind a normal shock, which becomes very low (subsonic) as M_1 becomes large.

The Mach angle $\mu_2 = \sin^{-1} 1/M_2$ is given for small deflection angle and large M, by

$$\mu_2 \to \frac{\sqrt{2\gamma(\gamma - 1)}}{2}\theta \to \frac{\sqrt{2\gamma(\gamma - 1)}}{\gamma + 1}\beta \quad (1.39)$$

Thus the positive Mach waves (those running away from the surface) are inclined to the flow direction behind the shock at an angle which is about twice that of the shock. Since the shock angle is only 20–30 per cent greater than the body angle, this has the practical consequences that for a curved slender body at high Mach numbers most of the outgoing Mach lines leaving the surface will run into the shock close to the body, causing the shock to become curved and also that the second family characteristics will reflect back on to the surface.

In supersonic flow, on the other hand, the shock angle is close to the Mach angle so that the effect of the outgoing waves on the shock is small, and most of the reflected family of Mach lines fall outside the body (figure 1.3).

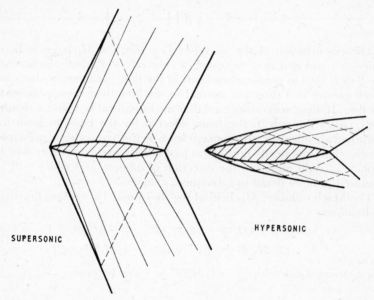

Fig. 1.3.—Supersonic and hypersonic flow past bi-convex aerofoil section.

Once again the Mach number appears in the above expressions, only in the forms $M_1\beta$ or $M_1\theta$ so that the Mach line pattern for small flow inclinations obeys the hypersonic similarity law, and a limiting pattern is reached for large values of the hypersonic similarity parameter.

1.3. Curved Shocks

The shocks surrounding bodies in hypersonic flow are often curved, and the differences of the flow properties on streamlines which cross different parts of the shock are associated with a rotational flow behind the shock.

For a flow having a constant total enthalpy the vorticity ζ is related to the gradient of the entropy S normal to a streamline by Crocco's theorem,

$$\zeta \times u = T \operatorname{grad} S \qquad (1.40)$$

Here u is the local velocity vector along the streamline (figure 1.4) and T is the static temperature.

Using the differential form of the conservation equations across the shock the entropy gradient may be related to the shock angle and the

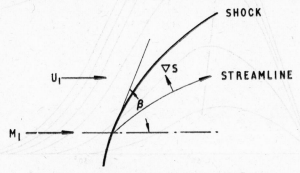

FIG. 1.4.—Curved shock and streamline.

following relationship (Hayes and Probstein, 1959b) may be obtained between the vorticity and, the shock curvature, K ($K = 1/R_s$ where R_s is the radius of curvature of the shock),

$$\zeta = \frac{\rho_2}{\rho_1} U_1 \left(1 - \frac{\rho_1}{\rho_2}\right)^2 \cos \beta . K \qquad (1.41)$$

This equation was shown by Lighthill (1957) to be valid for a general curved shock surface if the vorticity is chosen to be that component perpendicular both to the free stream direction and to the streamline behind the shock.

To illustrate the way in which the vorticity varies for the shock wave about a typical blunt body, figure 1.5 gives the distribution of the non-dimensional vorticity $\bar{\zeta} = \zeta d/U_1$ behind a given parabolic shock having the form $y_s/d = (x/d)^{\frac{1}{2}}$ for $\gamma = 1.4$ and for various Mach numbers. The body producing a given shock will of course become more and more slender as the Mach number decreases.

It is seen that the vorticity, which is zero at the nose reaches a maximum value close to the sonic point, and then decreases again. As the Mach number increases the vorticity also increases and reaches a limiting distribution as $M_1 \to \infty$. Figure 1.5 also serves to emphasise that because the vorticity at hypersonic Mach numbers is

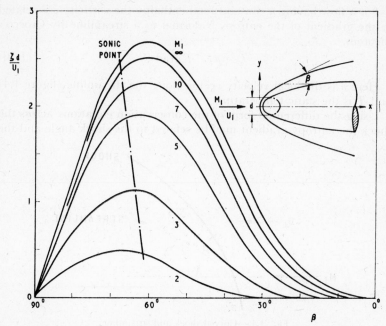

FIG. 1.5.—Vorticity behind shock of form $y/d = (x/d)^{\frac{1}{2}}$, $(\gamma = 1\cdot4)$.

much greater than at supersonic Mach numbers, we may expect the effect of interactions between the vortex surfaces and any expansion waves from the body to become a dominant feature of the flow field at high Mach numbers.

1.4. Prandtl–Meyer Expansion

In supersonic flow the expansion round a convex surface can take place without any shock wave forming, and the relationship between the angle, θ, turned through by the flow from the initial direction, the initial Mach number, M_1, and the local Mach number M_2 is given by the Prandtl–Meyer relation

$$\theta = \sqrt{\frac{\gamma+1}{\gamma-1}} \left[\tan^{-1} \sqrt{\frac{\gamma-1}{\gamma+1}(M_1{}^2-1)} \right.$$
$$\left. - \tan^{-1} \sqrt{\frac{\gamma-1}{\gamma+1}(M_2{}^2-1)} \right]$$
$$- [\tan^{-1} \sqrt{M_1{}^2-1} - \tan^{-1}\sqrt{M_2{}^2-1}] \qquad (1.42)$$

Assuming that both M_1 and M_2 are hypersonic, we may write approximately

$$\sqrt{M_1{}^2-1} \simeq M_1 \quad \text{and} \quad \sqrt{M_2{}^2-1} \simeq M_2$$

and using the expansion

$$\tan^{-1} M \simeq \frac{\pi}{2} - \frac{1}{M} + \cdots$$

we obtain, for M_1 and M_2 large

$$\theta \simeq \frac{2}{\gamma - 1} \left(\frac{1}{M_2} - \frac{1}{M_1} \right) \tag{1.43}$$

or

$$\frac{M_1}{M_2} \simeq 1 + \frac{\gamma - 1}{2} M_1 \theta \tag{1.44}$$

whence, from equation 1.11

$$\frac{p_1}{p_2} \simeq \left(\frac{M_1}{M_2} \right)^{\frac{2\gamma}{\gamma-1}} \simeq \left(1 + \frac{\gamma - 1}{2} M_1 \theta \right)^{\frac{2\gamma}{\gamma-1}} \tag{1.45}$$

The pressure coefficient is then given by

$$C_p = \frac{p_2 - p_1}{\frac{1}{2}\rho_1 U_1^2} \simeq \frac{2}{\gamma M_1^2} \left\{ \left(1 + \frac{\gamma - 1}{2} M_1 \theta \right)^{\frac{2\gamma}{\gamma-1}} - 1 \right\} \tag{1.46}$$

which may also be written in the form

$$\frac{C_p}{\theta^2} \simeq \frac{2}{\gamma M_1^2 \theta^2} \left\{ \left(1 + \frac{\gamma - 1}{2} M_1 \theta \right)^{\frac{2\gamma}{\gamma-1}} - 1 \right\} \tag{1.47}$$

This expression has the same form as the corresponding expression for the normal shock (1.35a), i.e.,

$$C_p = \theta^2 f(M_1 \theta, \gamma) \tag{1.47a}$$

Again, as for the compression through an oblique shock, the pressure coefficient varies with the square of the angle of inclination.

We may note from equation (1.45) that when the flow deflection angle is equal to $-2/(\gamma - 1)M_1$ the pressure after expansion becomes zero. Hence, for large values of M_1 it is only possible to expand through a relatively small angle before the pressure drops to zero; beyond this angle the flow must separate from the surface to form a 'cavitated' region, and in practice will probably separate some distance before this angle is reached.

The important consequence of this is that for a lifting surface at incidence the pressure on the upper (suction) surface will be low at high Mach number and most of the lift will be contributed by the lower surface (over which the pressure increases with M^2).

1.5. Hypersonic Flow Past Wedges, Cones and Flat Plates

The relationships obtained in section 1.2.2 for the flow through an oblique shock also represent the exact solution for the flow past a wedge having a semi-angle θ_W.

For the cone at zero incidence an exact solution of the equations of motion, the well known Taylor–Maccoll solution, may also be obtained. The properties of the flow field have been obtained from a numerical solution and are given in tables by Kopal (1947).

The variation of the shock angle with the semi-angle and with the Mach number is shown for wedges and cones at zero incidence in figures 1.6a and 1.6b.

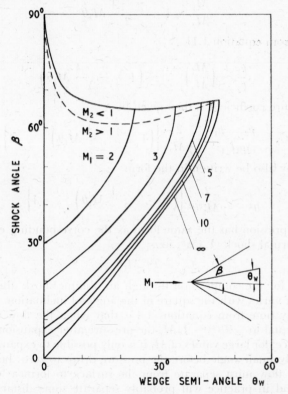

FIG. 1.6a.—Variation of shock angle with wedge semi-angle
($\gamma = 1{\cdot}4$).

The solutions to the equations of motion give two possible shock angles for each value of the wedge or cone angle, one corresponding to a strong shock and the other to a weak shock. Normally only the weak shock occurs, and only this part of the solution is shown in the figures. The close similarity between the solutions for the wedge and the cone is evident. For both flows there is, for a given Mach number, a maximum semi-angle for which an attached shock is possible. For

$M_1 = \infty(\gamma = 1 \cdot 4)$ this shock angle is 45·4° for the wedge, and is 58° for the cone. For larger angles than these the shock wave detaches and stands off from the nose by a finite amount.

Figures 1.6a and b show that except for very small wedge or cone angles, the shock angles change very little between $M_1 = 10$ and the

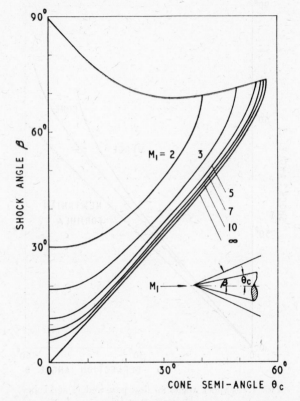

FIG. 1.6b.—Variation of shock angle with cone semi-angle
$(\gamma = 1 \cdot 4)$.

limiting value at $M_1 = \infty$, whereas there is a relatively large change with Mach number for hypersonic Mach numbers between 5 and 10.

At finite Mach numbers for the wedge flow there is a small range of semi-angles for which the flow behind the shock is subsonic (above the dashed curves in figures 1.6a). As M_1 increases this region becomes smaller and no longer exists at $M_1 = \infty$.

For small wedge angles in hypersonic flow the shock angle is also small, and as $M_1 \rightarrow \infty$ the ratio of shock to body angle approaches the value $(\gamma + 1)/2$ (equation 1.33).

For slender cones, approximate expressions for the ratio of the shock angle to the body angle, and for the pressure coefficient are given in section 2 of Chapter 4. As $M_1 \to \infty$, we obtain $\beta/\theta_c \to 2(\gamma + 1)/(\gamma + 3)$. Evidently, as $\gamma \to 1$, $\beta \to \theta_c$ as for the wedge flow.

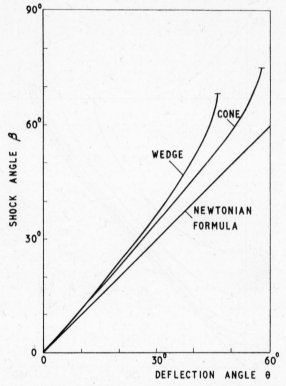

Fig. 1.7.—Shock angles for flow past wedges and cones $(M_1 = \infty, \gamma = 1\cdot4)$.

To bring out more clearly the similarities between wedge and cone flows, the shock-angle and the pressure coefficients for $M_1 = \infty$ have been plotted against the wedge or cone semi-angle in figures 1.7 and 1.8. It is evident that the two solutions are close together up to quite large values of the semi-angle. The pressure coefficient obtained from the Newtonian approximation is also shown on the figure and is discussed in Section 4.4.

Since for supersonic flow past a wedge the flow over the upper and lower surfaces are independent of each other, the flow past a wedge at incidence may be calculated using the oblique shock relationships by choosing different angles for the two surfaces. (For surfaces at negative incidence the Prandtl–Meyer solution must be used.)

Approximate solutions have also been tabulated (Kopal, 1947) for the flow past cones at incidence, and this and the wedge solution serve as useful models for checking the results of some of the methods discussed in later chapters, for calculating the flow past sharp nosed bodies with attached shocks.

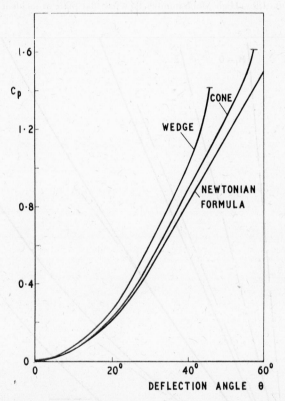

FIG. 1.8.—Pressure coefficients for flow past wedges and cones
$(M_1 = \infty, \gamma = 1\cdot4)$.

A limiting case of the flow past a wedge is the flow past an ideal flat plate of zero thickness at incidence α (figure 1.9), assuming no separation on the leeward surface, and that there is no shock-boundary layer interaction.

Here the oblique shock and the Prandtl–Meyer relationships may be used to determine the pressure coefficient on the two surfaces of the flat plate. Combining equations (1.35) and (1.46) we

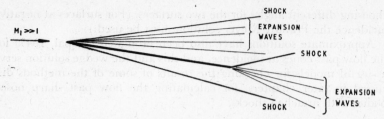

FIG. 1.9.—High Mach number flow past flat plate at incidence.

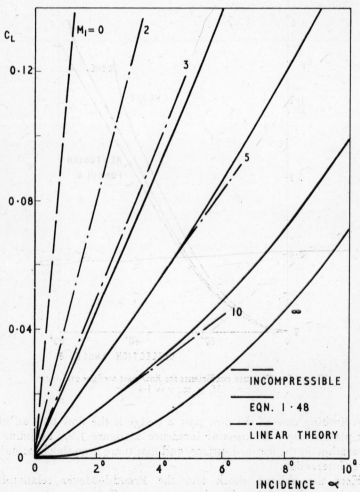

FIG. 1.10.—Variation of lift coefficient with incidence for flow
past flat plate ($\gamma = 1.4$) (Linnell, 1949).

see that for small angles of incidence the lift coefficient based on unit chord is

$$C_L = \frac{p_l - p_u}{\frac{1}{2}\rho_1 U_1^2} = \left\{\frac{\gamma + 1}{2} + \sqrt{\left(\frac{\gamma + 1}{2}\right)^2 + \frac{4}{M_1^2 \alpha^2}}\right.$$

$$\left. + \frac{2}{\gamma M_1^2}\left[1 - \left(1 + \frac{\gamma - 1}{2} M_1 \alpha\right)^{\frac{2\gamma}{\gamma - 1}}\right]\right\}\alpha^2 \qquad (1.48)$$

This relationship, which was obtained by Linnell (1949), is plotted in figure 1.10 for Mach numbers from 3 to ∞. (For $\gamma = 1.4$.)

Also shown on the figure (as dashed curves) are the incompressible values of 2π/radian, and the values obtained from linearised supersonic theory, which gives a lift curve slope of $4/\sqrt{M_1^2 - 1}$. The linearised theory evidently underestimates the lift at high Mach numbers and incidences.

As $M_1 \to \infty$, equation (1.48) simplifies to

$$C_L = (\gamma + 1)\alpha^2 \qquad (1.48a)$$

showing the proportionality of lift with α^2 which is a characteristic feature of the high Mach number flow past a flat plate.

assuming no separation

CHAPTER 2

GENERAL SIMILARITY PRINCIPLES AND CONCEPTS IN HYPERSONIC FLOW

2.1. Introduction

The results obtained for the simple flows discussed in the previous chapter suggest that two main regimes of hypersonic flow may be distinguished. For flow at moderate hypersonic Mach numbers, the shock shape and the flow quantities such as the density ratio and the pressure coefficient across the shock depend strongly on the value of the free stream Mach number, but for sufficiently high values of the Mach number the flow field about a given body changes only slowly as the Mach number is increased, and tends towards a limiting flow.

These two flow regimes are referred to in the Russian literature as 'high supersonic' and 'very high supersonic'. For the very high supersonic regime the term 'limiting hypersonic flow' will be used here. There seems however to be no clearly defined English term corresponding to the 'high supersonic' regime. For slender bodies with attached shocks, the term 'hypersonic' often refers to the region in which the hypersonic similarity parameter $M_1\tau$ is the governing parameter. Here we will call this the 'hypersonic similarity' regime. For blunt bodies, with attached or detached shocks, for which the hypersonic similarity law no longer holds, we will refer in addition to supersonic or hypersonic 'blunt body flows' depending on whether the free stream Mach number is below or above 5 (although some authors appear to refer to the flow past a blunt body with a detached shock as hypersonic for Mach numbers as low as 3).

In the present volume the limits of body semi-angle and Mach number for the regimes discussed above will be taken as:

1. Limiting hypersonic regime $M_1\tau > 5$.
2. Hypersonic similarity regime $\tau < 0.2$, $M_1 > 5$.
3. Hypersonic blunt body regime $M_1\tau < 5$, $\tau > 0.2$, $M_1 > 5$.

It will also be useful for the discussion in this and subsequent chapters to attempt to classify the types of body with which we will be concerned. Thus we distinguish between:

1. Blunt bodies with detached shock waves (figure 2.1a and b).
2. Blunt bodies with attached shocks (such as blunt wedges or cones having semi-angles below the attachment angle) (figure 2.1c).
3. Slender (pointed) bodies (with attached shocks, and semi-angles of less than 20°) (figure 2.1d).

4. Blunt nosed slender bodies (having slender afterbodies. The shock may be attached or detached) (figures 2.1e and f).

The existence of a limiting hypersonic flow, and the similarity laws which express the Mach number dependence of the hypersonic flow about slender bodies with attached shocks will be derived in the first

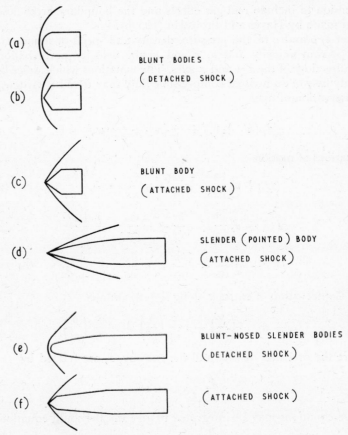

(a)

(b)

BLUNT BODIES

(DETACHED SHOCK)

(c)

BLUNT BODY

(ATTACHED SHOCK)

(d)

SLENDER (POINTED) BODY

(ATTACHED SHOCK)

(e)

BLUNT-NOSED SLENDER BODIES

(DETACHED SHOCK)

(f)

(ATTACHED SHOCK)

FIG. 2.1.—Classification of body types for hypersonic flight.

two sections of this chapter from the equations of motion and boundary conditions. These results are then extended to include the flow past bodies having blunt noses and slender afterbodies. The Newtonian flow model, valid for $M_1 \to \infty$ and $\gamma \to 1$, is introduced, and finally some discussion is given of the vortical layer associated with bodies at incidence.

2.2. Limiting Hypersonic Flow—The Mach Number Independence Principle

The concept of a limiting hypersonic flow appears first in a formal treatment by Oswatitsch (1951) (although Chernyi (1961) refers to an unpublished paper by Vallander written in 1949). Oswatitsch also extended the principle to include the flow past slender bodies, and an extension to include real gas effects and the boundary layer flow has been made by Hayes and Probstein (1959b).

Let p, ρ and a be the pressure, density and speed of sound, U_1 the free stream velocity and u, v and w the velocity perturbations in the directions of the x, y and z axes. The equations which describe the steady flow of an inviscid compressible fluid may then be written:
Conservation of mass

$$\frac{\partial}{\partial x}\left(\rho(U_1 + u)\right) + \frac{\partial}{\partial y}\left(\rho v\right) + \frac{\partial}{\partial z}\left(\rho w\right) = 0 \qquad (2.1)$$

Equations of motion

$$(U_1 + u)\frac{\partial u}{\partial x} + v\frac{\partial u}{\partial y} + w\frac{\partial u}{\partial z} = -\frac{1}{\rho}\frac{\partial p}{\partial x} \qquad (2.2a)$$

$$(U_1 + u)\frac{\partial v}{\partial x} + v\frac{\partial v}{\partial y} + w\frac{\partial v}{\partial z} = -\frac{1}{\rho}\frac{\partial p}{\partial y} \qquad (2.2b)$$

$$(U_1 + u)\frac{\partial w}{\partial x} + v\frac{\partial w}{\partial y} + w\frac{\partial w}{\partial z} = -\frac{1}{\rho}\frac{\partial p}{\partial z} \qquad (2.2c)$$

and Conservation of entropy along the streamline

$$(U_1 + u)\frac{\partial}{\partial x}\left(\frac{p}{\rho^\gamma}\right) + v\frac{\partial}{\partial y}\left(\frac{p}{\rho^\gamma}\right) + w\frac{\partial}{\partial z}\left(\frac{p}{\rho^\gamma}\right) = 0 \qquad (2.3)$$

where the pressure, density and the entropy, S, are related by

$$\frac{p}{\rho^\gamma} = \text{const. } e^{S/c_v}$$

These equations may be integrated to give the Bernoulli equation:

$$\tfrac{1}{2}[(U_1 + u)^2 + v^2 + w^2] + \frac{\gamma}{\gamma - 1}\frac{p}{\rho^\gamma} = \text{const.} \qquad (2.4)$$

The above equations hold for the flow upstream and downstream of the shock. Across the shock itself there is a discontinuous change of entropy, and the equations expressing the conservation of mass, momentum and energy across the shock must be used to relate the upstream and downstream flows. Since, however, the flow field remains unchanged by the presence of the body from infinity upstream to the shock envelope it is often convenient to treat the problem by regarding the conditions downstream of the shock as the boundary conditions for the flow past the body. These boundary conditions are given by equations (1.23) to (1.25) of Chapter 1. The variables in equations (2.1) to (2.4) then refer to the flow field between the shock and the body.

For the boundary conditions at the surface of the body, it is required that the flow be tangential to the body surface, i.e. that

$$(U_1 + u)l_x + vl_y + wl_z = 0 \qquad (2.5)$$

where l_x, l_y and l_z are the direction cosines of the normal to the surface. In order to study the behaviour of the flow when the Mach number becomes very large it is convenient to make the equations and boundary conditions non-dimensional by using the variables.

$$\bar{x} = x/l \qquad \bar{y} = y/l \qquad \bar{z} = z/l$$
$$\bar{u} = u/U_1 \qquad \bar{v} = v/U_1 \qquad \bar{w} = w/U_1$$
$$\bar{p} = p/\rho_1 U_1^2 \qquad \bar{\rho} = \rho/\rho_1 \qquad \bar{a} = a/U_1$$

Then the local Mach number is invariant, and the equations may be transformed to

$$\frac{\partial}{\partial \bar{x}}(\bar{\rho}(1 + \bar{u})) + \frac{\partial(\bar{\rho}\bar{v})}{\partial \bar{y}} + \frac{\partial(\bar{\rho}\bar{w})}{\partial \bar{z}} = 0 \qquad (2.6)$$

$$(1 + \bar{u})\frac{\partial \bar{u}}{\partial \bar{x}} + \bar{v}\frac{\partial \bar{u}}{\partial \bar{y}} + \bar{w}\frac{\partial \bar{u}}{\partial \bar{z}} = -\frac{1}{\bar{\rho}}\frac{\partial \bar{p}}{\partial \bar{x}} \qquad (2.7a)$$

$$(1 + \bar{u})\frac{\partial \bar{v}}{\partial \bar{x}} + \bar{v}\frac{\partial \bar{v}}{\partial \bar{y}} + \bar{w}\frac{\partial \bar{v}}{\partial \bar{z}} = -\frac{1}{\bar{\rho}}\frac{\partial \bar{p}}{\partial \bar{y}} \qquad (2.7b)$$

$$(1 + \bar{u})\frac{\partial \bar{w}}{\partial \bar{x}} + \bar{v}\frac{\partial \bar{w}}{\partial \bar{y}} + \bar{w}\frac{\partial \bar{w}}{\partial \bar{z}} = -\frac{1}{\bar{\rho}}\frac{\partial \bar{p}}{\partial \bar{z}} \qquad (2.7c)$$

and

$$(1 + \bar{u})\frac{\partial}{\partial \bar{x}}\left(\frac{\bar{p}}{\bar{\rho}^\gamma}\right) + \bar{v}\frac{\partial}{\partial \bar{y}}\left(\frac{\bar{p}}{\bar{\rho}^\gamma}\right) + \bar{w}\frac{\partial}{\partial \bar{z}}\left(\frac{\bar{p}}{\bar{\rho}^\gamma}\right) = 0 \qquad (2.8)$$

the boundary conditions at the body become

$$(1 + \bar{u})l_{\bar{x}} + \bar{v}l_{\bar{y}} + \bar{w}l_{\bar{z}} = 0 \qquad (2.9)$$

and the downstream shock conditions are

$$\bar{p}_2 = \frac{2}{\gamma + 1}\sin^2\beta\left\{1 - \frac{\gamma - 1}{2\gamma}\frac{1}{M_1^2\sin^2\beta}\right\} \rightarrow \frac{2}{\gamma + 1}\sin^2\beta \qquad (2.10a)$$

$$\bar{\rho}_2 = \frac{\gamma + 1}{\gamma - 1}\left\{1 + \frac{2}{\gamma - 1}\frac{1}{M_1^2\sin^2\beta}\right\}^{-1} \rightarrow \frac{\gamma + 1}{\gamma - 1} \qquad (2.10b)$$

$$\bar{u}_2 = \frac{2}{\gamma + 1}\left\{1 - \frac{1}{M_1{}^2 \sin^2 \beta}\right\} \to \frac{2}{\gamma + 1} \qquad (2.10c)$$

$$\bar{v}_2 = \frac{2}{\gamma + 1}\tan \beta \left\{1 - \frac{1}{M_1{}^2 \sin^2 \beta}\right\} \to \frac{2}{\gamma + 1}\tan \beta \qquad (2.10d)$$

In the reduced form of the equations (2.6) to (2.10), the Mach number appears only in the shock equations in the combination $M_1 \sin \beta$ (the component of the free stream Mach number normal to the shock). As $M_1 \sin \beta$ becomes large, the reduced pressure, density and velocity behind the shock tend towards the limiting values given on the right of equations (2.10). Thus the whole set of reduced equations then becomes independent of the value of the Mach number. (The flow field is sometimes said to be 'frozen'; this must not be confused with the same term as used to describe real gas flows in which the chemical state becomes frozen.)

The quantities which reach limiting values are those which determine the geometry of the flow behind the shock, i.e. the streamline inclination, the Mach angles and the streamtube areas. However, although the pressure coefficient also reaches a limiting value, the ratios of pressure and of temperature to the free stream values do not—they increase with the square of the normal Mach number for large values of the Mach number. The entropy jump across the shock also increases without reaching a limit—it varies as $c_v \ln M_1{}^2$. The 'Mach number independence principle' which results from the above analysis may be stated in the form that 'the flow past a given body reaches a limiting solution as $M_1 \to \infty$'. The principle has been extended to include real-fluid effects, including boundary layers, by Hayes and Probstein (1959), who also pointed out that in order to obtain a true limiting solution in real fluid, it is necessary for the Mach number to vary in such a way that ρ_1 and U_1 remain the same. This limitation does not apply if only perfect gas flows are considered.

For the flow to approach its limiting value, it is required that $M_1{}^2 \sin^2 \beta \gg 1$ and the value of free-stream Mach number for which the flow field becomes effectively independent of the Mach number will therefore depend on the geometry of the body, as well as on the value of γ. Thus the flow near the stagnation region of a blunt body with a detached shock will freeze at a lower Mach number than the flow at some distance from the nose, and the flow with an attached shock past, say, a relatively blunt cone will freeze at lower Mach numbers than the flow past a slender cone. Also, different flow quantities will become effectively frozen at different values of the Mach number, as may be seen from figure 1.2, which shows how the density ratio, the pressure coefficient and the Mach number downstream of an oblique shock vary with $M_1 \sin \beta$. It is, for instance, evident that the density ratio approaches its limiting value at a higher value of $M_1 \sin \beta$ than does the pressure coefficient.

It is found experimentally that for the flow past a slender body with a blunt nose, such as that shown in figure 2.2 the distribution of the local pressure coefficient along the body approaches its limiting value at surprisingly low values of the free-stream Mach number ($M_1 \sim 7$). The reason that this occurs becomes apparent if the limiting character-istic AB, from the shock to the rear of the body is considered.

The flow conditions near the body are seen to be influenced only by the strong part of the bow shock between the stagnation point S

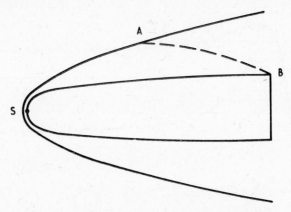

Fig. 2.2.—Hypersonic flow past blunt-nosed body.

and A, which would be expected to approach the limiting flow at fairly low hypersonic Mach numbers. It is experimentally confirmed that this part of the shock does not alter as the Mach number increases beyond say 7, and even further back there is surprisingly little change in the shock shape with increase of Mach number—although a long way from the nose the shock must degenerate to a Mach wave.

The concept of Mach number independence is an important one, for not only do many practical blunt body flow fields of interest approach the limiting flow at quite moderate Mach numbers, but the limiting flow may be treated theoretically as a first approximation for the flow at finite Mach numbers. (See Chapter 5.)

Experimentally the Mach number independence principle is fairly well confirmed for the drag coefficient of blunt bodies. Figure 2.3 shows some ballistic range measurements of the way in which the drag of spheres and blunt cones varies with Mach number. (Charters and Thomas (1945), Hodges (1957) and Stevens (1950).) It may be seen that the drag coefficient is nearly constant for Mach numbers greater than about 7.

Some caution must however be exercised when dealing with slender body flows if the normal component of the Mach number at the shock falls below about 2. As may be seen from figure 1.2, quantities such as the density ratio and the pressure coefficient behind the shock start to change very rapidly with further decrease in Mach number, and there is then a marked departure from the limiting conditions for parts of the flow outside the region of influence of the strong part of the bow

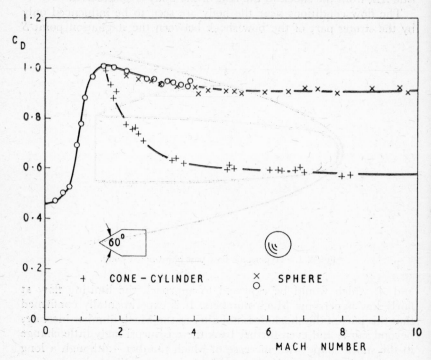

Fig. 2.3.—Ballistic range measurements of drag of spheres and cone-cylinders (○ Charters and Thomas (1945), × Hodges (1957), + Stevens (1950)).

shock. The effect of this on the shock shape for the flow over slender cones or wedges may be seen from the curves given in figures 1.6a and b. Thus, for semi-angles less than about 10°, the difference between the shock angles for $M_1 = 10$ and $M_1 = \infty$ is much greater than for larger semi-angles (for which $M_n > 2$).

Vas, Bogdonoff and Hammitt (1958) showed experimentally that for the flow of helium past blunted flat plates, the surface pressure varied with $M^{2.2}$ (and not with M^2) for a range of Mach numbers between 11 and 17.

2.3. Hypersonic Similarity Laws for the Flow Past Slender Bodies

The similarity laws for the hypersonic flow past slender bodies were first derived by Tsien (1946) for two-dimensional and axisymmetric irrotational flow field without shock waves, and Fal'kovich (1947) used a somewhat different method to derive the same result for two-dimensional flows. Hayes (1947) extended the derivation to include rotational and three dimensional flows, and showed that the equations were equivalent to those for unsteady flow in one less space dimension —the so-called 'equivalence principle'. More detailed studies of the small perturbation equations were made by Goldsworthy (1952) and van Dyke (1954) and others, and in Russia by Bam-Zelikovich, Bunimovich and Mikhailova (1949) Il'yushin (1956) and Telenin (1956).

At supersonic speeds, the equations of motion can be considerably simplified if the flow past slender bodies with attached shock waves is considered. Because the shock waves are weak the flow field can be considered to be irrotational and the perturbations of densities, pressures and velocities in the flow field are found to be small compared with the free stream values. It is then possible to linearise the equations, and a wave equation may be obtained for the velocity potential having solutions which can be superposed. For hypersonic flows, although the perturbation of the velocities due to the body may be small compared with the free stream velocity, the pressure changes can be large, and it is no longer possible to neglect certain of the terms which led to linearisation of the equation for supersonic Mach numbers. Nevertheless the approximate equations for hypersonic flow past slender bodies, although non-linear, are still easier to handle than the complete equations, and permit certain similarity laws to be deduced.

The difference between the flows past slender bodies for supersonic and hypersonic Mach numbers is illustrated qualitatively in figure 2.4.

In supersonic flow the disturbance velocities produced by the body are small compared with the ambient speed of sound, a_1, and the nose of the body may be thought of as sending out weak disturbance fronts travelling only slightly faster than the speed of sound: these fronts move back with the main stream, so that the resulting shock envelope is nearly a Mach cone, and since the Mach angle is large, the distance between the body and the shock is large compared with the body thickness.

In hypersonic flow the disturbance velocities may be comparable with or greater than a_1, and the disturbances travel outwards as a series of relatively strong fronts which attenuate as they move away from the body, and which are 'blown back' by the high velocity to form a curved shock envelope lying close to the body, and which only degenerates into a Mach cone a long way back from the nose.

The ratio of a typical disturbance velocity, v, to the ambient speed of sound may be expressed in terms of the Mach number and the mean body slope $\tau = d/l$. For a slender body the flow velocity along the

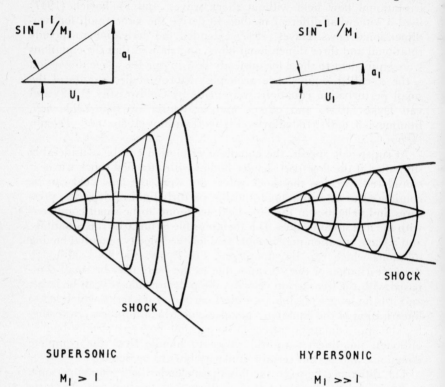

FIG. 2.4.—Shock envelopes for flows past axisymmetric slender bodies.

surface does not differ greatly from the free stream velocity at all Mach numbers, and we may write

$$\frac{v}{U_1} \sim \frac{dy}{dx} \sim \frac{d}{l} \sim \tau$$

Hence

$$\frac{v}{a_1} = \frac{U_1}{a_1} \tau = M_1 \tau$$

and $M_1\tau$ is seen to be the parameter characterising the strength of the disturbances produced by a slender body. For supersonic flow past a slender body, the parameter $M_1\tau$ can have quite small values. However, since there is a practical limit to the degree of slenderness of a body, we see that as the Mach number becomes large, we must have $M_1\tau \geqslant 1$. This means that in setting up approximate equations for hypersonic flow it is not possible, as is the case for the linearised supersonic equations, to neglect terms of order $M_1\tau$.

2.3.1. The Small Disturbance Equations

The orders of magnitude of the various parameters in hypersonic slender body flows may be obtained from the shock equations, or from the flow past simple bodies such as the wedges and cones discussed in the previous chapter, and are set out in the Table below:

TABLE 2.1

Quantity	Order	From Eqn.
$\Delta p/p_1$	$\dfrac{\gamma(\gamma+1)}{2} M_1^2\tau^2 \sim \gamma M_1^2\tau^2$	(1.25)
$\Delta\rho/\rho_1$	$\dfrac{\gamma+1}{\gamma-1}$	(1.24)
$\Delta T/T_1$	$\dfrac{\gamma+1}{2}\tau^2 \sim \tau^2$	(1.23)
$\Delta u/U_1$	$\dfrac{\gamma+1}{2}\tau^2 \sim \tau^2$	(1.36)
$\Delta v/U_1$	τ	(1.37)

Using these orders of magnitude, the following non-dimensional variables may be used to transform the flow equations and boundary conditions for a body of unit length; they are chosen to be of order unity when $M_1\tau \gtrsim 1$ and $\tau \ll 1$.

$$\tilde{x}=x, \qquad \tilde{y}=y/\tau, \qquad \tilde{z}=z/\tau$$

$$\tilde{u}=\frac{u}{U_1\tau^2}, \qquad \tilde{v}=\frac{v}{U_1\tau}, \qquad \tilde{w}=\frac{w}{U_1\tau}$$

$$\tilde{p}=\frac{p}{\gamma M_1^2\tau^2 p_1}, \qquad\qquad \tilde{\rho}=\frac{\rho}{\rho_1}$$

If these variables are substituted into the full equations and boundary conditions (2.7 to 2.9), and terms of order τ^2 are neglected, the resulting small disturbance equations are:

$$\frac{\partial\tilde{\rho}}{\partial\tilde{x}}+\frac{\partial(\tilde{\rho}\tilde{v})}{\partial\tilde{y}}+\frac{\partial(\tilde{\rho}\tilde{w})}{\partial\tilde{z}}=0 \qquad (2.11)$$

$$\frac{\partial \tilde{u}}{\partial \tilde{x}} + \tilde{v}\frac{\partial \tilde{u}}{\partial \tilde{y}} + \tilde{w}\frac{\partial \tilde{u}}{\partial \tilde{z}} = -\frac{1}{\tilde{\rho}}\frac{\partial \tilde{p}}{\partial \tilde{x}} \qquad (2.12a)$$

$$\frac{\partial \tilde{v}}{\partial \tilde{x}} + \tilde{v}\frac{\partial \tilde{v}}{\partial \tilde{y}} + \tilde{w}\frac{\partial \tilde{v}}{\partial \tilde{z}} = -\frac{1}{\tilde{\rho}}\frac{\partial \tilde{p}}{\partial \tilde{y}} \qquad (2.12b)$$

$$\frac{\partial \tilde{w}}{\partial \tilde{x}} + \tilde{v}\frac{\partial \tilde{w}}{\partial \tilde{y}} + \tilde{w}\frac{\partial \tilde{w}}{\partial \tilde{z}} = -\frac{1}{\tilde{\rho}}\frac{\partial \tilde{p}}{\partial \tilde{z}} \qquad (2.12c)$$

and

$$\frac{\partial}{\partial \tilde{x}}\left(\frac{\tilde{p}}{\tilde{\rho}_z{}^\gamma}\right) + \tilde{v}\frac{\partial y}{\partial \tilde{y}}\left(\frac{\tilde{p}}{\tilde{\rho}_z{}^\gamma}\right) + \tilde{w}\frac{\partial}{\partial \tilde{z}}\left(\frac{p}{\tilde{\rho}_z{}^\gamma}\right) = 0 \qquad (2.13)$$

the body boundary conditions are

$$l_x + \tilde{v}l_y + \tilde{w}l_z = 0 \qquad (2.14)$$

and the shock conditions are

$$\tilde{\rho} = \frac{\gamma + 1}{\gamma - 1}\left\{\frac{\left(\dfrac{d\tilde{r}}{d\tilde{x}}\right)^2}{\left(\dfrac{d\tilde{r}}{d\tilde{x}}\right)^2 + \dfrac{2}{\gamma - 1}\dfrac{1}{M_1{}^2\tau^2}}\right\} \qquad (2.15a)$$

$$\tilde{p} = \frac{2}{\gamma + 1}\left\{\left(\frac{d\tilde{r}}{d\tilde{x}}\right)^2 - \frac{\gamma - 1}{2\gamma}\frac{1}{M_1{}^2\tau^2}\right\} \qquad (2.15b)$$

$$\tilde{u} = -\frac{2}{\gamma + 1}\left\{\left(\frac{d\tilde{r}}{d\tilde{x}}\right)^2 - \frac{1}{M_1{}^2\tau^2}\right\} \qquad (2.15c)$$

and

$$\tilde{v} = \left\{\frac{2}{\gamma + 1}\left(\frac{d\tilde{r}}{d\tilde{x}}\right)^2 - \frac{1}{M_1{}^2\tau^2}\right\}\left(\frac{d\tilde{r}}{d\tilde{x}}\right)^{-1} \qquad (2.15d)$$

Here, $d\tilde{r}/dx$ is the shock slope in reduced coordinates ($= \beta/\tau$) and the free stream conditions are

$$\tilde{u} = \tilde{v} = \tilde{w} = 0 \qquad \tilde{\rho} = 1 \text{ and } \tilde{p} = \frac{1}{\gamma M_1{}^2\tau^2}$$

These equations have two important properties. Firstly the variable $\tilde{u}$ appears only in equation (2.12a) which means that the equations may be solved first for $\tilde{v}$, $\tilde{w}$, $\tilde{\rho}$ and $\tilde{p}$ and that $\tilde{u}$ may be subsequently obtained from the Bernoulli equation, which, in small disturbance form, becomes

$$\tilde{u} + \frac{\tilde{v}^2 + \tilde{w}^2}{2} + \frac{\gamma}{\gamma - 1}\frac{\tilde{p}}{\tilde{\rho}} = \frac{1}{\gamma - 1}\frac{1}{M_1{}^2\tau^2} \qquad (2.16)$$

(Substitution of $\tilde{p}$, $\tilde{\rho}$, $\tilde{v}$ and $\tilde{w}$ from the shock equation shows that the form of $\tilde{u}$ given in (2.15c) is consistent with this form of the Bernoulli equation). The second important property is that the Mach number and the body slope appear only in the combination $M_1\tau$, the 'hypersonic similarity parameter'. This means that the flow past affinely related slender bodies of similar geometrical shapes obtained by expanding or contracting the dimensions normal to the free stream direction will have the same values of the non-dimensional variables if the Mach number is altered in such a way that $M_1\tau$ remains constant. The hypersonic similarity concept can also be applied to a body at a small incidence α and similarity is obtained, if, for a given value of $M_1\tau$, α and τ are altered in such a way that the ratio α/τ remains constant.

The lift, drag, and moment coefficients for a body may also be expressed in terms of the non-dimensional variables. Thus, for a given body of form $f(\tilde{x},\tilde{y},\tilde{z})$ at incidence (basing the lift and drag on the cross-sectional area τ^2) we obtain for the drag coefficient

$$
\begin{aligned}
C_D &= \frac{D}{\gamma M_1{}^2 p_1 \tau^2} \\
&= \frac{1}{\gamma M_1{}^2 \tau^2 p_1} \int\int p \cdot dy\, dz = \tau^2 \tilde{D}\left(M_1\tau, \gamma, \frac{\alpha}{\tau}, x, \frac{y}{\tau}, \frac{z}{\tau}\right)
\end{aligned}
\tag{2.17}
$$

for the lift coefficient

$$
\begin{aligned}
C_L &= \frac{L}{\gamma M_1{}^2 p_1 \tau^2} \\
&= \frac{1}{\gamma M_1{}^2 p_1 \tau^2} \int\int p \cdot dx \cdot dy = \tau \tilde{L}\left(M_1\tau, \gamma, \frac{\alpha}{\tau}, x, \frac{y}{\tau}, \frac{z}{\tau}\right)
\end{aligned}
\tag{2.18}
$$

and for the moment coefficient (based on the area τ^2 and on unit body length)

$$
\begin{aligned}
C_M &= \frac{M}{\gamma M_1{}^2 \tau^2 p_1} \\
&= \frac{1}{\gamma M_1{}^2 p_1 \tau^2} \int\int p \cdot x \cdot dx \cdot dy = \tau \tilde{M}\left(M_1\tau, \gamma, \frac{\alpha}{\tau}, x, \frac{y}{\tau}, \frac{z}{\tau}\right)
\end{aligned}
\tag{2.19}
$$

where $\tilde{D}$, $\tilde{L}$ and $\tilde{M}$ are non-dimensional drag, lift and moment functions. It may be noted that since α/τ is constant for similar flows, $M_1\alpha$ may be used in place of $M_1\tau$ in the above formulae.

The application of the similarity concept to winged bodies at incidence is illustrated in figure 2.5.

The lateral extent of the wings is characterised by the aspect ratio $\mathcal{R} = b/l$ and if $\tau/\mathcal{R} \sim 1$ then to obtain similarity between the two bodies at two different Mach numbers and angles of incidence in addition to $M_1\tau$ being constant, α/τ and $\tau/\mathcal{R}$ ($\simeq d/b$) must be constant.

For a wing having a large aspect ratio such that $\tau/\mathcal{R} \ll 1$ the form of similarity required becomes simplified, because the shock over the wings in hypersonic flow will be flat and will lie close to the body, and both u and w will be small compared with v. The equations of motion then reduce to a one-dimensional form which is independent of aspect ratio and only the two parameters $M_1\tau$ and α/τ are required. Essentially this means that the similarity law is valid on chordwise strips on the surface of the wing and this form of similarity is known as 'strip theory'.

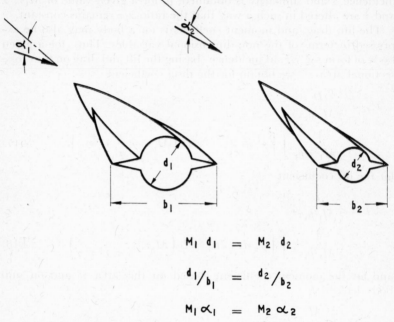

$$M_1 \; d_1 \;=\; M_2 \; d_2$$

$$d_1/b_1 \;=\; d_2/b_2$$

$$M_1 \, \alpha_1 \;=\; M_2 \, \alpha_2$$

Fig. 2.5.—Hypersonic similarity for slender wing-body configuration.

2.3.2 Oscillating Aerofoils

For unsteady flow fields, such as those due to an oscillating aerofoil, the similarity principle may be used, provided that the aerofoil is thin, if a reduced time variable $\tilde{t} = U_1 t$ is used. By using the transformation $\tilde{x} = \tilde{x} - \tilde{t}$, the unsteady flow equations which involve the time derivative in the form $(\partial/\partial\tilde{t} + \partial/\partial\tilde{x})$, reduce to the same form as the small perturbation equations (2.12)–(2.14). (This means that space axes are used instead of body axes.) The variable τ may be interpreted as the angle of deflection of the streamlines and since τ must be small, the theory will not apply for large amplitude or high frequency oscillations. The extension of the similarity law to unsteady flows was first made by Hamaker, Neice and Wong (1953) and Lighthill (1953) derived the expressions for the aerodynamic derivatives of oscillating aerofoils using piston theory, in which the flow is assumed to be similar to that caused by an oscillating piston in a tube. Piston theory is developed further in a paper by Ashley and Zartarian (1956).

2.3.3. Unified Supersonic-hypersonic Similitude

As given above, the small disturbance equations are valid only for $M_1\tau \gtrsim 0(1)$, and cannot be used for the flow past slender bodies at supersonic Mach numbers. The difficulty arises because of the form chosen for the reduced variable; thus the pressure $\tilde{p} = p/\gamma M_1^2 p_1\tau \to \infty$ as $M_1\tau \to 0$. Van Dyke (1951) showed that this could be overcome by using the pressure difference $p - p_1$ in place of p (and $\rho - \rho_1$ for the density) and that the theory could be extended to include the normal linearised Prandtl–Glauert theory by replacing M_1 by $\sqrt{M_1^2 - 1}$. (This reduces to M_1 as M_1 becomes large.) The unified supersonic hypersonic similarity parameter is then $\sqrt{M_1^2 - 1} \cdot \tau$.

A different method of deriving the small disturbance equations so as to include both the hypersonic and supersonic theory was given by Il'yushin (1956) who used $(\tau + 1/M_1)$ in place of τ.

2.3.4. Limiting Hypersonic Flow for Slender Bodies

For very large values of the Mach number for the flow past a body of given thickness τ, the value of $M_1\tau$ will become sufficiently large for the shock equations (2.15) to reduce to their strong shock form

$$\tilde{p} = \frac{2}{\gamma + 1}\left(\frac{d\tilde{r}}{d\tilde{x}}\right)^2 \tag{2.20a}$$

$$\tilde{\rho} = \frac{\gamma + 1}{\gamma - 1} \tag{2.20b}$$

$$\tilde{u} = -\frac{2}{\gamma + 1}\left(\frac{d\tilde{r}}{d\tilde{x}}\right)^2 \tag{2.20c}$$

$$\tilde{v} = \frac{2}{\gamma + 1}\left(\frac{d\tilde{r}}{d\tilde{x}}\right) \tag{2.20d}$$

Since the Mach number no longer appears explicitly in the equation of motion or the boundary condition, a limiting flow is obtained as $M_1\tau$ becomes large, a result which is in accordance with the limiting flow discussed in the last section although, for small values of τ, the value of Mach number needed for the flow field to freeze may be unrealistically high.

2.3.5. Application of Similarity Principle to Hypersonic Flows

The application of the hypersonic similarity law to hypersonic flows is illustrated by the flow past wedges and cones shown in figures 2.6a and 2.6b.

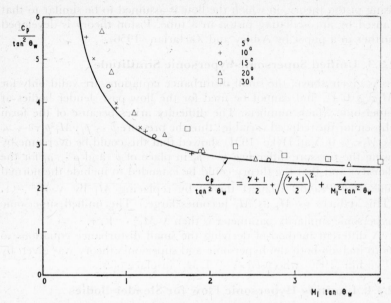

$$\frac{c_p}{\tan^2 \theta_w} = \frac{\gamma + 1}{2} + \sqrt{\left(\frac{\gamma + 1}{2}\right)^2 + \frac{4}{M_1^2 \tan^2 \theta_w}}$$

FIG. 2.6a.—Surface pressure coefficients on wedges ($\gamma = 1\cdot4$).

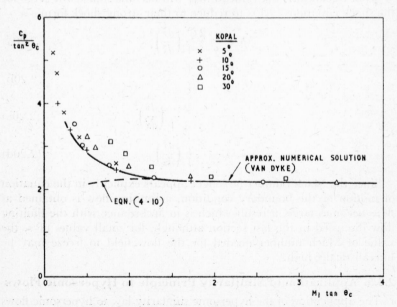

FIG. 2.6b.—Surface pressure coefficients on cones ($\gamma = 1\cdot4$).

In figure 2.6a is shown the pressure coefficient for the flow past a wedge plotted in the form $C_p/\tan^2 \theta_w = f(M_1 \tan \theta_w)$ where θ_w is the wedge semi-angle. Evidently satisfactory correlation is obtained for values of $M_1 \tan \theta_w \gtrsim 0{\cdot}5$ and for $\theta_w < 20°$ (by using the unified similarity parameter, with $\sqrt{M_1{}^2 - 1}$. $\tan \theta_w$ in place of $M_1 \tan \theta_w$ the correlation may be extended into the supersonic range).

The correlation for cones is given in figure 2.6b where the exact results for cones are obtained from the numerical calculations of Kopal (1947). The full line curve on figure 2.6a is the approximate relationship for wedge flows given by equation (1.34). The full-line in figure 2.6b is an approximate numerical solution for cones obtained by van Dyke (1954) (Section 4.6) and the dashed curve is an approximate formula given in Section 4.3 (equation (4.10)).

By taking as a criterion for hypersonic similarity the requirement that the exact value of the surface pressure coefficient should not differ by more than, say, 5 per cent from the limiting value obtained for wedges or cones of small angle, at the same value of $M_1 \tan \theta$, it is possible to obtain more precise limits for the region of applicability of the similarity laws. These limits are shown for wedges in figure 2.7a and for cones in figure 2.7b. The similarity laws may be taken to be valid in the unhatched region of the figures.

Neice and Ehret (1951) suggest that a similar criterion for the flow past ogives of different thickness ratio may be obtained from figure 2.7b by assuming that the flow obeys the same similarity relationship as that for a cone of the same nose angle. Thus the similarity parameter $M_1 \tan \theta_w$ for the cone is replaced by $M_1 d/l$ for the corresponding ogive. This was confirmed by characteristics calculations of the flow about ogives. (Actually ogives of different thickness ratio are not affinely related but for small thickness ratios the difference of shape is negligibly small.)

Only a very few systematic experiments seem to have been made to confirm the hypersonic similarity laws. The results of some experimental measurements at supersonic Mach numbers of slender cones at incidence (Neice and Ehret (1951)) are given in figure 2.8, which shows some measurements of the pressure on two cones made in the Ames Laboratory 10×14 inch supersonic tunnel.

The tests were made at two different values of the Mach number (4·46 and 2·75) and the cone semi-angles were chosen to give a constant value of 0·91 for the parameter $M_1 \tau$.

The incidence was then altered to give values of α/τ between -8 and $+16$, and the figure shows a comparison between the pressure ratios $(p_c - p_1)/p_1$ measured at corresponding points on the surface for the two cones. Apart from some separation effects which occur on the low pressure side of the cones, the pressure coefficients are the same at the corresponding positions as predicted by the similarity law.

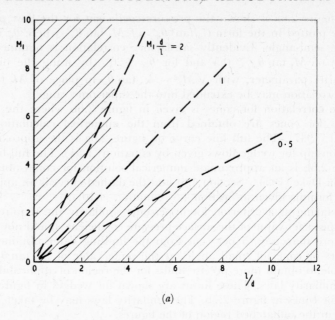

(a)

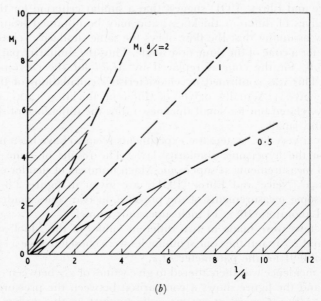

(b)

FIG. 2.7.—Range of applicability of similarity law for flow past
(a) wedges. (b) cones ($\gamma = 1\cdot4$).

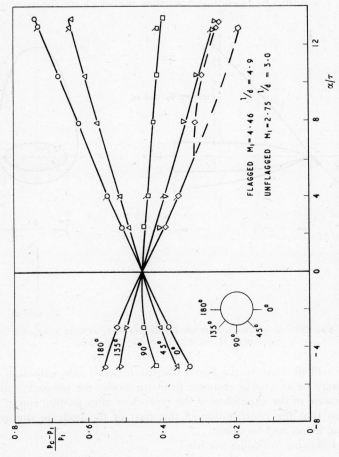

FIG. 2.8.—Measurements of surface pressure on two cones with M_1. $d/l = 0.91$ (Neice and Ehret (1951)).

2.3.6. Flow Past Bodies at Large Incidence

The similarity laws have been extended by Sychev (1960b) to include the flow past slender bodies at high incidence in hypersonic flow (figure 2.9).

For high values of the Mach number, the cross flow Mach number, $M_1 \sin \alpha$ will also be fairly large, so that the shock on the windward

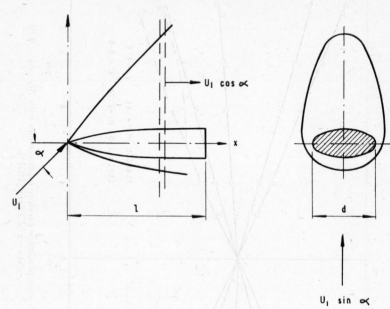

Fig. 2.9.—Equivalence principle for slender body at large angle of incidence ($M_1 \sin \alpha \gg 1$) (Sychev (1960b)).

surface will lie close to the body. On the leeward side, although the shock may be at a large distance from the body, the pressure will be low because of the expansion of the cross-flow after passing round the body, so that the contribution of this part of the body to the aerodynamic forces will be small.

The following variables are used

$$\bar{\bar{x}} = x/l, \quad \bar{\bar{y}} = y/d, \quad \bar{\bar{z}} = z/d$$

$$\bar{\bar{u}} = (U_1 + u)/U_1 \cos \alpha, \quad \bar{\bar{v}} = v/U_1 \sin \alpha, \quad \bar{\bar{w}} = w$$

$$p = p/\rho_1 U_1^2 \sin \alpha \text{ and } \bar{\rho} = \rho/\rho_1$$

and after substituting these into the equations of motion the shock equations and the body boundary conditions, the small perturbation equations which are valid for the problem are obtained. The flow is found to depend only on the two parameters

$$K_1 = M_1 \sin \alpha \text{ and } K_2 = \frac{d}{l} \cot \alpha.$$

The expression for the normal and axial force coefficients and the moment coefficient may then be written

$$C_N = \frac{N}{\frac{1}{2}\rho_1 U_1^2 ld} = \sin^2 \alpha \; \overline{\overline{N}} \, (K_1, K_2, \gamma) \tag{2.21}$$

$$C_D = \frac{D}{\frac{1}{2}\rho_1 U_1^2 ld} = \frac{d}{l} \sin^2 \alpha \; \overline{\overline{D}} \, (K_1, K_2, \gamma) \tag{2.22}$$

$$C_M = \frac{M}{\frac{1}{2}\rho_1 U_1^2 l^2 d} = \sin^2 \alpha \; \overline{\overline{M}} \, (K_1, K_2, \gamma) \tag{2.23}$$

For very high incidences for which $M_1^2 \sin^2 \alpha \gg 1$ Sychev notes that the strong shock solution becomes valid and that the Mach number independence principle applies to the pressure on the windward surface of a body at high incidence in hypersonic flow.

2.4. The Equivalence Principle (Law of Plane Sections)

2.4.1. The Equivalence Principle for Slender Bodies

It was noted by Hayes (1947) that if the substitution $x = U_1 t$ (or $\tilde{x} = \tilde{t}$) is made in the small perturbation equations and boundary conditions (2.12) to (2.13), then they become identical with the equations for unsteady flow in one less space dimension. This relationship between the steady and unsteady problems is called by Hayes the 'equivalence principle', and in the Russian literature (Il'yushin (1956)) the 'law of plane sections'.

The principle rests on the concept that when a slender body moving with hypersonic velocity passes through a thin plane layer of gas perpendicular to the motion of the body, and initially at rest, the gradient of the flow quantities normal to the layer are small compared with those parallel to the layer so that the resulting gas motion is largely confined to the plane layer. This is illustrated in figure 2.10a for a two-dimensional body and in figure 2.10b for an axisymmetric body.

That the value of the u perturbation velocity is an order of magnitude less than v has been noted in Section 2.3 of Chapter 1 (see also Table 2.1). In the small perturbation equations, u appears only in the x momentum equation (2.12a) and in the shock condition (2.15c). Thus the unsteady flow problem in the y,z-plane in figure 2.10b reduces to one in p,v,w and t (z and w are redundant for a two dimensional flow) and the value of u can, if required, be determined, after transferring back to the steady problem, from the Bernoulli relationship. The magnitude of u thus determined then serves as a check on whether the basic assumption made (i.e. that $u \ll v$) is correct.

(a)

(b)

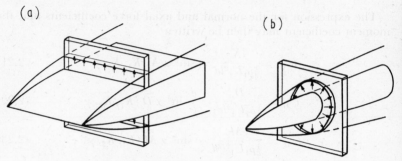

FIG. 2.10.—Equivalence principle for (a) plane, and (b) axisymmetric slender bodies.

The equivalence principle may alternatively be thought of (in a coordinate system in which the body is at rest) as applying to the gas layer between two planes of infinitesimal distance apart moving with a relative velocity U_1 past the body (figure 2.11). The body surface then behaves like a piston and produces an unsteady motion in the gas layer as shown in the y-t diagram.

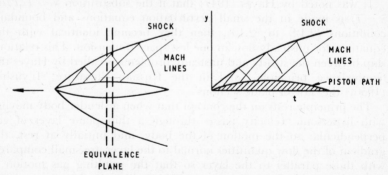

FIG. 2.11.—Equivalence between steady flow past slender body and unsteady piston motion.

The equivalence principle is important because it means that a number of existing methods and solutions for unsteady flow problems become available for steady hypersonic flows, and an important extension of the principle has resulted in methods of treating the effects of nose blunting on the flow past a slender body. A superficial resemblance may be noted between the equivalence principle and the

Munk–Jones cross-flow theory in supersonic flow. For the supersonic flow it follows from the form of the linearised potential equation, i.e.

$$(M_1{}^2 - 1)\phi_{xx} + \phi_{yy} + \phi_{zz} = 0,$$

that for a flow past a slender body for which $\phi_{xx} \ll \phi_{yy}$ and ϕ_{zz} near the surface, the problem of determining the force on a body at incidence α may be reduced to that of determining the unsteady flow on a y,z-plane due to a cross-flow velocity $M_1 \sin \alpha$. It is only near the body that $u \ll v$ in supersonic flow—near the shock $u \sim v$, and the method only holds locally for the flow close to the body. In hypersonic slender body flow $u \ll v$ near the shock as well and the equivalence principle is valid for the whole flow field between the shock and the body for a slender pointed body.

2.4.2. Extension of Equivalence Principle to the Blunted Slender Body—The Entropy Layer

A configuration of interest for hypersonic vehicle design is a slender body or wing for which the nose or leading edge is blunted in order to reduce the heat transfer to the stagnation region. At hypersonic Mach numbers the influence of the blunted nose can dominate the flow field for a considerable distance downstream of the nose, and a reappraisal of the validity of the small disturbance equations and of the equivalence principle must be made.

The discussion of hypersonic similitude and of the equivalence principle in the previous section was confined to slender bodies with attached shock waves. The derivation of the small disturbance equations demanded a small flow deflection; this breaks down near a blunt nose, although this does not exclude one possibility that at some distance downstream of the nose there may be regions of flow where the flow deflection is small and the Mach number still sufficiently high for the small disturbance equations to be locally valid.

The streamline pattern for the hypersonic flow past a body having a blunted nose and a slender afterbody is shown in figure 2.12.

The most striking feature of the flow field is that the streamtubes which cross the shock near the nose of the body expand rapidly downstream whereas those crossing a part of the shock having a small inclination remain initially fairly close to the shock. The streamline whose local inclination after crossing the shock is 20° (this is chosen to give a value of $M_1\tau \geqslant 0(1)$ for $M_1 \geqslant 5$) may be considered as separating the flow field into two parts, an outer 'shock layer' and an inner 'entropy layer' near the surface. The entropy layer is so-called because the flow which has crossed the almost normal part of the shock near the nose has undergone an entropy change which is large compared with that for the flow which has crossed the weaker parts of the shock outboard of the dividing streamline.

It is to be expected that the small perturbation equations will be valid in the shock layer. In addition we note that, if we exclude the nose region, the streamline inclination can also be small over much of the entropy layer, and we must then ask whether, in spite of the large entropy change which occurred when the streamlines in the entropy layer crossed the shock, the small perturbation equations will be valid, or, what is of more practical importance, whether the equivalence principle will hold.

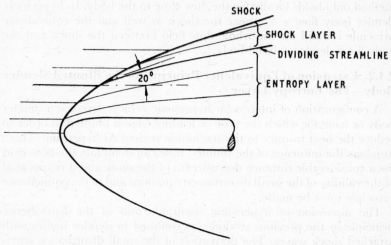

SHOCK

SHOCK LAYER

DIVIDING STREAMLINE

20°

ENTROPY LAYER

FIG. 2.12.—Streamlines for flow past blunt-nosed slender body.

The effect of the large entropy change on streamlines crossing the shock near the nose is to produce a large change of streamtube area, which results in a displacement of the shock from the position it would occupy if the nose were not blunted. Thus hypersonic similarity based on a parameter $M_1\tau$ where τ is the body fineness parameter will not be expected to hold for a blunted slender body, except for special cases where the flow field including the entropy layer can be affinely related, or where the displacement effect of the entropy layer can be shown to be small (cf. chapter 4, section 6).

For the equivalence principle to hold, however, it is required that the u perturbations are much smaller than the v perturbations on an equivalence plane moving with the free stream velocity past the body. It is shown later that because of the large entropy change near the nose, the condition that $u \ll v$ is not normally valid in the entropy layer downstream of the blunted nose. However it can be shown that $u \ll U_1$ some distance downstream of a blunt nose, and also that the change of pressure across the entropy layer is small. It is this rather fortuitous combination of circumstances which accounts in part for the apparent success of blast-wave methods in predicting surface pressure distributions. This is discussed further in Chapter 5.

2.5. Newtonian Flow

The free stream Mach number may be expressed as the ratio of the directed kinetic energy of the gas to its random thermal energy, i.e.

$$M^2 = \frac{U^2/2}{a^2/2} = \frac{U^2/2}{\gamma RT/2} \propto \frac{\text{directed (kinetic) energy}}{\text{random (thermal) energy}} \quad (2.24)$$

Evidently as the Mach number becomes large the directed energy becomes large compared with the thermal energy. This means that the effect of the random collisions between the atom or molecules of the flowing gas is of relatively little importance compared with the directed motion and the gas may be regarded as a stream of non-interacting particles. This bears a superficial resemblance to the gas model which was envisaged by Newton of a 'rare' gas consisting of small particles having a large distance between them. For large velocities he showed that if the particles do not interact with each other, then the resistance of a body on which the particles impinge will vary as the square of the velocity. Also by assuming no transfer of tangential momentum, and that the normal momentum of the particles is destroyed at the surface, he obtained the result that the force on a plate at incidence varies with the square of the angle of incidence. Epstein (1931) showed that with these assumptions the pressure on the plate is given by

$$p - p_1 = \rho_1 U_1^2 \sin^2 \theta$$

or

$$C_p = 2 \sin^2 \theta \quad (2.25)$$

and the agreement between this result and that of Newton and the relevance to hypersonic flow was noted by Busemann (1933) and Sänger (1933).

For the flow over a wedge, the correct result corresponding to (2.25) for $M_1 \to \infty$ is

$$C_p = \frac{4}{\gamma + 1} \sin^2 \theta \quad (2.26)$$

and evidently as $\gamma \to 1$ this agrees with Newtonian result.

It has also been shown in Chapter 1 that for large Mach numbers the relation between the shock angle β and the body angle is

$$\frac{\beta}{\theta} = \frac{\gamma + 1}{2}$$

so that as $\gamma \to 1$, the shock and the body become coincident, and the density ratio across the shock, $\rho_1/\rho_2 = (\gamma + 1)/(\gamma - 1)$, becomes infinite;

there is thus a layer of high density gas lying next to the surface, the 'Newtonian Shock Layer'. This may be regarded as the limit of the region between the shock and the body as the density ratio becomes infinite, and as the shock coincides with the surface.

For particles flowing round a curved surface, even although the gas layer is infinitesimally thin, there must be a centrifugal pressure gradient normal to the surface, and, for a surface which is convex to the oncoming flow, the surface pressure will be reduced. An expression for this centrifugal pressure gradient was given by Busemann (1933).

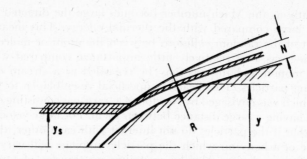

Fig. 2.13.—Assumed shock-layer structure.

In order to determine the centrifugal pressure gradient, it is necessary to attribute a structure to the shock layer. Thus, in figure 2.13 particles entering the shock layer at $y = y_s$ are assumed to continue round the surface as an identifiable layer. Following the derivation of Eggers, Resnikoff and Dennis (1957) the change in pressure from the surface to the shock due to the centrifugal forces is (figure 2.13)

$$\Delta_p = \int_0^N \frac{\rho U_1^2}{R} \, dN \simeq \frac{\bar{U}}{\bar{R}} \int_0^N \rho U dN \qquad (2.28)$$

where $\bar{U}$ and $\bar{R}$ are the mean values of the velocity and of the radius of curvature of a layer of gas of thickness dN. The mass of air flowing past a section on the body is given by

$$m = 2\pi y \int_0^N \rho U dN \simeq \pi y^2 \rho_1 U_1 \qquad (2.29)$$

(since in the limit $y_s \to y$).

Thus combining (2.28) and (2.29) the pressure change is

$$\Delta p = \frac{\bar{U}}{\bar{R}} \cdot \frac{y}{2} \rho_1 U_1 \text{ or } \Delta C_p = \frac{y}{R} \cdot \frac{\bar{U}}{U_1} \qquad (2.30)$$

Now if it is assumed that a particle entering the shock with a tangential velocity $U_1 \cos \theta$ retains that velocity (this is true as $M_1 \to \infty$ and $\gamma \to 1$) then the mean velocity

$$\bar{U} = \frac{1}{\pi y^2} \int_0^y 2\pi y \, . \, U_1 \cos \theta \, dy \qquad (2.31)$$

and, since, for an infinitely thin layer, $y/\bar{R} = y \sin \theta \, d\theta/dy$, we obtain

$$\Delta C_p = \frac{2 \sin \theta}{y} \frac{d\theta}{dy} \int_0^y \cos \theta \, . \, y \, . \, dy \qquad (2.32)$$

Expressing the result in terms of the cross-sectional area $A = \pi y^2$, the expression for the surface pressure is then that given by Busemann namely

$$C_p = 2 \left(\sin^2 \theta + \sin \theta \frac{d\theta}{dA} \int_0^A \cos \theta \, . \, dA \right) \qquad (2.33)$$

where the first term is that given by the Newtonian flow, and the second is the centrifugal pressure term. This is known as the Newtonian –Busemann relationship.

As will be discussed in Chapters 3 and 4 the Newtonian–Busemann theory does not give very good agreement with more exact calculations or with experiment for $\gamma = 1\cdot4$. However the behaviour predicted for $\gamma \to 1$ and $M_1 \to \infty$ is of interest in the sense that it may contain certain embryo features of which there are still vestigial remains at higher values of γ and at finite M_1 and it serves as the basis for methods involving some form of expansion in powers, for instance, of the density ratio $(\gamma + 1)/(\gamma - 1)$ or of the Mach number.

For a sphere the pressure according to equation (2.33) is given by

$$C_p = 2 \left(1 - \frac{4}{3} \sin^2 \theta \right) \qquad (2.34)$$

which vanishes for $\theta = 60°$ (measured from the forward stagnation point). Lighthill (1957) suggested that the shock wave separates from the surface at this point because the assumption of negligible streamtube area begins to break down as the pressure and hence the density decrease rapidly near this point (figure 2.14).

The separated shock layer is often referred to as a Newtonian 'free layer'. Since most of the streamlines remain close to the shock after separation, the shape of the shock wave may be determined by assuming that the centrifugal pressure drop across the separated shock layer reduces the pressure to zero—or from (2.33)

$$0 = \sin^2 \theta + \sin \theta \frac{d\theta}{dA} \int_0^A \cos \theta \, . \, dA \qquad (2.35)$$

This may be solved to give a shock shape which tends asymptotically to the form

$$y \sim x^{1/3}$$

This may be contrasted with the result (Chapter 5, Section 2)

$$y \sim x^{1/2}$$

obtained from the Blast Wave Theory for the shock shape at some distance from the nose. A recent study by Freeman (1960) has shown how it is possible to reconcile the two results.

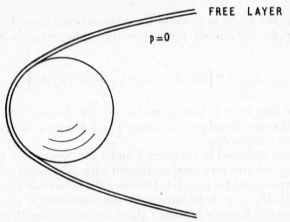

FIG. 2.14.—Separation of shock layer for flow past sphere.

2.6. Incidence Effects—The Vortical Layer

For a body at incidence in supersonic or hypersonic flow the flow field is further complicated by the appearance of what is called the vortical layer. For simplicity we will consider the case of a cone of circular cross section.

For a cone at zero incidence, the angle between the cone generators and the stream direction is constant, so that the entropy is constant and the flow field is everywhere irrotational. The radial surfaces of constant entropy for the flow past a cone are shown in figure 2.15. (These surfaces are the traces on a unit sphere of the surfaces joining all the streamlines which have entered the shock along a given generator.)

When a cone is at incidence the shock wave, which is also of conical form, is inclined. This means that although the local surface shape is constant along each generator of the shock, it will vary from generator to generator so that there will be circumferential gradients of the flow quantities behind the shock. There are then different values of entropy on streamlines entering at different parts of the shock, and the flow field is rotational; that is, vorticity is present.

Ferri (1951) pointed out that the surface of the cone must have a constant value of entropy, and suggested that the streamline traces, instead of being radial, must commence to diverge away from the lower generator of the cone, as they approach the cone surface, and converge towards a 'vortical singularity' situated, at any rate for small angles of incidence, at the upper generator. Along this vortical singularity the entropy would be many-valued, and the surface of the body itself could then be at constant entropy. (At high angles of incidence it is possible that the singularity might occur off the body, or that there might be

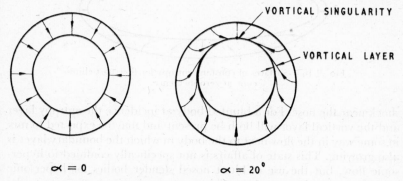

$\alpha = 0$ $\alpha = 20^{\circ}$

FIG. 2.15.—Surfaces of constant entropy for flow past cone.

more than one singularity). Ferri's solutions for the flow field show that the surfaces of constant entropy, which must be radial close to the shock, form a thin 'vortical layer' close to the surface of the cone across which a large change of vorticity takes place.

The thickness δ_v of this vortical layer was shown by Guiraud (1960) to be given by

$$\delta_v \simeq \frac{\bar{\gamma} - 1}{\bar{\gamma} + 1} \, \exp\left[- \frac{\bar{\gamma} + 1}{\alpha(\bar{\gamma} - 1)} \right], \qquad (2.36)$$

where $\bar{\gamma}$ is a mean fictitious adiabatic index representing the thermodynamic properties of the gas downstream of the shock and α is the angle of incidence. A similar analysis was made by Cheng (1960a and 1962) who also showed that even for high values of the density ratio a vortical 'sub-layer' is still distinguishable at the base of the shock layer.

A vortical layer will also be present in the flow past non-circular conical bodies at zero incidence, because for these also the value of entropy varies from generator to generator. The lines of constant entropy for the flow past an elliptic cone are shown in figure 2.16.

Such bodies have been considered by Briggs (1959), Stocker and Mauger (1962), Mauger (1960), Radnakrishnan (1958) and Chapkis (1961).

The discussion thus far has been confined to conical bodies with attached shocks having straight generators. If the shock has longitudinal curvature there will also be entropy changes throughout the flow field, and, in particular, if the body has a detached shock wave about a blunted nose, there will be the entropy layer arising from the large entropy changes associated with those streamlines which cross the

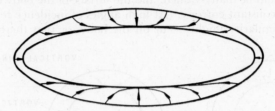

FIG. 2.16.—Surfaces of constant entropy for flow past elliptic cone at zero incidence.

shock near the nose. For a blunted body at incidence the entropy layer and the vortical layer will both be present and may be expected to mix in some way in the flow next to the body in which the boundary layer is also growing. This state of affairs is not specifically confined to hypersonic flow, but the use of blunt nosed slender bodies for hypersonic vehicles means that aerodynamicists are now having to face up to the problems of the effect of vorticity in the external field on the boundary layer development and on the heat transfer.

CHAPTER 3

SUPERSONIC AND HYPERSONIC BLUNT BODY FLOW

3.1. Introduction

Bodies having a blunt nose region are often used in hypersonic vehicle design (as, for instance, the Mercury and Jupiter capsules illustrated in figure 2 of the Introduction). Also, since, without special means of protection, the high heat transfer rates to a sharp nose will result after a time in the nose melting and becoming blunted by an ablation process, it is necessary to be able to calculate the local flow round the blunt nose in order to provide a starting point for the calculation of the flow over an afterbody. Such afterbody flows are considered in Chapters 4 and 5; in the present chapter we are concerned solely with the flow round the blunt portion of a body, behind a detached shock wave.

Normally for a blunt nose of, for instance, hemispherical, large angle conical, or disc-like shape, there will be a single shock standing off from the nose as shown in figure 3.1.

The stand-off distance Δ_s may, for small M_1^{-2} and for a small

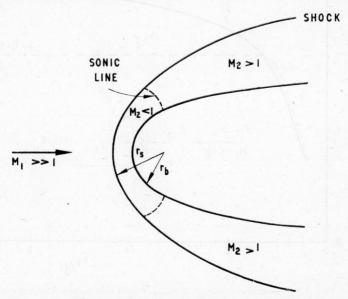

Fig. 3.1.—Subsonic and supersonic regions for flow past blunt body.

density ratio $\epsilon = \rho_1/\rho_2 = (\gamma - 1)/(\gamma + 1)$ be simply related to the body radius for a spherical body. Hayes (1955a and b) shows that Δ_s is given approximately for this case by

$$\Delta_s \simeq \frac{\epsilon r_b}{1 + \sqrt{2\epsilon}} \tag{3.1}$$

and that the flow velocity is nearly constant along the streamlines.

The flow mechanism for bodies having a more general shape was developed by Hayes (1955a and b), and is discussed further in review articles by Lees (1957) and Mangler (1959). It is clear from these studies that the stand-off distance is governed principally by the flow in the region of the sonic point on the body. Physically this seems reasonable since a finite stand-off distance results because the gas compressed by the shock near the nose must expand round the shoulder, and the mass flow will be governed principally by the disance between the sonic point on the body and at the shock, just as the mass flow in a convergent–divergent supersonic nozzle is governed by the throat diameter.

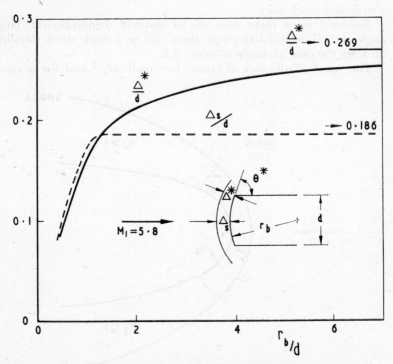

FIG. 3.2.—Variation of stand-off distance with nose radius. Experiments at $M_1 = 5\cdot8$ (Fraasa and Wisenbaker, 1957).

Figure 3.2 gives some measurements by Fraasa and Wisenbaker (1957) of the way in which the stand-off distances Δ_s at the nose and Δ^* at the shoulder vary with the nose radius for a series of blunt-nosed models ranging from flat-faced to hemispherical at $M_1 = 5\cdot8$.

The measurements show that three regions of the flow occur. Sonic choking occurs for these models from $r_b/d = 1\cdot3$ to ∞ ($90° > \theta^* > 69°$) and that Δ_s/d is effectively constant in this region, although

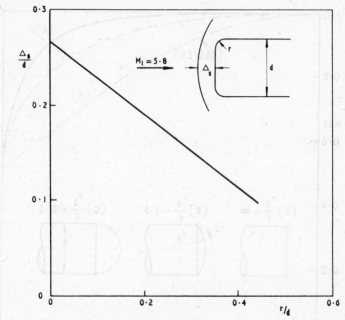

FIG. 3.3.—Variation of shock stand-off distance with shoulder radius, $M_1 = 5\cdot8$ (Fraasa and Wisenbaker, 1957).

Δ^*/d increases slowly with nose radius. For smaller values of r_b/d ($67° > \theta^* > 45°$) the sonic point on the shoulder remains fixed, and that on the shock moves towards the axis, whereas for $\theta^* < 45°$ (nearly spherical noses) both sonic points move towards the axis and Δ^* decreases almost linearly with r_b.

Some further measurements showing the way in which rounding-off the shoulder of a flat faced body affects the nose stand-off distance at $M_1 = 5\cdot8$ are given in figure 3.3.

As the shoulder radius increases, the stand-off distance decreases almost linearly. This illustrates the way in which the body radius of curvature in the sonic region controls the bow shock shape when the flow at the shoulder is choked.

The surface pressure, on the other hand, is affected mainly by the local body shape. Figure 3.4 shows measured surface pressure distributions for $r_b/d = 1\cdot3$, and ∞ together with the distribution measured by Oliver (1956) on a hemispherical nose. The pressure has been plotted against the distance along the surface referred to the distance s^* between the stagnation point and the sonic point on the body, and the local surface pressure may be seen to be a strong function of the body shape.

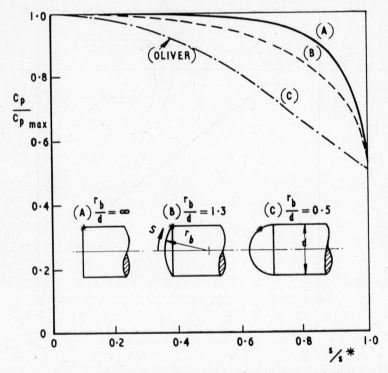

FIG. 3.4.—Surface pressure distributions on three blunt-nosed bodies at $M_1 = 5\cdot8$ (Fraasa and Wisenbaker, 1957).

For certain blunt shapes it is possible for a composite shock system to form as shown for the truncated cone in figure 3.5.

Such a flow can result if the flow on the conical part of the afterbody is asymptotically subsonic so that after the subsonic flow behind the leading shock has accelerated round the corner to a supersonic velocity, a second shock must exist to produce a subsonic flow again to match up with the afterbody flow. For the remainder of this chapter, however, we will consider mainly accelerating flows (see Vaglio–Laurin, 1962), that is to say, flows in which the velocity increases monotonically in the downstream direction along the shock, along the body surface, and along streamlines, and for which no secondary shock occurs. For such bodies we require to determine for supersonic or hypersonic Mach numbers the flow variables in the field between the detached shock wave and the body.

This field is normally separated into two regions by the sonic line, as shown in figure 3.1. At the nose is a region where the flow behind the

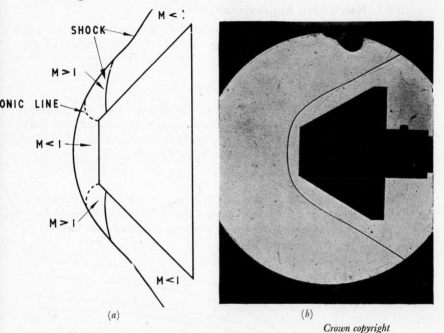

(a)   (b)

Crown copyright

FIG. 3.5.—Flow past truncated blunt cone (a) diagram, (b) shadowgraph of flow past a truncated cone at $M_1 = 6.85$ (R.A.E. Hypersonic Tunnel)

shock is subsonic and in which the governing equations are of elliptic type. Beyond the sonic line the flow becomes supersonic, and the governing equations are of hyperbolic type. The flow in the hyperbolic region can be determined by the method of characteristics once conditions are known along the sonic lines. The major computational difficulties arise in the subsonic region, and to date no exact analytical solutions are available so that recourse has to be made to numerical methods. In addition a number of approximate methods of determining various flow parameters have been used. To discuss blunt body flows further we will follow, at least in part, the excellent review by van Dyke (1958b) of this subject. The various methods discussed here are:

1. Newtonian approximations.
2. Potential flow approximation.

3. Incompressible approximation.
4. Taylor series expansion from shock.
5. Indirect numerical methods.
6. Direct numerical methods.

3.2. Approximate Methods of Calculating Blunt Body Flows

3.2.1. Newtonian Approximation

For Newtonian flow it is assumed that the normal component of momentum is destroyed at the surface and that the tangential component remains unchanged. This, as discussed in Chapter 2, leads to the *Newtonian Formula*

$$C_p = 2 \sin^2 \theta \qquad (3.2)$$

for the pressure coefficient on a surface at an angle θ to the free stream.

An empirical modification to this formula suggested by Lees (1955) is to adjust this formula so that it is exact at the stagnation point on the nose, thus giving the '*Modified Newtonian Formula*'

$$C_p = C_{p_0} \sin^2 \theta \qquad (3.3)$$

where C_{p_0} is the stagnation point pressure coefficient. The value of C_{p_0} may be determined using the integral Bernoulli equation together with the usual shock equations, and is given by the Rayleigh formula

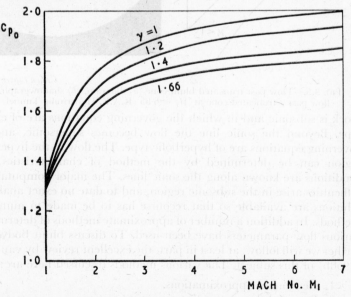

FIG. 3.6.—Variation of **stagnation** pressure coefficient C_{p_0} with M_1 and γ.

$$C_{p_0} = \frac{2}{\gamma M_1^2} \left[\left(\frac{\gamma + 1}{2\gamma M_1^2 - \gamma + 1} \right)^{\frac{1}{\gamma - 1}} \left(\frac{\gamma + 1}{2} M_1^2 \right)^{\frac{1}{\gamma - 1}} - 1 \right] \qquad (3.4)$$

C_{p_0} is shown in figure 3.6 as a function of Mach number for different values of γ. It is seen that as $\gamma \to 1$ and $M_1 \to \infty$, $C_{p_0} \to 2$ as given by the Newtonian formula.

Busemann showed that strictly speaking the centrifugal effects in the shock layer must be included, and, if this is done, the *Newtonian–Busemann* formula (Equation 2.50)

$$C_p = 2 \left(\sin^2 \theta + \frac{\sin \theta}{2} \frac{d\theta}{dA} \int_0^A \cos \theta \, . \, dA \right) \qquad (3.5)$$

is obtained where A is the cross-sectional area of the body normal to the free stream direction.

Again this may be modified to be exact at the nose, giving the *Modified Newtonian–Busemann Formula*

$$C_p = C_{p_0} \left(\sin^2 \theta + \frac{\sin \theta}{2} \frac{d\theta}{dA} \int_0^A \cos \theta \, . \, dA \right) \qquad (3.6)$$

Figures 3.7a and 3.7b show a comparison between numerical calculations of the surface pressure distributions for the flows over a cylinder and over a sphere at $M = \infty$ and $\gamma = 1 \cdot 4$ and the results given by the first three of the above formulae.

The closest agreement for both flows for $\gamma = 1 \cdot 4$ is given by the Modified Newtonian formula. This agreement is to some extent fortuitous since the surface pressure must depend on the body shape, on the Mach number, and on the value of γ. For $M = \infty$ and $\gamma = 1$ the pressure coefficient at the nose must approach the value 2, and the actual surface pressure distribution should tend to that given by the Newtonian–Busemann formula.

Chester (1956) has tried to extend the Newtonian–Busemann method for blunt bodies to apply to finite Mach numbers and $\gamma > 1$ by expanding the flow as a double power series in $(\gamma - 1)/(\gamma + 1)$ and M^{-2}, and, for $M \to \infty$, an expansion in $(\gamma - 1)/(\gamma + 1)$ only has been used by Freeman (1956). (A double series expansion method used by Cole (1957) for slender-body Newtonian flows is considered later in Chapter 4.)

Van Dyke points out that the series such as that used by Chester converges rather slowly for practical values of γ and that it is unlikely to yield useful results for the surface pressure for instance.

As discussed in section 5 of Chapter 2, a difficulty which arises with the Newtonian–Busemann formula is that it predicts zero pressure at the surface of a typical round-nosed body near $\theta = 60°$. Lighthill (1957) suggested that this difficulty may be overcome by assuming that the flow separates to form a free layer as $\gamma \to 1$. The singularity has also been studied in more detail by Freeman (1956).

For plane faced bodies ($\theta = 90°$), the simple Newtonian theories break down completely, and for bluff bodies having large values of the

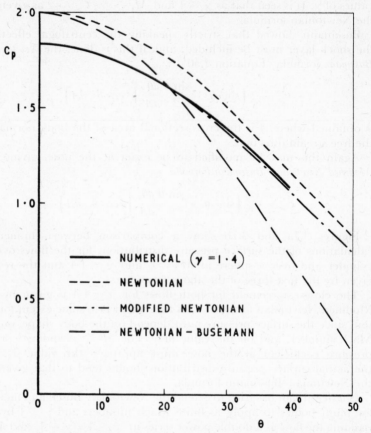

FIG. 3.7a.—Surface pressure distributions for flow past circular cylinder ($M_1 = \infty$, $\gamma = 1.4$) (van Dyke, 1958b).

nose radius of curvature, very poor agreement with other methods is obtained. A modification of Newtonian theory which permits the treatment of such bodies is given in a paper by Freeman (1959).

3.2.2. Potential Flow Approximations

The basis of these methods is an attempt to relate the actual flow between the shock wave and the body to some feature of the subsonic potential flow past the same body. Examples are given in papers by Laitone and Pardee (1947), Nagamatsu (1949) and Kawamura (1950).

The theories predict primarily the shock stand-off distance ahead of the body and figure 3.8 shows a comparison made by van Dyke between the results of a numerical solution and the stand-off distance for the flow past a sphere predicted by the different approximate methods.

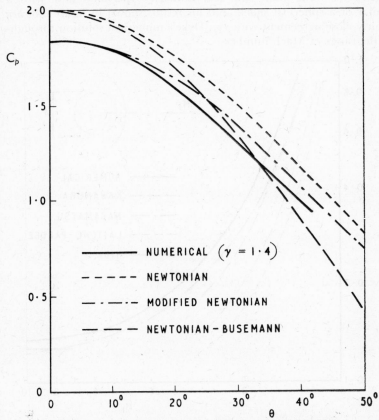

FIG. 3.7b.—Surface pressure distributions for flow past sphere $(M_1 = \infty, \gamma = 1\cdot4)$ (van Dyke, 1958b).

It is evident that none of these potential flow approximation methods gives a very close approximation to the numerical calculation—particularly for high Mach numbers.

3.2.3. Incompressible Approximations

Because the variation of density between the shock and the stagnation point on a body is small, a reasonable approximation would seem to be to solve the equations of rotational incompressible flow using the boundary conditions downstream of the shock waves. This method has been employed by Lighthill (1957) for the flow past a sphere and by Whitham (1957) and Hayes and Probstein (1959b), for the flow past a cylinder. (For both these examples the shock is concentric with the body.) Hida (1953) using a similar method, obtained the stand-off distance for both plane and axisymmetric sypersonic flow with a circular or a spherical shock, and his results shown in figure 3.8, are in fairly close agreement with van Dyke's numerical solution throughout the range of Mach numbers.

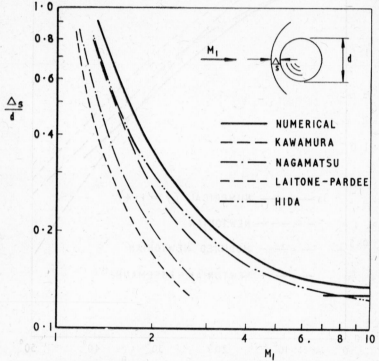

FIG. 3.8.—Stand-off distance of shock from sphere ($\gamma = 1 \cdot 4$) (van Dyke, 1958).

The results may be used to illustrate the relative importance of rotation and compressibility in the approximations. For $M_1 = \infty$ the numerical solution gives $\Delta_s/r_b = 0 \cdot 128$, whereas the value obtained by Hida and Lighthill is $0 \cdot 120$, and the incompressible potential flow approximation of Kawamura gives $0 \cdot 094$.

Thus we may write

$$\frac{\Delta_s}{r_b} = \underbrace{0 \cdot 094}_{\substack{\text{Incompressible} \\ \text{Potential}}} + \underbrace{0 \cdot 026}_{\text{Rotation}} + \underbrace{0 \cdot 008}_{\text{Compressibility}}$$

The compressibility increment thus appears to be small compared with the effect of rotation. A calculation by Heybey (1953) in which he tried to correct the potential flow approximation for the effect of compressibility appeared to overestimate the effect since he obtained an increment of 0·024 over Kawamura's incompressible solution.

3.2.4. Taylor Series Expansion from Shock

In the series expansion methods it is assumed that the shock shape is known. The flow variables downstream of the shock may then be determined from the oblique shock equations (since conditions are locally two-dimensional) and their derivatives may be obtained using the equations of motion. Using these values the flow variables are then represented as Taylor series in terms of distance from the shock, and it is hoped that by taking a sufficient number of terms, the whole region between the shock and the body can be represented; examples of this method are given in papers by Lin and Rubinov (1948), Lin and Shen (1951) and Cabannes (1951). However, as shown by van Dyke, successive terms of the Taylor series diverge as the body is approached. An explanation for this behaviour, which is given by van Dyke (1958b), is that upstream of the shock the Taylor series expansion has an analytic continuation which possesses a limiting line. Van Dyke suggests that if the shock wave is closer to the limiting line than to the body, the radius of convergence of the Taylor series will not include the body. He determines the limiting line for the flow past a sphere and shows that for this example the body does indeed lie outside the radius of convergence; he also suggests that the situation will be worse in plane flow, for certain other body shapes, and for regions far from the nose. Nevertheless, in practice, for a paraboloidal shock in axisymmetric flow at $M_1 = \infty$ he shows that the first three terms of a Taylor series are able to predict the ratio of stand-off distance to body radius within 0·8 per cent, although the solution breaks down before the sonic point is reached.

3.3. Numerical Methods

None of the approximate methods developed to date are able to give reasonable accuracy for the calculation of the flow field for flow at all supersonic Mach numbers and values of γ and we now consider various numerical methods of solving the blunt-body problem. Fairly complete reviews of these methods for symmetrical shapes at zero angle of attack are given by van Dyke (1958b) and Hayes and Probstein (1959b) and here we consider only those methods in common use and which are suitable for present-day electronic computing machines.

Basically there are two methods of solving the numerical problem. In the *direct method* the free-stream conditions and the body shape are given and the shock wave and the flow field must be determined, where-as in the *inverse method* the free stream conditions and shock wave shape are given and the position and shape of the body producing that shock, and the flow field are required. Obviously the direct solution is more satisfactory, although in the inverse methods it is normally possible to iterate the solution until the flow past a desired body is obtained. A fundamental difficulty with the inverse method, which at one time was considered by many theoreticians to exclude the use of such numerical methods for the blunt body problem, is that in the subsonic flow region up to the sonic line the initial value problem for an elliptic governing equation is unstable, so that any numerical errors, due for instance to rounding-off, will grow exponentially. However, experience has shown that the use of modern electronic computers having large storage capacity makes it possible to commence the calculation with a sufficient number of significant figures to still retain a reasonable accuracy after taking the required number of steps between the shock and the body.

3.3.1. Inverse Methods

The inverse method in most common use is that developed inde-pendently by van Dyke (1958b), and Mangler and Evans (1957). Essentially the method consists of numerically integrating the flow equations from the shock to the body by a marching technique.

The method has been applied principally to shocks having a shape which is a conic section. This is not unreasonable since schlieren photo-graphs of the flow past bodies having spherical or elliptical noses have shock shapes which are very nearly conic sections, so that by starting with a shock of this form one might expect to arrive at a useful body shape.

A shock shape which is a conic section may be described by

$$y^2 = 2r_s x - B_s x^2 \qquad (3.7)$$

where B_s is a shock bluntness parameter and r_s is the radius of curvature at the apex of the shock. Thus, $B_s = 0$ is a parabola, $B_s = -1$ a hyper-bola, $B_s = 1$ a circle, and other values of $B_s > 0$ represent prolate or oblate ellipses depending on whether $B_s < 1$ or $B_s > 1$.

For convenience a curvilinear orthogonal coordinate system (η, ξ) is employed which contains the shock surface as one coordinate. Van Dyke uses

$$x = \frac{B}{B_s} [1 - \sqrt{(1 - B_s \xi^2)(1 - B_s + B_s \eta^2)}] \qquad (3.8a)$$

$$y = B\xi\eta \qquad (3.8b)$$

where B is the bluntness parameter. The shock surface is then given by $\eta = 0$ and the upstream axis by $\xi = 0$.

Substituting these into the exact, inviscid, non heat-conducting equations of continuity, momentum and energy, and obtaining the values of the flow variables behind the shock from the oblique shock relations yields two coupled partial differential equations for the density and stream functions which can then be integrated numerically, by a marching technique, from the shock to the body. Van Dyke and Gordon (1959) have published a collection of solutions of both plane and axisymmetric flows obtained using this method for a wide range of values of shock bluntness, Mach number and γ.

The stand-off distance for a sphere in air as calculated by van Dyke is compared in figure 3.9 with experimental results; it is seen that extremely good agreement is obtained.

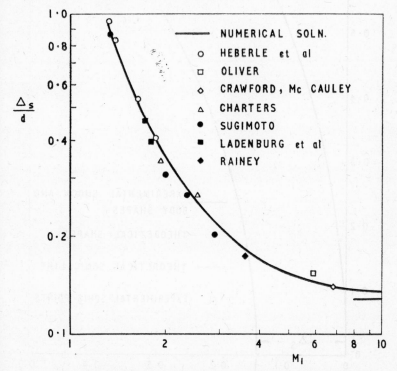

Fig. 3.9.—Stand-off distance for sphere. Comparison between numerical solution of van Dyke (1958b) and experimental results.

As another example of a calculation made using a similar method by Mangler and Evans (1957), figure 3.10 shows the shock and sonic line shapes for flow at $M = 7$ past a hemisphere compared with measurements made in air in the R.A.E. Hypersonic tunnel at $M = 6.8$. The sonic line position was traced using a probe ahead of the shock to produce a disturbance which was reflected at the sonic line to form a

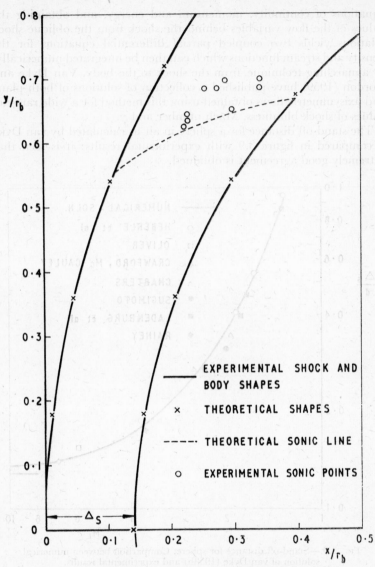

FIG. 3.10.—Comparison of theoretical shock shape and sonic line position for flow past hemispherical nose.

Theoretical	Experimental
$B_b = 0.964$	$B_b = 1.0$
$B_s = 1.0$	$r_b = 1.25$
$r_b/r_s = 0.743$	
$\Delta_s/r_b = 0.144$	$\Delta_s/r_b = 0.148$
$M_1 = 7.0$	$M_1 = 6.8$

cusp. Good agreement was obtained between theory and experiment.

An elegant method of solving the inverse problem is that due to Garabedian and Lieberstein (1958). To avoid the instability in the subsonic region, the initial data are continued into an imaginary third dimension where the flow equation becomes hyperbolic. This means that the method of characteristics can be used to obtain solutions and that proofs of convergence can be constructed. Van Dyke showed that there was good agreement between this method and his own for the flow past a body supporting a hyperboloidal shock at $M = 5\cdot8$ and $\gamma = 1\cdot4$.

A basic weakness of the inverse methods seems to be that shock shapes which are barely distinguishable from each other can lead to

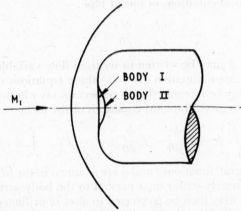

M_1

BODY I

BODY II

Fig. 3.11.—Different bodies having same shock.

radically different body shapes. An extreme example (given by Vaglio-Laurin (1962)) of two bodies having almost indistinguishable shock shapes is shown in figure 3.11.

The apparent insensitivity to body shape in this example arises principally because local disturbances near the body in the subsonic region tend to damp out fairly rapidly as one proceeds away from the body.

Vaglio-Laurin and Ferri (1958) suggest that some of the limitations of the inverse method can be overcome by computing the velocity along the stagnation streamline (after a transformation of variables) and also by using some information on the limiting line upstream of the shock (referred to in 2.4 above) which intersects the shock at the sonic line. This means that some information about the velocity distributions in the neighbourhood of the sonic line can be fed into the calculation. The problem can then be solved if desired by marching upstream from the body in the transformed plane; as an example the flow past a disc was solved by this technique.

3.3.2. Direct Problem—Method of Integral Relations

A method which is becoming widely used for the direct problem is the method of integral relations of Dorodnitsyn (1957). The technique is to assume a polynomial variation of certain flow quantities across a series of N strips between the shock and the body. By substituting in the equations of motion, a system of ordinary differential equations may be obtained which may be integrated across the strips.

We follow here the description of the method given by Chushkin and Shchennikov (1960). Using polar coordinates (r, θ) it is found that the equations of motion may be expressed in the form of first order partial differential equations of mixed type:—

$$\frac{\partial F}{\partial r} + \frac{\partial f}{\partial \theta} = \phi \qquad (3.9)$$

where F, f and ϕ may be written in terms of flow variables.

For the first approximation ($N = 1$) three equations of form (3.9) result. These may be integrated with respect to, say r between the body and the shock to give 3 integral equations of the form

$$\frac{d}{d\theta} \int_{r_b}^{r_s} f \cdot dr + f_b \frac{dr_b}{d\theta} - f_s \frac{dr_s}{d\theta} + F_s - F_b = \int_{r_b}^{r_s} \phi \cdot dr \qquad (3.10)$$

The 'subintegral' functions f and ϕ are assumed in the first approximation to vary linearly with r on a normal to the body surface, and the equations (3.9) may then be converted to a set of ordinary differential equations in one independent variable θ.

i.e.
$$\frac{df_s}{d\theta} + \frac{df_b}{d\theta} = \Phi \qquad (3.11)$$

where

$$\Phi = \phi_s + \phi_b + \frac{2}{r_s - r_b} \left[-F_s - F_b + \tfrac{1}{2}(f_s - f_b) \left\{ \frac{dr_s}{d\theta} + \frac{dr_b}{d\theta} \right\} \right] \qquad (3.12)$$

Equations (3.11) may then be expressed in terms of the flow variables and their derivatives at the shock, and the equations integrated numerically between the shock and the body.

Conditions at the sonic position must be obtained by an iterative process. An initial value of stand-off distance is assumed, and varied until the flow either passes smoothly through the sonic position for a smooth body, or becomes sonic at the corner for a sharp cornered body.

To obtain a second approximation ($N = 2$) a mean line is chosen between the shock and the body at $(r_s + r_b)/2$ and six independent integral relations of the form (3.9) are obtained—three from the shock to the mean line, and three from the mean line to the body. Second order polynomials are assumed for the flow variables, and the resulting ordinary differential equations may be integrated over the two strips. Extension to N strips is obvious—although for most examples given to date not more than 3 strips have been used because of the labour involved, particularly in the iteration process for conditions at the sonic line, which requires making the flow pass smoothly through N sonic 'throats'.

For further details the reader is referred to papers by Belotserkovski (1958), (1960), Traugott (1962), Holt (1958), Holt and Hoffmann (1961) and Holt (1961).

3.4. Blunt Bodies at Incidence

Numerical methods of solving the inverse problem for the flow past a body of incidence have been proposed by Mangler (1960), Vaglio-Laurin and Ferri (1958) and Vaglio-Laurin (1962). Mangler's method is an extension of his marching technique, Vaglio-Laurin and Ferri use a first order perturbation of the flow about a body at zero incidence, and Vaglio-Laurin employs the successive refinements of an approximate solution by the PLK (Poincaré–Lighthill–Kuo) method.

All three methods depend however, on the assumption that the stagnation streamline crosses the shock at right angles (i.e. it is also the streamline of maximum entropy). Mangler (1960) advances plausible physical arguments as to why this should be the case. Thus, if the stagnation streamline and the maximum entropy streamline are separated, a rather improbable situation results in which the rotation changes sign behind the shock in crossing the maximum entropy streamline and then has to change sign again in the same direction across the stagnation streamline.

An inverse numerical calculation by Swigart (1962) of the flow past a round nosed body using a series expansion method apparently gave a solution for which the stagnation and separation streamline were not coincident—although they were fairly close together. It is unfortunately not clear whether this arises because of some inaccuracies in the numerical solution, or whether it is a fundamental feature of the flow. It is to be hoped that this point will be clarified by further numerical calculations.

CHAPTER 4

HYPERSONIC FLOW PAST SLENDER BODIES

4.1. Introduction

The exact calculation of the flow past a pointed slender body at zero incidence for which the flow behind the attached shock is everywhere supersonic is simplified, compared with the blunt body flows considered in the previous chapter, because the flow at the nose, being either wedge or cone-like, is known exactly, and by using the method of characteristics for a rotational flow field, the flow downstream of the nose may be determined to any required degree of accuracy. The amount of computational effort required is, however, considerable, and although, using a high speed computer, a library of solutions can be obtained for the flow past families of bodies, this can never completely supplant the deeper understanding of the flow behaviour which often comes from even an approximate analytical treatment of a flow field. For this reason most of this chapter is concerned with approximate methods of calculating the flow past slender bodies, although the results of applying the approximate methods will be checked against the exact characteristics solutions where these are available.

Slender bodies having $\tau \ll 1$ represent an important class of bodies for practical applications particularly for sustained flight at hypersonic velocities where there is a need for reducing the drag in order to achieve aerodynamic efficiency. The slender form makes possible simplifications in the theoretical treatment of flow fields. Thus, for instance, the small disturbance form of the governing equations may often be used and the hypersonic similarity laws discussed in Chapter 2 are available for extending the results obtained for a given Mach number and thickness ratio to other flows having the same value of the hypersonic similarity parameter, $M_1\tau$. Although most of this chapter deals with bodies having pointed noses with attached shock waves, it also considers classes of slender bodies—for instance power law bodies having the form $y \sim x^m (1 > m \gtrsim 0.7)$—for which, although the nose is blunt, with a detached shock, the effects of the blunting nevertheless are confined to the nose region and to an entropy layer next to the body which is sufficiently thin for the small disturbance equations to hold over most of the field.

The approximate methods discussed in this chapter are:

1. The shock-expansion method.
2. The tangent wedge and cone methods.

3. The Newtonian–Busemann approximations and Newtonian Slender Body Theory.

4. Hypersonic Small Disturbance Theory.

5. Similarity Solutions.

4.2. Shock-expansion Method

This section concerns the flow past aerofoils or bodies of revolution having pointed noses and with an attached shock wave, such as the shapes shown in figure 4.1.

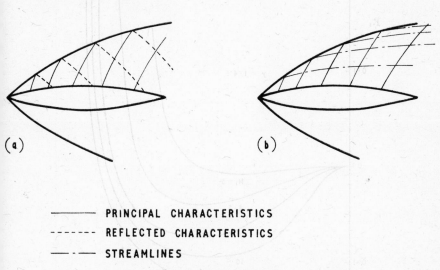

——————— PRINCIPAL CHARACTERISTICS

- - - - - - REFLECTED CHARACTERISTICS

—— · —— STREAMLINES

Fig. 4.1.—Principal and reflected characteristics for flow
past slender body.

Figure 4.1a shows the characteristics network for hypersonic flow past a convex body with the first family characteristics running out from the body to meet the shock and causing it to become curved, and being reflected at the shock to form a second family of characteristics running towards the surface. The shock-expansion method which, in its simplest form, was first suggested by Epstein (1931) amounts to considering only the first family characteristics as in figure 4.1b and assuming that the waves incident upon the shock are completely absorbed there, so that the second family characteristics may be ignored. The flow conditions round the surface of the body are then simply obtained from the known wedge or cone conditions at the nose, followed by using the Prandtl–Meyer relationship based on the local surface inclination.

A simple example of shock-expansion theory is the flow past a flat plate at incidence considered in Chapter 1, in which there was a straight shock on the lower surface and a centred Prandtl–Meyer expansion on the upper surface. The shock-expansion method is also employed implicitly in the treatment of thin aerofoils at supersonic speeds where it is normally assumed that the exact relationships for the shock waves and expansions may be replaced by the leading terms of a power series valid for small values of $M_1\tau$. (The Busemann series.)

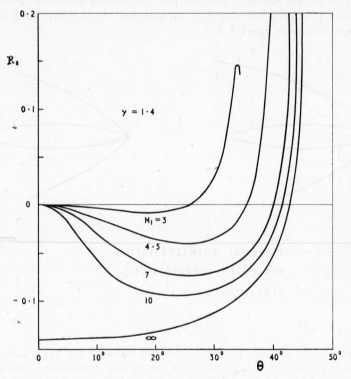

FIG. 4.2a.—Variation of reflection coefficient $\mathfrak{R}_s$ with Mach number for $\gamma = 1\cdot4$.

There are in fact two types of wave interaction which are assumed to be neglected in the shock expansion method—firstly the reflected waves from the shock, and secondly the reflected disturbances arising from the interaction between the outgoing waves and the stream surfaces, across which, behind the curved shock, an entropy gradient exists.

We first consider the reflection of an expansion wave at a shock.

A quantity which characterises the strength of the reflection of an incident wave from a shock is the ratio of the change of pressure, δp_r, along the Mach waves reflected from the shock to the pressure change, δp_i, along the incident waves coming from the surface, i.e.

$$\mathfrak{R}_s = \frac{\delta p_r}{\delta p_i} \tag{4.1}$$

This quantity has been evaluated by various authors (Lighthill (1949), Chu (1952), Eggers and Syvertson (1952)) and it is shown in figure 4.2a as a function of the free stream Mach number for $\gamma = 1 \cdot 4$. (A negative sign means that the reflection takes place with a change of sign; thus a compression is changed after reflection at a shock to an expansion for $\mathfrak{R}_s < 0$, but remains a compression for $\mathfrak{R}_s > 0$.)

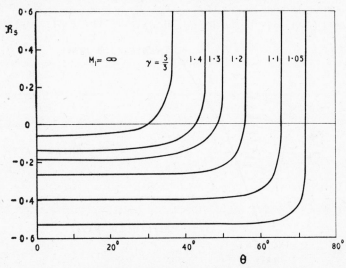

Fig. 4.2b.—Variation of reflection coefficient $\mathfrak{R}_s$ with flow deflection angle and γ for $M_1 = \infty$.

Except very close to the detachment angle $(M_2 \to 1)$ $\mathfrak{R}_s$ is small compared with unity (the maximum negative value is $-0 \cdot 14$ for $M = \infty$). The variation of $\mathfrak{R}_s$ with γ is shown in figure 4.2b and it is seen that $\mathfrak{R}_s$ becomes large as $\gamma \to 1$; however for a wide range of values of M_1 and for γ not too near unity, it is evident that it is a reasonable approximation to consider that waves incident upon a shock are absorbed there.

The second type of interaction which is important is that between an incident wave and a shear layer in the flow. Such interactions have been considered by Waldman and Probstein (1961). In a similar fashion to equation (4.1), a reflection coefficient can be defined by the ratio of the pressure rise across the reflected wave to that across an incident wave

$$\mathfrak{R}_v = \frac{\delta p_r}{\delta p_i} \tag{4.2}$$

Following Hayes and Probstein (1959b) the possible importance of this parameter may be considered by discussing the reflection of a wave from a shear layer characterised by the two different values of Mach number in the flow on the two sides of the layer (figure 4.3).

The reflection coefficient is given by

$$\Re_v = \left(\frac{\gamma M_B{}^2}{\sqrt{M_B{}^2 - 1}} - \frac{\gamma M_A{}^2}{\sqrt{M_A{}^2 - 1}} \right) \bigg/ \left(\frac{\gamma M_B{}^2}{\sqrt{M_B{}^2 - 1}} + \frac{\gamma M_A{}^2}{\sqrt{M_A{}^2 - 1}} \right)$$

(4.3)

For a weak shear layer $(M_B \to M_A)$, $\Re_v \to 0$ and the strength of the reflected wave may be neglected. However if $M_B \gg M_A$, and M_A is

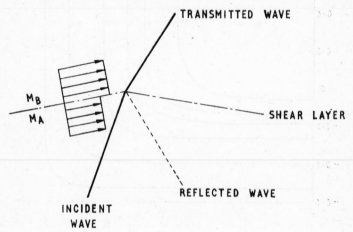

FIG. 4.3.—Reflection of waves from a shear layer.

not too close to unity, the value of $\Re_v \to + 1$, and the incident wave reflects from the shear layer as if it were a solid wall. Thus for a large entropy gradient in the flow, the effect of the reflection from the shear layers may be more important than that from the shock. The interaction of a wave with a shear layer has also been considered by Lighthill (1954).

Thus whereas, for M_1 not too close to unity, an expansion wave will reflect from a shock as a compression, it will reflect from a shear layer as an expansion, and the two effects may partially cancel each other out in the flow behind a curved shock. This at least partially helps to explain the sometimes astonishingly good accuracy obtained in the calculation of surface pressures by shock expansion methods.

To calculate the shock shape and the quantities in the flow field between the shock and the body, Eggers and Syvertson (1952) suggested in their 'generalised shock-expansion method' the use of a modified characteristic calculation in which only the first family characteristics and their interaction with the stream surfaces are taken into account. Thus, as shown in figure 4.1b, the first family characteristics would be curved, but, as in shock-expansion theory, the second family reflections from the shock and from the vortex surfaces are neglected. In calculating the flow field two procedures are possible. Either the pressure may

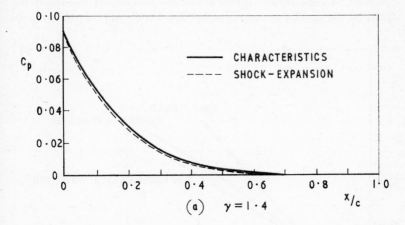

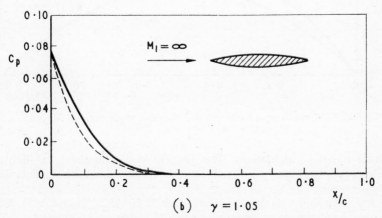

FIG. 4.4.—Surface pressure distribution on 10 per cent thick bi-convex aerofoil section for $M_1 = \infty$ (Eggers and Syvertson, 1952).

be assumed constant along a characteristic and the flow deflection and Mach angle calculated, or the flow deflection assumed constant and the pressure change and Mach angle calculated. To remove the arbitrariness associated with this choice, Hayes and Probstein (1959b) suggested averaging the shock angle obtained from the two assumptions at each step in the computation.

An example of the use of the shock expansion method to calculate the surface pressure distribution on a bi-convex aerofoil (10 per cent thick) at zero incidence (Eggers and Syvertson (1952)) is given for $M = \infty$ and $\gamma = 1\cdot4$ in figure 4.4a, where the results are compared with numerical characteristics calculations.

For all Mach numbers up to $7\cdot5$ it was found that the results obtained by the shock expansion method were indistinguishable from the

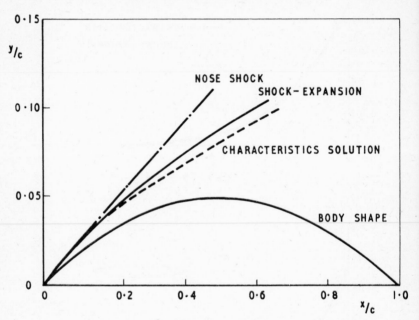

FIG. 4.5.—Shock wave for 10 per cent thick-bi-convex aerofoil. $M_1 = \infty$, $\gamma = 1\cdot4$ (Eggers *et al.*, 1955).

characteristics calculations. For higher Mach numbers, a slightly lower pressure was predicted by the shock expansion calculation (figure 4.4a).

Fig. 4.4b shows the results of calculations for $M = \infty$ and $\gamma = 1\cdot05$. As expected the shock expansion method yields poor agreement with the exact calculation for the low value of γ, for which the reflection coefficients are large.

A calculation of the shock shape for the same aerofoil for $M = \infty$ and $\gamma = 1\cdot4$ using the generalised shock expansion method is shown in figure 4.5. Fair agreement is obtained with the shock shape obtained from a full characteristic calculation.

The shock expansion method may also be used for determining the surface pressures on slender lifting bodies and surfaces provided that the inclination of the nose does not approach the detachment angle.

The flat plate at incidence was considered in Chapter 1, and the lift and drag of various aerofoil sections may be readily determined

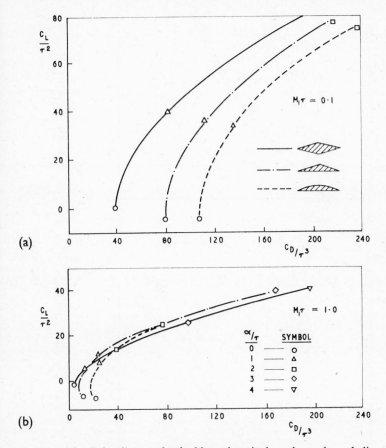

(a)

(b)

Fig. 4.6.—Polar diagram for double wedge, single wedge and parabolic arc profiles (Linnell, 1949).

using the exact shock and Prandtl–Meyer relationships, and assuming that the second family of waves reflected from the shock and also the vortex surface interactions may be neglected.

The lift and drag polar diagrams for triangular and diamond aerofoil sections and for parabolic arc aerofoils were calculated by Linnell (1949) and the results for two different values of the hypersonic similarity parameter $M_1\tau$, 0·1 and 1, are shown in figures 4.6a and 4.6b.

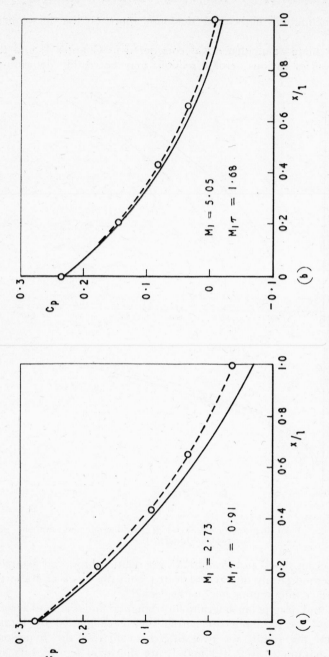

FIG. 4.7.—Pressure distribution over $l/d = 3$ ogive at zero incidence
o Experiment; – – – Characteristics; —— Shock Expansion
($\gamma = 1\cdot4$) (Eggers *et al.*, 1955).

At $M_1\tau = 1$, it may be seen that the triangular section gives higher L/D ratios than the diamond section except for small values of incidence (the same result is obtained using the Newtonian approximation in the next section) and that both give higher values than the parabolic arc aerofoil.

So far the discussion has been confined mainly to plane flows. Eggers, Savin and Syvertson (1955) extended the shock-expansion theory to bodies of revolution. In order to be able to apply the method, the flow must be considered to be locally two dimensional, that is to say the rate of divergence of streamlines in planes tangential to the surface must be small compared with the rate of divergence of streamlines in planes normal to the surface, so that the surface streamlines will be practically coincident with the geodesics. For a body of revolution at zero incidence the relevant geodesics are the meridian lines. The shock expansion method may then be applied to a pointed body of revolution by assuming that the flow at the nose is known (either from exact cone theory or from experiment) and then the Prandtl–Meyer expansion equations are used to obtain the surface pressure along meridian lines. The flow between the body and the shock on meridian planes may be constructed, if desired, using the two dimensional generalised shock expansion method.

Figure 4.7a and b show a comparison made by Eggers *et al.* (1955) between the pressure coefficient obtained using the shock-expansion method and the results of a characteristics calculation for an ogive of revolution having $l/d = 3$ at zero incidence.

Two values of the hypersonic similarity parameter are shown, $M_1\tau = 0.91$ and 1.68. At the lower value the shock-expansion theory gives results which are somewhat low but for $M_1\tau = 1.68$ the two methods are in better agreement. Some experimental results obtained in the Ames 10 inch × 14 inch supersonic tunnel are also shown in the figures.

For inclined bodies of revolution there will be a lateral pressure gradient since the pressure will be different along different surface streamlines and the streamlines will diverge from the geodesics. However, Eggers *et al.* suggest that it may still be possible to obtain the surface pressure by assuming that the streamlines follow the meridian lines.

Inclined cone theory or experimental values are used to obtain the pressures at the pointed nose, and, again, the two dimensional Prandtl–Meyer expansion relationships are used to obtain the surface pressure along meridian lines.

An example of the application of this method to the flow over an ogive at $\alpha = 5°$ and $\alpha = 15°$ is shown in figures 4.8a and b.

The shock-expansion calculation was made using the experimentally measured nose pressures, and extremely good agreement is obtained with the experimental pressure distribution; even at $\alpha = 15°$ it is only on the extreme leeward side of the body, where viscous cross flow effects are to be expected that the measured pressures lie slightly above the calculated values.

Figure 4.9 shows that for ogives good agreement is also obtained between the experimentally observed shock shapes, and the shocks s/v obtained using the generalised shock-expansion calculation.

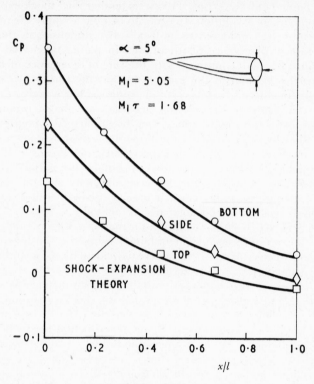

Fig. 4.8a.—Pressure distribution over $l/d = 3$ ogive at $M_1 = 5\cdot05$ and $\alpha = 5°$ (Eggers et al., 1955).

One of the main limitations of shock-expansion theory for predicting surface pressures is that the Prandtl–Meyer relationship predicts constant conditions along straight line elements of a surface. Thus, for a wedge followed by a flat plate or for a cone-cylinder the theory yields a constant pressure over the afterbody, whereas in practice the pressure changes gradually from its value at the corner to a value close to the free stream pressure at the rear of a long afterbody. In an attempt to overcome this difficulty, Syvertson and Dennis (1957) suggested allowing the pressure to vary with the distance s from the corner as

$$p = b + ce^{-as}$$

where the constants a, b and c are evaluated by using the pressure at the corner, its first derivative $\partial p/\partial s$, and the asymptotic value along the afterbody.

This failure of the simple theory to predict the pressure for bodies with straight line elements is a particular case of the error which can

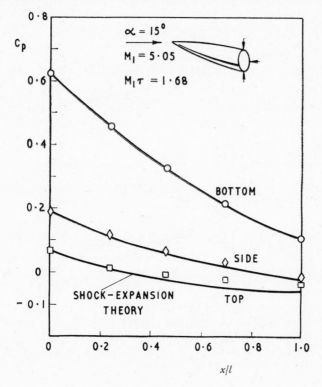

FIG. 4.8b.—Pressure distribution over $l/d = 3$ ogive at $M_1 = 5·05$ and $\alpha = 15°$ (Eggers *et al.*, 1955).

arise when the body curvature at the nose is large compared with the curvature on the afterbody. Essentially this is because the concentrated expansion fan associated with the nose leads to a large shock curvature in that region and to a strong entropy gradient, so that the reflections from the vortex lines, which are omitted in the simple theory, can lead to incorrect results for the afterbody pressure.

In general we may say that only for sharp-nosed aerofoils or bodies with smoothly varying curvature, and for values of γ not too close to unity, may the shock expansion methods be expected to yield good results.

Second-order shock expansion theories which include the effects of both the entropy variations and of the reflections from the shock have been given by Stocker (1958) and Waldman and Probstein (1961) and a three-dimensional shock expansion method in which the deviation of the streamlines from the geodesics is taken into account has been developed by Mauger (1963).

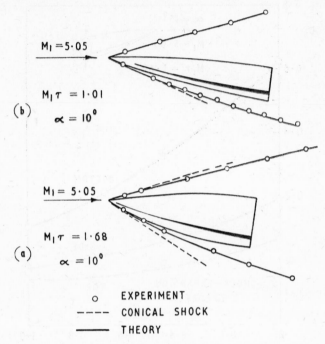

FIG. 4.9.—Shock shape for (a) $l/d = 3$ and (b) $l/d = 5$ ogives at $M_1 = 5.05$ and $\alpha = 10°$ (Eggers *et al.*, 1955).

4.3. Tangent-wedge and Tangent-cone Approximations

Methods of predicting body surface pressures in terms of the local inclination angle, although often empirically based, are extremely useful in practice. In the tangent wedge and cone methods, it is assumed that the local pressure is equal to the exact value of the pressure on a wedge or cone having the same inclination to the flow direction as the surface, and with the same value of free stream Mach number.

The exact wedge or cone values may of course be used. However there are no explicit expressions for the pressure on the cone or wedge in terms of the surface inclination, although for slender wedges at hypersonic speeds the approximate expressions obtained in Chapter 1 may be used.

Thus for the wedge, we have from equations (1.32) and (1.34) for the pressure ratio

$$\frac{p_w}{p_1} = 1 + \frac{\gamma(\gamma+1)}{4}(M_1\theta_w)^2 + \gamma M_1\theta_w \sqrt{1 + \left(\frac{\gamma+1}{4}\right)^2 (M_1\theta_w)^2}$$
(4.5)

and for the pressure coefficient (1.35)

$$\frac{C_p}{\theta_w{}^2} = \frac{2}{\gamma M_1{}^2\theta_w{}^2}\left(\frac{p_w}{p_1}-1\right) = \left[\frac{\gamma+1}{2} + \sqrt{\left(\frac{\gamma+1}{2}\right)^2 + \frac{4}{(M_1\theta_w)^2}}\right]$$
(4.6)

Here we may note that for small values of $M_1\theta_w$ the expression for the pressure reduces to

$$\frac{p_w}{p_1} = 1 + \gamma M_1\theta_w + \frac{\gamma(\gamma+1)}{4}(M_1\theta_w)^2 + \frac{\gamma(\gamma+1)^2}{32}(M_1\theta_w)^3 \ldots$$
(4.7)

The first three terms of this series are identical with the Busemann series used in supersonic aerofoil theory (Busemann 1935), and with the expansion of the Prandtl–Meyer relationship (Equation 1.45).

For the flow past bodies of revolution, the approximate tangent cone expressions corresponding to those for the wedge were derived by Lees (1951) for the condition that $(\beta - \theta_c)/\theta_c$ is small (i.e. that the shock lies close to the body) and that $1 < M_1\theta_c < \infty$. The pressure ratio is given by

$$\frac{p_c}{p_1} = 1 + \frac{2\gamma}{\gamma+1}\{(K_c)^2 - 1\} + \gamma(K_s - K_c)^2\left\{\frac{\gamma+1}{\gamma-1+2/K_c{}^2}\right\}$$
(4.8)

where $K_c = M_1\theta_c$

and
$$K_s = \frac{\gamma+1}{\gamma+3}K_c + \sqrt{\left(\frac{\gamma+1}{\gamma+3}\right)^2 K_c{}^2 + \frac{2}{\gamma+3}}$$

and the pressure coefficient is given by

$$\frac{C_p}{\theta_c{}^2} = \frac{2}{\gamma M_1{}^2\theta_c{}^2}\left(\frac{p_c}{p_1}-1\right) = \frac{4}{\gamma+1}\left(\frac{K_s{}^2-1}{K_c{}^2}\right)$$
$$+ \frac{2(K_s - K_c)^2}{K_c{}^2}\left\{\frac{\gamma+1}{\gamma-1+2/K_c{}^2}\right\}$$
(4.9)

for $M_1 \to \infty$, this becomes

$$\frac{C_p}{\theta_c^2} = \frac{2(\gamma + 1)(\gamma + 7)}{(\gamma + 3)^2} \qquad (4.10)$$

A comparison between the approximate formulae for C_p for the wedge and the cone and the exact values has already been given in figure 2.6a and b.

An example of the application of the tangent cone method by Probstein and Bray (1955) to the calculation of the pressure distribution over circular-arc ogives, is given in figure 4.10. Agreement with exact

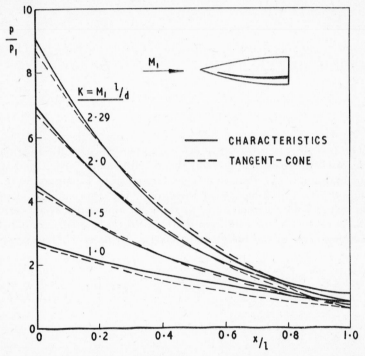

FIG. 4.10.—Surface pressure distribution on ogives (Probstein and Bray, 1955).

rotational characteristic calculations by Rossow (1951) is good over the range of parameters considered.

The main limitations of the method arise because it predicts only the surface pressure, and gives no detail of the flow field between the shock and the body. In the limit, as $\gamma \to 1$ and $M_1 \to \infty$ the approximate expressions for the wedge and cone flows degenerate to the Newtonian flow expressions. The method ignores the effects of the centrifugal pressure gradient and of the changes of the flow inclination between the shock and the body. Lees (1955) suggested a way of correcting the tangent wedge method for these two effects. His corrected expression for the surface pressure is

$$\frac{p_w}{p_1} = \frac{\gamma}{2}(\gamma + 1)M_1^2\theta_w^2 + M_1^2\frac{y_b}{R_b}[\gamma - (\gamma^2 - 1)] \qquad (4.11)$$

where R_b is the radius of curvature of the body, and y_b is the body ordinate. As $\gamma \to 1$ this expression tends to the Newtonian–Busemann expression for a slender body.

The tangent wedge and cone methods are of somewhat wider application than the shock-expansion methods because the expressions used are valid as $\gamma \to 1$. However, a constant pressure is incorrectly predicted on the rear part of blunted flat plates and cylinders in hypersonic flow and as with the shock expansion methods, the tangent wedge and cone methods should only be used for bodies which do not have too abrupt changes of curvature. The method is employed in Chapter 8 to predict the induced pressure distributions caused by boundary layers.

Both the tangent wedge and tangent cone methods may also be used as an approximation to obtain the pressure distribution for inclined surfaces. Thus Ivey and Cline (1950) used expressions equivalent to those of equation (4.5) to determine the lift and drag coefficients for a diamond aerofoil, and Dorrance (1952) determined closed-form solutions for the lift and drag coefficients of a number of simple aerofoil shapes using the three-term expansion of equation (4.7) for the pressure.

4.4. Newtonian Approximations

The Newtonian flow concept may be employed for calculating the flow over slender bodies with or without attached shock waves. As in the methods discussed in the previous two sections, the surface pressure may be expressed in terms of the local inclination angle, and for that reason, it is relatively easy to apply.

The Newtonian formulae used for the blunt bodies may also be applied to slender body flows. Thus, for the local pressure coefficient we have:

1. The simple Newtonian formula $C_p = 2\sin^2\theta \simeq 2\theta^2$ \qquad (4.12)

2. The modified Newtonian formula $C_p = C_{p_0}\sin^2\theta \simeq C_{p_0}\theta^2$ (4.13)

(Here C_{p_0} is the exact value of the pressure coefficient at the nose of the body.)

3. The Newtonian–Busemann formula, including a centrifugal force term:

$$C_p = 2\left(\sin^2\theta + \sin\theta\frac{d\theta}{dA}\int_0^A \cos\theta \, . \, dA\right) \qquad (4.14)$$

which, for slender bodies becomes,

$$C_p \simeq 2(\theta^2 + y\theta') \qquad \text{for plane flow (4.15a)}$$

and

$$C_p \simeq 2\left(\theta^2 + \frac{r\theta'}{2}\right)$$

$$\text{for axi-symmetric flow (4.15b)}$$

4. The modified Newtonian–Busemann slender body formulae

$$C_p = C_{p0}(\theta^2 + y\theta') \qquad \text{for plane flow (4.16a)}$$

and

$$C_p = C_{p0}\left(\theta^2 + \frac{r\theta'}{2}\right)$$

$$\text{for axi-symmetric flow (4.16b)}$$

For a body which does not have a curved surface the centrifugal correction term is zero, and either the Newtonian or the modified Newtonian formulae may be used to determine the pressure and the force and moment coefficients. As noted in the section on Newtonian theory in Chapter 2, only for the Newtonian–Busemann formulae is there some mathematical justification, but the empirically based Newtonian theory yields results which often give good agreement with exact calculations for finite Mach numbers and $\gamma = 1\cdot4$, and will be considered here for that reason.

An example of the extent to which the simple Newtonian formula can be expected to yield agreement with the results of more exact calculations is given by the flow past wedges and cones. The comparison between the exact flow for $M_1 = \infty$ and $\gamma = 1\cdot4$ for a wedge and a cone and the Newtonian formula was given in figure 1.8. The agreement is surprisingly good for semi-angles up to 20°, although the Newtonian curve is closer to the cone than to the wedge curves. This comparison gives some confidence that the results obtained from simple Newtonian theory are not completely meaningless when applied to slender bodies. The limiting expression given in Chapter 1 for the pressure coefficient for a slender wedge as $M \to \infty$ is

$$C_{p_w} = (\gamma + 1)\theta_w^2 \qquad (4.17)$$

and both this, and the approximate expression for a slender cone

$$C_{p_c} = \frac{2(\gamma + 1)(\gamma + 7)}{(\gamma + 3)^2} \theta_c^2 \qquad (4.18)$$

tend to the Newtonian formula as $\gamma \to 1$.

In place of the modified Newtonian formula (4.13) equations (4.17) and (4.18) may be used to obtain the pressure coefficients for slender wedges and cores.

For a curved body one would expect that a centrifugal correction must be made. Figures 4.11a and b show how the modified Newtonian and the modified Newtonian–Busemann results for the flow at $M_1 = \infty$ past a 10 per cent thick circular arc aerofoil compare with a calculation by the method of characteristics by Eggers, Syvertson and Kraus

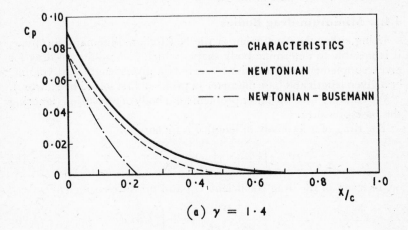

(a) $\gamma = 1 \cdot 4$

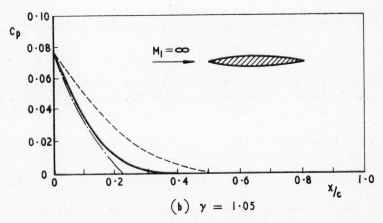

(b) $\gamma = 1 \cdot 05$

FIG. 4.11.—Surface pressure distribution on 10 per cent thick bi-convex aerofoil section for $M_1 = \infty$ (Eggers *et al.*, 1953).

(1953). For $\gamma = 1 \cdot 4$ (figure 4.11a) the Newtonian formula is in better agreement with the characteristics values than the Newtonian–Busemann formula. Such agreement must, as in the blunt body flows, be regarded as fortuitous, and presumably arises because for $\gamma = 1 \cdot 4$ the pressure behind the shock is greater than the pressure near the body, so that there is a pressure gradient which tends to cancel out the centrifugal pressure gradient.

That this is probably the true explanation may be seen from figure 4.11b where the characteristic values for $\gamma = 1{\cdot}05$, when the shock is much closer to the body, lie fairly close to the Newtonian–Busemann result over a large part of the chord.

4.4.1. Minimum-drag Bodies

Using either the Newtonian or the Newtonian–Busemann formulae, it is possible to determine body shapes which give minimum drag for given supplementary conditions—such as a given length and volume, or a given length and base diameter (a problem first solved by Newton).

We consider here the latter problem for a body of revolution (ignoring the base pressure).

The drag of a forebody of length l is given by

$$D = \int_0^l 2\pi r \,(p - p_1) \cdot \frac{dr}{dx} \cdot dx \tag{4.19}$$

or, in terms of the drag coefficient, C_D and pressure coefficient C_p

$$C_D = \frac{D}{\frac{1}{2}\rho_1 U_1{}^2 \pi r_b{}^2} = 2 \int_0^l C_p rr' dx \tag{4.20}$$

(taking the body radius, r_b, to be unity).

If the modified Newtonian slender body expression (4.13) is used

$$C_D = 2 \int_0^l \frac{2rr'^3}{1 + r'^2} \cdot dx \tag{4.21}$$

(since $\sin^2 \theta = r'^2/(1 + r'^2)$).

The problem in variational calculus which has to be solved is to minimise the integral in equation (4.21) taking into account the given supplementary conditions.

For a given length and base diameter the integrand to be minimised is

$$f = \frac{rr'^3}{1 + r'^2} \tag{4.22}$$

and the function $r(x)$ which minimises this must satisfy the Euler equation

$$\frac{d}{dx}\left(\frac{\partial f}{\partial r'}\right) - \frac{\partial f}{\partial r} = 0 \tag{4.23}$$

This may be integrated w.r.t. r (since the integrand does not contain the independent variable) to give

$$r' \frac{\partial f}{\partial r'} - f = \text{const.} \tag{4.24}$$

and if (4.22) is substituted into this, we obtain

$$\frac{rr'^3}{(1+r'^2)^2} = \text{const.} = C_1 \tag{4.25}$$

This is readily integrated to give the parametric equations (having $r' = \tan\theta$ as parameter).

$$x = C_1 \left\{ \frac{3}{4r'^4} + \frac{1}{r'^2} + \ln r' \right\} + C_2 \tag{4.26a}$$

and, from (4.25)

$$r = \frac{C_1(1+r'^2)^2}{r'^3} \tag{4.26b}$$

The constants C_1 and C_2 may be chosen to give a convex body. It should be noted that, for a given fineness ratio, a small but finite value of r is obtained at the nose $(x = 0)$ and that the body slope there is 45°. As pointed out by Eggers et al. (1957) this applies only if the length is fixed. If the length is free; for instance if it is desired to minimise for a given base diameter and volume, a pointed body is obtained.

The profile obtained for a minimum-drag body having a fineness ratio $l/d = 6·18$ is shown in figure 4.12. To the scale of the figure the finite nose ordinate is too small to be distinguished. For slender bodies it is found that except at the nose, the minimum-drag shape may be closely approximated by the power law body of the form $r \propto x^{3/4}$, also shown on the figure.

The minimum drag bodies may also be obtained using the Newtonian–Busemann formula in place of the Newtonian formula.

Thus expression (4.14) may be written

$$C_p = 2\frac{d}{dA} \cdot \left\{ A - \cos\theta \int_{A_0}^{A} \cos\theta \cdot dA \right\} \tag{4.27}$$

(where A_0 is the area of the body at the nose) and integrating to determine the drag of the forebody, and transforming to variables $r(x)$ and x for a body of revolution gives

$$C_D = 2\left\{ 1 - \frac{\cos\theta(l)}{r(l) - r(0)} \int_0^l \frac{rr'}{(1+r'^2)^{1/2}} \cdot dx \right\} \tag{4.28}$$

This is the relationship for which a minimum value must be found. The integral, and the expression $\cos\theta(l)/(r(l) - r(0))$ may be minimised separately. $\theta(l)$ is not necessarily the body angle at $x = l$ but is the flow deflection angle after leaving the base of the body. Thus the flow can in principle be deflected to give $\theta(l) = 0°$, and hence a minimum value for cos $\theta(l)/(r(l) - r(0))$, by using a turning vane (a Newtonian 'thrust-cowl') at the rear of the body. The extra drag reduction effectively results from the thrust associated with the free shock-layer behind the body.

Two values of the minimum drag coefficient will thus be obtained depending on whether $\theta(l)$ is taken as the body angle at $x = l$, or as $0°$ if a thrust cowl is fitted. Hayes and Probstein (1959b) point out that an even lower drag can be obtained if the shock layer is allowed to separate when the pressure has fallen to zero, and to just reach the base of the body.

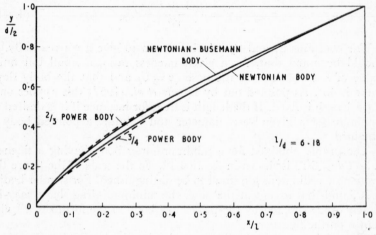

FIG. 4.12.—Minimum drag body shapes for $l/d = 6\cdot18$ (Eggers *et al.*, 1957).

By minimising equation (4.28) for the flow without a thrust cowl, the minimum drag shape for a slender body may be obtained. As with the previous example a small finite nose ordinate is obtained. The resulting body shape for $l/d = 6\cdot18$ is compared in figure 4.12 with that obtained using the modified Newtonian formula. A $\frac{2}{3}$ power law body is seen to be a close approximation to the Newtonian–Busemann minimum drag shape.

The drag coefficients for minimum drag bodies can be considerably less than those of the cone or wedge having the same thickness ratio. The table below gives a comparison between the drag of a slender cone and various optimum power law slender bodies which are approximations to the minimum drag bodies obtained using the Newtonian (N) or Newtonian–Busemann (N–B) expressions. The table also shows how the results obtained for two-dimensional bodies—for which the minimum Newtonian drag shape is a wedge fitted with a thrust cowl, compares with the drag of a 0·866 power law body derived by the slender body method of Cole (see next section), which is associated with the Newtonian–Busemann expression.

TABLE 4.1

Axi-Symmetric	$C_D/C_{D_{cone}}$
$\frac{3}{4}$ Power (N)	0·702
$\frac{2}{3}$ Power (N–B)	0·666
Min Drag Body (N–B) (with thrust cowl)	0·422

Two-Dimensional	$C_D/C_{D_{wedge}}$
0·866 Power (Cole) (N–B)	0·918
Min Drag Body (N) (Wedge + Thrust Cowl)	0·500

Figure 4.13 shows the results of some experiments by Eggers *et al.* (1957) on power law bodies of revolution having different values of the exponent and with $l/d = 3$ and 5, in which the measured drag is compared with that of a cone of the same thickness ratio. (The base drag, determined from the measured base pressure, was subtracted from the measured drag.)

The experimental agreement is best with the curves calculated by the Newtonian–Busemann formula, and it is confirmed that minimum drag for power law bodies of revolution lies between $\frac{1}{2}$ and $\frac{3}{4}$.

The power law bodies on which measurements were made had blunt noses so that at finite Mach numbers the shock wave was detached over a small region at the nose; this will introduce effects due to the entropy layer which are not taken into account in the Newtonian theory (see remarks on this in section 4.7).

4.3.2. Newtonian Approximation for Bodies at Incidence

For bodies at incidence the Newtonian formulae may be used to calculate the pressure distribution over those parts of surfaces inclined at positive incidence to the oncoming stream (the "wetted area").

As an example, for small thickness ratios the lift and drag coefficients of a triangular section aerofoil of thickness ratio τ are given, using the Newtonian formula, by

$$\frac{C_L}{\tau^2} = 2\left(\frac{\alpha}{\tau}\right)^2 - \left(2 - \frac{\alpha}{\tau}\right)^2 \qquad (4.29a)$$

$$\frac{C_D}{\tau^3} = 2\left(\frac{\alpha}{\tau}\right)^3 - \left(2 - \frac{\alpha}{\tau}\right)^3 \qquad (4.29b)$$

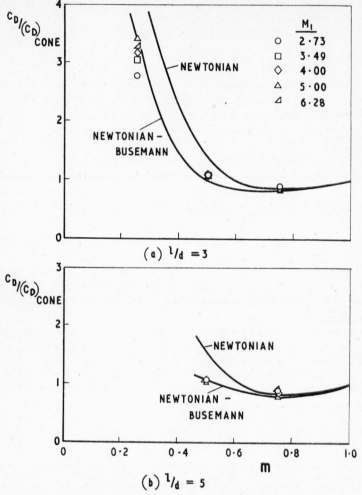

FIG. 4.13.—Ratio of drag of power law bodies ($r \propto x^m$) to drag of cone
(For experiments $\gamma = 1\cdot4$). (Eggers *et al.*, 1957).

where the second term is needed only for $\alpha/\tau < 2$, and, for a diamond
section aerofoil having the same thickness ratio,

$$\frac{C_L}{\tau^2} = \left(1 + \frac{\alpha}{\tau}\right)^2 - \left|1 - \frac{\alpha}{\tau}\right|^2 \qquad (4.30a)$$

$$\frac{C_D}{\tau^2} = \left(1 + \frac{\alpha}{\tau}\right)^3 + \left(1 - \frac{\alpha}{\tau}\right)^2 \left|1 - \frac{\alpha}{\tau}\right| \qquad (4.30b)$$

where the second term applies only if $\alpha/\tau < 1$.

The polar diagrams for these two aerofoil sections obtained using these formulae are shown in figure 4.14.

We see that in agreement with the result of using shock expansion theory (figure 4.6b) for values $\alpha/\tau > 1\cdot2$, C_L for the triangular aerofoil is greater than that for the diamond aerofoil over most of the range of

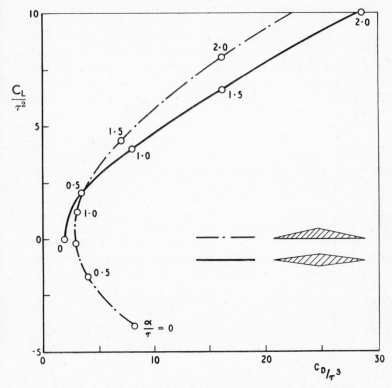

FIG. 4.14.—Polar diagrams for diamond and triangular aerofoils (Newtonian formula).

incidence; this is the opposite of the situation at moderate supersonic velocities (figure 4.6b) where, because of the influence of the relatively large pressure on those parts of the surface at negative incidence, the diamond aerofoil gives the best performance.

For curved two dimensional aerofoils either the simple Newtonian or the Newtonian–Busemann formulae are available. The Newtonian–Busemann formula has been used by Ivey, Klunker and Bowen (1948) for determining the pressure distribution on, for instance, a bi-convex aerofoil. The addition of the centrifugal force term leads to a pressure which may fall to zero some fraction of the chord back from the leading edge, even when the lower surface is at positive incidence, and as in the case of the same aerofoil at zero incidence (figure 4.11) the use of the simple or modified Newtonian formula gives better agreement with experimental results than the Newtonian–Busemann formula for finite values of Mach number and for $\gamma = 1\cdot4$.

For the flow over bodies of revolution at incidence the possibility of a cross flow will exist since, if the Newtonian formula is applied locally to every part of the surface at positive incidence, lateral pressure gradients will exist. For Newtonian flow (having an infinite density) it is shown by Hayes (1958) and Guiraud (1960) that the streamlines are the longitudinal geodesics of the body surface.* Cheng (1960a) refers to the 'stiffness' property of the streamlines, i.e. they tend to keep to their original direction along the geodesics even in the presence of transverse gradients, for high Mach number flow.

The behaviour of streamlines in Newtonian flows as $M_1 \to \infty$ and $\gamma \to 1$ has been investigated theoretically by Guiraud (1960). He introduces a correction for the path of the surface streamlines and shows that they diverge from the geodesic lines, and that close to the surface a vortical layer is formed. (See Chapter 2.) He obtained a second approximation for the circular cone at incidence, and expressions are also given for a general body of revolution which, for slender bodies, reduce to those of Cole discussed in the next section.

For Newtonian flow over a cone at incidence, the only geodesic family which passes through the vertex is that given by the generators, and the question of a centrifugal correction does not then arise. The polar diagrams obtained by applying the Newtonian formula to a cone and to a half-cone having the same cross-sectional area are shown in figure 4.15 for different values of α/δ.

The half-cone has a higher lift to drag ratio than the cone, and Sänger (1939) suggested this should be the basic form to be used for hypersonic lifting bodies.

The surface pressure distribution on a 10° cone has been determined experimentally by McClellan (1951) at $M_1 = 6\cdot9$, and in figure 4.16 the results for $\alpha = 6\cdot7°$ and 14° are compared with the surface pressures predicted by the Newtonian formula. At $\alpha = 6\cdot7°$ very satisfactory agreement is obtained with the experimental results over most of the surface, although the experimental pressures on the leeward generators are somewhat higher than the Newtonian values. At $\alpha = 14°$ the incidence angle is greater than the semi-angle of the cone and the theory predicts zero pressure over about the upper 30 per cent of the leeward

---

* This may be inferred since, if friction is neglected, the reaction of the shock layer fluid and of the centrifugal forces must be normal to the surface and the fluid paths will be the same as for the constrained motion of a particle on a curved surface; that is, the osculating plane at every point on a streamline must be normal to the surface. Hence the fluid particles will follow geodesic paths, or more precisely, the family of geodesics defined by initial conditions at the stagnation point.

surface. Very low pressures are in fact measured in this region and there is good agreement between the Newtonian formula and the measured pressure over the rest of the cone.

For pointed bodies of revolution the only family of geodesics which pass through the vertex and which do not intersect each other are the

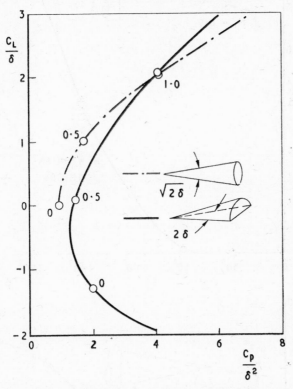

FIG. 4.15.—Polar diagrams for cone and half-cone having same base area (Newtonian formula). (Numbers by circles refer to values of α/δ.)

meridian lines, and the Newtonian formula may be applied along these lines, or, where the meridian lines are curved, centrifugal effects may be included by using the Newtonian–Busemann formula.

Grimminger, Williams and Young (1950) have derived general expressions for the lift and drag of inclined bodies of revolution. For determining which parts of the surface are at positive incidence they assume that the streamlines remain parallel and leave the surface in a streamwise direction as shown in figure 4.17.

For high Mach numbers the pressure in the 'aerodynamic shadow' —the shaded region of the figure—is assumed to be zero, although for

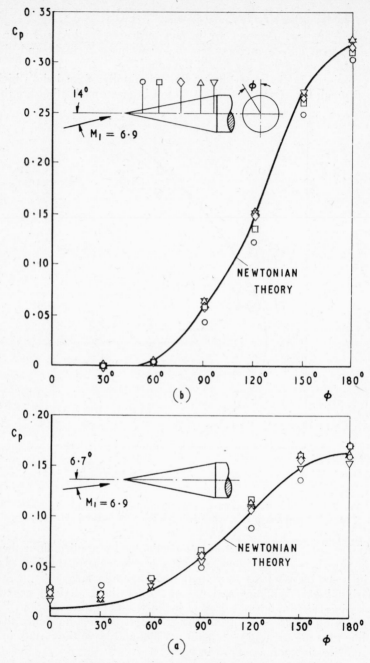

FIG. 4.16.—Pressure distribution around conical nose at incidence
(a) α = 6·7° (b) α = 14° (McClellan, 1951).

moderate hypersonic Mach numbers it is suggested that a correction for the pressure in this region should be made if the shape is simple enough for the pressure to be determined by assuming, say, a Prandtl–Meyer expansion. The Newtonian formula is employed to calculate the pressure on the wetted position of the body and, because the Newtonian–Busemann formula overestimates the centrifugal effects,

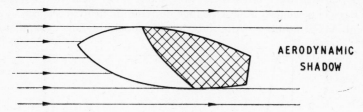

FIG. 4.17.—Flow past body at incidence on Newtonian model.

Grimminger *et al.* suggest an approximate method for correcting for the centrifugal pressure gradient for bodies for which the streamline geodesics are curved. Thus they estimate that the centrifugal pressure correction on an infinite cylinder at incidence including the effect of the boundary layer, is to reduce the normal force by about 10 per cent below the Newtonian value. Grimminger *et al.* also give methods for calculating the lift and drag of composite bodies such as cone-cylinders which yield satisfactory agreement with experiments by McLellan (1951) at $M = 6.9$.

However, it is found that at high Mach numbers the Newtonian formula can give poor agreement with experimental results for blunt-nosed cylinder flare bodies. This occurs because the Newtonian model assumes a shock layer close to the body as in figure 4.18a whereas the shock wave actually lies at some distance from the body

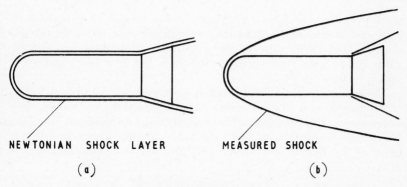

FIG. 4.18a. and b.—Assumed and measured shock shapes for hypersonic flow past flared body.

surface (figure 4.18b) and, in addition, a secondary shock is formed ahead of the flare. A photograph of the flow about a cone-cylinder-flare at $M_1 = 6.85$ is given in figure 4.18c: the secondary shock over the flare may be clearly seen.

This type of flow has been discussed by Seiff (1962).

If a typical streamline which reaches the region of the flare is considered, it will have crossed the bow shock fairly near the nose, and will have experienced a large change of dynamic head across the shock at high Mach numbers. After crossing the shock the flow expands to a

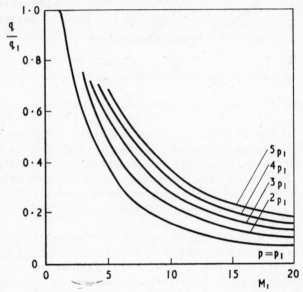

FIG. 4.19.—Dynamic pressure downstream of normal shock wave.

static pressure of perhaps a few times the free stream value at the flare. The way in which the dynamic pressure ratio q/q_1 downstream of a normal shock varies with the free stream Mach number, and with the value of the local static pressure to which the flow has expanded, is shown in figure 4.19.

The loss of dynamic head is much more pronounced at high values of the free stream Mach number than at relatively low values. Seiff suggests that the pressure on the flare should be calculated using the Newtonian formula with the local value of the impact pressure in place of the free stream value. Thus the pressure coefficient on the flare, C_{p_f}, is given by

$$C_{p_f} = C_{p_2} + 2 \frac{q_2}{q_1} \sin^2 \theta_f \qquad (4.31)$$

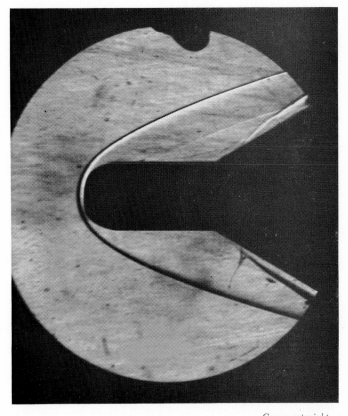

FIG. 4.18c.—Schlieren photograph of flow about a cone-cylinder-flare at $M_1 = 6\cdot85$. (R.A.E. Hypersonic Tunnel).

where C_{p_2} is the local static pressure coefficient ahead of the flare shock, and the Newtonian term is multiplied by the ratio of the dynamic head (calculated by assuming that the flow has expanded to the static pressure ahead of the flare shock wave) to the free-stream value.

The flare pressure coefficient calculated using equation (4.31), including real gas equilibrium effects, for a hemisphere-cylinder-flare model at high Mach numbers is shown in figure 4.20 as a function of

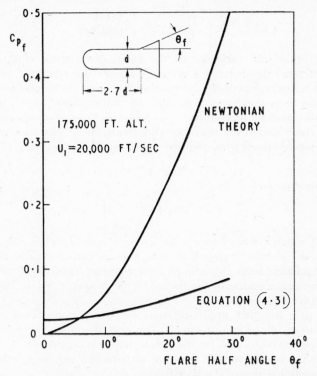

FIG. 4.20.—Variation of flare pressure coefficient with flare half-angle
(Seiff 1962).

the flow angle. The local static pressure at the commencement of the flow was assumed to be obtained using blast wave theory (Chapter 5). The flare pressure is much less than the value which would be given by the Newtonian formula applied in the usual way, and it is evident that great care must be taken when applying Newtonian theory to composite bodies at high Mach numbers.

4.5. Newtonian Slender Body Theory

A study of the behaviour of the small disturbance equations as $\gamma \to 1$ and as $M_1 \to \infty$ was made by Cole (1957). He introduced two parameters, the density ratio $\epsilon = (\gamma - 1)/(\gamma + 1)$ (whence $\gamma = 1 + 2\epsilon + 2\epsilon^2$ . . .) and a hypersonic similarity parameter

$$H = \frac{1}{M_1{}^2\theta_0{}^2}$$

(where θ_0 is the nose semi-angle).

The ratio of these Cole called the Newtonian flow parameter

$$N = \frac{H}{\epsilon} = \frac{\gamma + 1}{\gamma - 1}\frac{1}{M_1{}^2\theta_0{}^2}$$

By expanding the variables in the small disturbance equations in terms of these parameters, a set of equations was obtained of which the first terms represent the Newtonian flow, and the second terms the departure from the Newtonian flow for finite values of M_1 and for values of γ greater than unity.

The most important result of this treatment is that the pressure coefficients obtained from the first approximations are

$$C_p = 2\theta_0{}^2(y'^2 + yy')$$

for plane flow and

$$C_p = 2\theta_0{}^2\left(r'^2 + \frac{rr'}{2}\right)$$

for axisymmetric flow, where a dash over a symbol means d/dx.

Thus, for slender bodies Cole was able to show formally that the centrifugal force term, introduced somewhat empirically by Busemann, arises from proceeding to the limits $M_1 \to \infty$ and $\gamma \to 1$ in the small disturbance equations.

Although the first approximation for the pressure coefficient is independent of the parameter N, the corresponding expressions for other flow variables and for the shock shape do depend on N. This is an example of the surface pressure distribution reaching a limiting value before the rest of the flow field.

Cole used the theory to derive first and second approximations for the flow over wedges and cones, and also obtained bodies of the form $r \propto x^m$ for which the shock shape is proportional to the body shape. For these bodies he showed that a finite drag is only possible if $1 > m > \frac{2}{3}$ for plane flow or $1 > m > \frac{1}{2}$ for axisymmetric flow. The formulae for the drag coefficients are

$$\frac{C_D}{\theta_0{}^2} = m^2\left[\frac{2m - 1}{3m - 2}\right] \qquad \text{for plane flow}$$

$$\frac{C_D}{\theta_0{}^2} = m^2\left[\frac{3m - 1}{2m - 1}\right] \qquad \text{for axisymmetric flow}$$

For minimum drag $m = 0.866$ for plane flow and $\frac{2}{3}$ for axisymmetric flow. These values are close to the minimum-drag body shapes obtained using the Newtonian–Busemann formulae.

The results obtained by Cole from the second approximation for cones are discussed in the next section, where they are compared with a different approximate method.

4.6. Hypersonic Small-disturbance Theory

In the previous section a method of solution of the small disturbance equations by expansion in series was discussed. Another method of solution, by numerical integration of the equations was developed by van Dyke (1954).

For axisymmetric flow it is convenient to use non-dimensional variables $\tilde{x}$, $\tilde{r}$ and $\tilde{v}$ defined as in Section 2.3.1 (where $\tilde{v}$ is the velocity component in the $\tilde{r}$ direction).

The small disturbance equations (2.11)–(2.14) then become

$$\frac{\partial \tilde{\rho}}{\partial \tilde{x}} + \frac{\partial (\tilde{\rho}\tilde{v})}{\partial \tilde{r}} + \frac{\tilde{\rho}\tilde{v}}{\tilde{r}} = 0 \qquad (4.32a)$$

$$\frac{\partial \tilde{v}}{\partial \tilde{x}} + \tilde{v}\frac{\partial \tilde{v}}{\partial \tilde{r}} + \frac{1}{\tilde{\rho}}\frac{\partial p}{\partial \tilde{x}} = 0 \qquad (4.32b)$$

and

$$\left\{\frac{\partial}{\partial \tilde{x}} + \tilde{v}\frac{\partial}{\partial \tilde{r}}\right\}\frac{\tilde{p}}{\tilde{\rho}^\gamma} = 0 \qquad (4.32c)$$

(For plane flows, $\tilde{r}$ becomes $\tilde{y}$ and the last term on the L.H.S. of 4.32a is zero.)

To reduce these equations to a form suitable for integration a stream function ψ satisfying the continuity equation identically is introduced such that

$$\frac{\partial \psi}{\partial \tilde{r}} = \tilde{r}\tilde{\rho} \qquad (4.33a)$$

and

$$-\frac{\partial \psi}{\partial \tilde{x}} = \tilde{r}\tilde{\rho}\tilde{v} \qquad (4.33b)$$

All the flow quantities appearing in equations (4.32), may be written in terms of the stream function ψ and, letting $w(\psi) = \tilde{p}/\tilde{\rho}^\gamma$ and substituting in the momentum equations (4.32) yields

$$\left(\frac{\partial \psi}{\partial \tilde{r}}\right)^2 \frac{\partial^2 \psi}{\partial \tilde{x}^2} - 2\left(\frac{\partial \psi}{\partial \tilde{x}}\right)\left(\frac{\partial \psi}{\partial \tilde{r}}\right)\left(\frac{\partial^2 \psi}{\partial \tilde{x}.\partial \tilde{r}}\right) + \left(\frac{\partial \psi}{\partial \tilde{x}}\right)^2 \cdot \left(\frac{\partial^2 \psi}{\partial \tilde{r}^2}\right)$$

$$= \frac{1}{\tilde{r}^{\gamma-1}}\left(\frac{\partial \psi}{\partial \tilde{r}}\right)^{\gamma+1}\left[\gamma w\left(\frac{\partial^2 \psi}{\partial \tilde{r}^2} - \frac{1}{\tilde{r}}\frac{\partial \psi}{\partial \tilde{r}}\right) + \frac{\partial w}{\partial \tilde{r}}\left(\frac{\partial \psi}{\partial \tilde{r}}\right)\right]$$

with a corresponding equation for plane flows.

This equation was integrated by van Dyke for the flows past a number of body shapes such as wedges, cones and ogives.

Results for the pressure coefficient for a cone are compared in table 4.2 with the second approximation obtained using Cole's slender body theory. (The value of $C_p/\theta_c{}^2$ for his 1st approximation is 2.)

TABLE 4.2

$\gamma = 1{\cdot}4$ $M_1 \tan \theta_c$	$C_p/\tan^2 \theta_c$ Cole 2nd Approx.	$C_p/\tan^2 \theta_c$ van Dyke
0·6599	3·232	2·646
1·150	2·462	2·333
2·469	2·166	2·154
3·988	2·166	2·116
∞	2·084	2·091

As may be seen from the full-line curve of figure 2.6b, van Dyke's results for a cone are close to the exact values for slender cones calculated by Kopal.

Cole's second approximation lies above the values obtained by van Dyke for small values of the parameter $M_1 \tan \theta_c$ but as this parameter becomes large, good agreement is obtained between the different methods. This illustrates the importance of the parameter N in Cole's method; only for values of $N < 2$ to 3 can the Newtonian expansion procedure be expected to yield useful results.

4.7. Similarity Solutions for Power Law Bodies

In general the flow equations, and even the small perturbation equations for the flow past slender bodies, represent a complex set of non-linear partial differential equations which can only be solved by numerical methods. However, there is a certain class of self-similar motions for which the partial differential equations reduce to ordinary differential equations, thus introducing a considerable simplification and even leading, in some cases, to analytical solutions. Here, the concept of 'self-similar' refers to flows in which the distributions of the flow variables such as the pressure, density and velocity between the shock and the body are similar to each other at different stations along the body.

Since, for slender bodies, the equivalence principle is valid (see chapter 11), one method of approach which has been extensively adopted in the Russian literature, is to solve the problem of the unsteady flow generated by an expanding piston, and then to obtain the corresponding steady flow by using the transformation $x = U_1 t$. For the unsteady motions self-similar flows are flows in which the distributions of flow variables between the shock and the piston are similar at different times.

The use of the equivalence principle means that a number of self-similar solutions previously obtained for unsteady flow problems become available for calculating steady flows. A review of solutions obtained in this way and of approximate methods of solving the unsteady flows is given in the book by Chernyi (1961).

The relatively simple case of the flow generated by a plane piston moving with a constant velocity may be transformed to the flow past a wedge and Chernyi shows for a slender wedge, that the expression for the pressure coefficient is the same as that given in equation (1.35). The more complicated case of the flow due to an expanding cylindrical piston was solved by Bam–Zelikovitch et al. (1949), and, after transformation, leads to the flow past a cone. Another useful solution, for cylindrical pistons having a motion given by $r \sim t^m$, and from which the flow past power law bodies may be obtained, is given, for the case of a strong shock, by Velesko et al. (1956). Other self-similar solutions considered in the Russian literature include a piston expanding according to an exponential law $r = r_0 e^{t/t_0}$ (Sedov, 1959 and Gusev, 1957), and the problem of a violent explosion (Sedov, 1959) which is applied to blunt slender body flows in the next chapter.

Here, instead of using the equivalence principle, we shall investigate steady flows which may be obtained from similarity solutions of the small perturbation equations for axisymmetric bodies. The approach adopted is similar to that followed by Lees and Kubota (1957) and Mirels (1959).

First we introduce non-dimensional variables f, g and h for the radial velocity, pressure and density which for similarity, must be functions only of the variable $\eta = \tilde{r}/\tilde{r}_s$ (where $\tilde{r}_s$ is the reduced shock radius, r_s/τ) and which are defined by

$$\tilde{v}(\tilde{x}, \tilde{r}) = \tilde{r}'_s f(\eta) \qquad (4.35a)$$

$$\tilde{p}(\tilde{x}, \tilde{r}) = \frac{\tilde{r}'^2_s}{\gamma} g(\eta) \qquad (4.35b)$$

and

$$\tilde{\rho}(\tilde{x}, r) = h(\eta) \qquad (4.35c)$$

(where $\tilde{r}'_s = d\tilde{r}_s/dx$)

If it is assumed that the shock is strong (i.e. $\frac{1}{2}(\gamma - 1)M_1^2\beta^2 \gg 1$), the boundary conditions at the shock ($\eta = 1$) become (equations 2.15a, b, c and d)

$$f(1) = \frac{2}{\gamma + 1}$$

$$g(1) = \frac{2\gamma}{\gamma + 1}$$

$$h(1) = \frac{\gamma + 1}{\gamma - 1}$$

Substituting in the small disturbance equations (equation 4.32) we obtain, since

$$\frac{\partial f(\eta)}{\partial r} = \frac{1}{\tilde{r}_s} \cdot \frac{\partial f}{\partial \eta} \text{ and } \frac{\partial f(\eta)}{\partial \tilde{x}} = - \frac{\eta \tilde{r}_s'}{\tilde{r}_s} \frac{\partial f}{\partial \eta} \text{ etc.}$$

$$(\eta - f)h' - hf' - \frac{hf}{\eta} = 0 \tag{4.36a}$$

$$(\eta - f)f' - \frac{g'}{\gamma h} = f\frac{r_s r_s''}{r_s'^2} \tag{4.36b}$$

$$(\eta - f)\left(\frac{g'}{g} - \frac{\gamma h'}{h}\right) = \frac{2r_s r_s''}{r_s'^2} \tag{4.36c}$$

For a similar solution to apply, the equations must be independent of r_s. This can only be the case if

$$\frac{r_s r_s''}{r_s'^2} = \text{const.} = \alpha \tag{4.37}$$

Integrating this gives

$$r_s' = Ar^\alpha \tag{4.38}$$

and

$$r_s = \left(\frac{A}{m}\right)^m \cdot x^m \tag{4.39}$$

where

$$m = \frac{1}{1 - \alpha}$$

The shock shape is thus of the form

$$r_s = C_1 x^m \tag{4.40}$$

where C_1 is constant, and, since at the body,

$$\frac{v_b}{v_s} = \frac{f(\eta_b)}{f(1)} \tag{4.41}$$

then for flow similarity, η_b is constant along the body,

i.e. $$\frac{r_b}{r_s} = \text{const.} \qquad (4.42)$$

Hence the body shape is similar to the shock shape and is given by

$$r_b = C_2 x^m$$

A similar analysis can be applied to a plane body whose ordinate is y_b.

The ratio of the body to the shock radius and the distribution of the flow variables between the shock and the body must be obtained from a solution of the flow equations. However it is possible to say something about the values of m for which similar flows may exist by considering the drag of a plane ($\sigma = 0$) or axisymmetric ($\sigma = 1$) body, which is given by (since $p_b \propto r_s'^2$)

$$D = 2^\sigma \pi^\sigma \int_0^l r_b^\sigma p_b \left(\frac{dr_b}{dx}\right) . dx = \text{const.} \int_0^{r_s} r_s^{\sigma+2\alpha} dr_s \qquad (4.43)$$

$$\text{or } D = \text{const.} \left[r_s^{\sigma+1+2\alpha}\right]_0^{r_s} \qquad (4.44)$$

D is then finite only when

$$-2\alpha \leqslant 1 + \sigma$$

or

$$m \geqslant \frac{2}{3+\sigma}$$

(for $m = 2/(3+\sigma)$, D has a constant value).

Also, if we consider the relationship between the rate of change of the specific energy E associated with the fluid in a transverse plane moving past the body with velocity U_1, and the rate at which work is done by the pressure forces on the body, we have

$$\frac{dE}{dt} = U_1 \frac{dE}{dx} = 2^\sigma \pi^\sigma r_b^\sigma p_b v_b \qquad (4.45)$$

We see that $r_b = 0$ if $dE/dx = 0$, that is, if the drag D has a constant value. (It follows also that $v_b = 0$.) Thus, $m = 2/(3+\sigma)$ corresponds to a body having zero radius, but for which a finite amount of energy has been imparted to the flow at the nose. This type of flow may be associated with the blunt-nosed cylinder or flat plate which is discussed in Chapter 5.

It should be noted that the apparent breakdown of the similarity

5

method for $m < 2/(3 + \sigma)$ does not imply that no flow exists past a body having these values of m, but only that there is no similarity solution. This question is discussed in some detail in a paper by Freeman (1962).

The value $m = 1$ corresponds, as has been noted, to a wedge or cone flow. m cannot be less than $2/(3 + \sigma)$ as the drag would be infinite at the nose. If $m > 1$ the body is cusped with r_b increasing with x, and

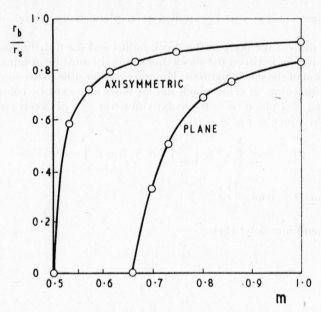

FIG. 4.21.—Ratio of body radius to shock radius for flow over power law bodies ($\gamma = 1\cdot4$) (Kubota, 1957).

although the solutions may be able to represent the flow for some distance from the nose, they must sooner or later break down. (For further discussion of these points, the reader is referred to Mirels (1959) and (1962).)

In the rest of this chapter we concentrate on power law bodies for which $1 \geqslant m \geqslant 2/(3 + \sigma)$.

4.7.1. Solutions for Power Law Bodies

To obtain the actual values of the flow variables between the shock and the body, the equations themselves must be solved. If the set of equations (4.36) with the corresponding boundary conditions are integrated numerically, the resulting ratio of the body to shock radius (for plane and axisymmetric flows) and the pressure, density and velocity distributions between the shock and the body are given in figures 4.21, 4.22a, b, and c (Kubota, 1957b) for a power-law body of revolution ($\gamma = 1\cdot4$).

Figure 4.21 shows that the ratio of the shock to the body radius stays fairly constant for values of $m \geqslant 0\cdot6$ for axisymmetric bodies and for $m \geqslant 0\cdot8$ for plane bodies. The ratio becomes smaller as m

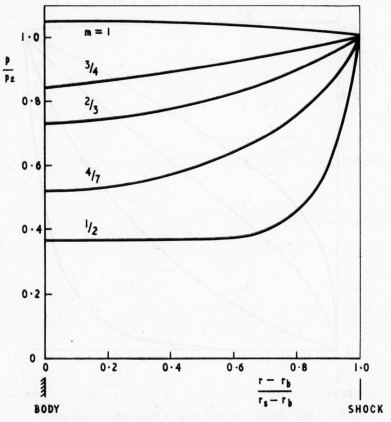

FIG. 4.22a.—Pressure distribution between shock and body for power law bodies of revolution ($\gamma = 1\cdot4$) (Kubota, 1957b).

decreases below these values, and is zero for $m = \frac{1}{2}$ for axisymmetric bodies and for $m = \frac{2}{3}$ for plane bodies. Thus, for these limiting values of m, the body radius falls to zero. It is shown in the next chapter that these flows can be used to represent the flow over blunt-ended cylinders or flat-plates; for the present, however, the discussion will be mainly restricted to values of m not too far different from unity.

The shock and body shapes for a number of different values of the exponent m are shown in figure 4.23. The figure emphasises that all the bodies considered, with the exception of the cone, have blunt noses. The effect of this blunting is considered in the next section.

The pressure distribution between the shock and a power law body of revolution is shown in figure 4.22a. For a cone the pressure increases

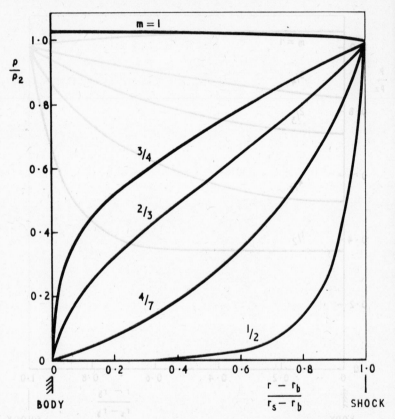

Fig. 4.22a.—Density variation between shock and body for power law bodies of revolution ($\gamma = 1.4$) (Kubota, 1957b).

slightly between the shock and the body. For a power law body with $m = 0.925$ the pressure at the body is equal to that at the shock, and for smaller values of m, the pressure at the body decreases as m decreases, reaching a limiting value of $p/p_2 = 0.36$ for $m = \frac{1}{2}$.

Figure 4.22b shows that for all values of m other than unity, the density is zero near the surface. As m decreases the region of low density extends further from the wall, and as $m \rightarrow \frac{1}{2}$ most of the mass of the gas is confined to a layer near the shock front.

The transverse velocity varies fairly smoothly from its value at the body to that at the shock for all values of m (figure 4.22c). As $m \to \frac{1}{2}$, $v \to 0$ at the body.

The drag coefficient based on the area of the base is given by

$$\frac{C_D}{\tau^2} = \frac{2^{\sigma-1}}{\gamma} \frac{m^3}{m(\sigma+3)-2} \frac{g(\eta_b)}{\eta_b^2} \qquad (4.46)$$

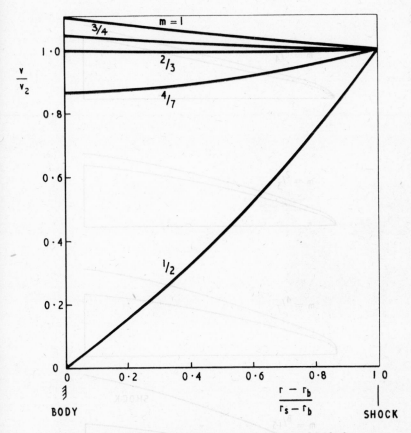

Fig. 4.22c.—Velocity distribution between shock and body for power law bodies of revolution ($\gamma = 1\cdot4$) (Kubota, 1957b).

The drag coefficient for bodies of revolution is shown in figure 4.24. For $\gamma = 1\cdot4$ the minimum value of C_D occurs for $m = 0\cdot71$. This lies between the value $\frac{2}{3}$ and $\frac{3}{4}$ deduced from the Newtonian formulae. The figure also shows the drag coefficient for plane bodies (Mirels, 1959). For this case the minimum drag occurs when $m = 0\cdot92$.

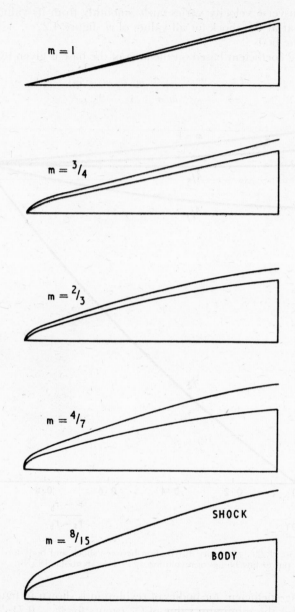

Fig. 4.23.—Family of power law bodies showing theoretical shock shapes
$(\gamma = 1 \cdot 4)$.

The effect of the value of γ on the shock to body radius is shown in figure 4.25a for axisymmetric flow and in figure 4.25b for plane flow.

As is to be expected the distance between the shock and the body decreases as the value of $\gamma \to 1$. (For $\gamma = 1$, the shock and body are coincident.) An approximate method of solving the problem of the

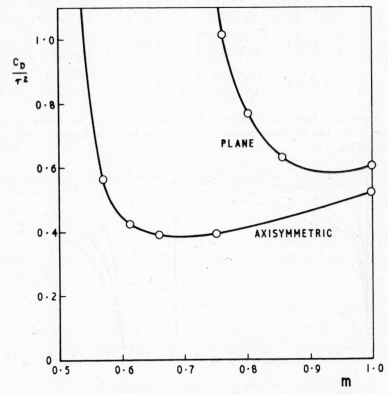

FIG. 4.24.—Drag coefficient for power law bodies (given thickness ratio)
$(\gamma = 1\cdot4)$.

flow past power law bodies has been given by Mirels (1959). The method employs the asymptotic form of the flow in the neighbourhood of the body surface to obtain approximate expressions for the dependent variables. Both first and second approximations have been obtained by Mirels, and the results are in quite good agreement with numerical integrations of the equations of motion, particularly when m and γ are close to 1.

A second approximation to the similarity solutions for axisymmetric bodies valid for shocks of finite strength, has been obtained by Kubota (1957b) by expanding the equations as power series in $x^{2(1-m)}/M_1{}^2\beta^2$.

The resulting equations are integrated numerically. It is interesting to compare his results for $\gamma = 1\cdot4$ for the ratio of shock to body radius with those obtained by Cole (1957).

m	Kubota (2nd Approx.)	Cole
$\frac{3}{4}$	$1\cdot143\left[1 + \dfrac{0\cdot518\ (x/l)^{\frac{1}{2}}}{M_1^2(d/l)^2}\right]$	$1\cdot123\left[1 + \dfrac{0\cdot866\ (x/l)^{\frac{1}{2}}}{M_1^2\ (d/l)^2}\right]$
$\frac{2}{3}$	$1\cdot192\left[1 + \dfrac{0\cdot558\ (x/l)^{\frac{2}{3}}}{M_1^2\ (d/l)^2}\right]$	$1\cdot202\left[1 + \dfrac{1\cdot077\ (x/l)^{\frac{2}{3}}}{M_1^2\ (d/l)^2}\right]$
$\frac{4}{7}$	$1\cdot379\left[1 + \dfrac{0\cdot457\ (x/l)}{M_1^2\ (d/l)^2}\right]$	$1\cdot439\left[1 + \dfrac{1\cdot333\ (x/l)}{M_1^2\ (d/l)^2}\right]$

Agreement between the two approximations is good for values of m near unity, but becomes poorer as m tends towards the limiting critical value of $\frac{1}{2}$.

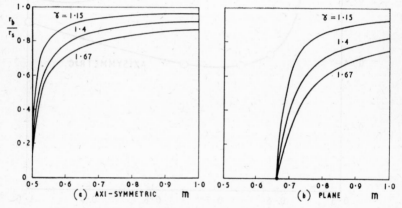

Fig. 4.25.—Variation of body to shock radius ratio with γ for power law bodies.

4.7.2. Limitations of Similarity Solutions for Power Law Bodies

The first order solutions are based on the strong shock relationships, and will hold only if $\frac{1}{2}(\gamma - 1)M_1^2\beta^2$ is large. Thus for a finite hypersonic Mach number, the solution may be expected to break down towards the rear of a slender body as the shock becomes weaker and the shock angle approaches the Mach angle. At the same time a region near the nose of a power law body is excluded because the solutions are based on the use of the small disturbance equations which must break down where the flow deflection is large.

The similarity solutions for $m < 1$ predict a density which falls to zero at the body surface. Since the pressure is finite, the entropy (or p/ρ^γ) will become infinite as the surface is approached. In the equivalent unsteady flow of an expanding piston, this arises because of the initially infinite piston velocity which generates a 'hot core' of gas next to the surface. In a steady flow, the entropy change on the streamlines next to the body which have crossed a nearly normal part of the shock is limited, and, as discussed in chapter 2, there is an entropy layer next to the surface in which the small perturbation equations are no longer valid, and which must be excluded from the solutions obtained using the similarity method.

A calculation of the extent of this layer is given in the next chapter. For the time being it will be noted that for values of m less than unity but greater than about 0·6 for axisymmetric flows, and greater than 0·8 for plane flows, the entropy layer thickness is small relative to the distance between the shock and the body. Since it can be shown that the pressure difference across the entropy layer is also small, the effects of the entropy layer for these values of m can be considered to be negligible in calculating most of the flow field.

CHAPTER 5

HYPERSONIC FLOW PAST BLUNT-NOSED SLENDER BODIES

5.1. Introduction

The previous chapter dealt with the flow past pointed slender bodies having attached shock waves, and with those slender power law bodies having self similar flows for which the effects of the blunt nose are confined to the nose region and to an entropy layer close to the surface. In this chapter we will consider the modifications to the flow over a slender afterbody which arise when the nose of a body of revolution or the leading edge of a two dimensional wing has a finite dimension which is nevertheless small compared with the length of the afterbody.

It is, of course, impossible to manufacture an infinitely sharp nose, so that in practice even so-called sharp leading edges and noses have a small finite dimension, and so long as this is large compared with the ambient mean free path, there will be a small local region where the shock is detached. (The slip flow effects which arise when the nose dimension is of the order of the mean free path or less are considered in chapter 9.)

The influence of nose blunting in hypersonic flow can be significant for hundreds of nose dimensions downstream, and it is important to derive methods of calculating the effect of the blunt nose on the flow field. In a practical flight vehicle the nose will normally be rounded in order to reduce the heat transfer to the stagnation region; it is in any event likely that even if the nose were not deliberately rounded, the large heat transfer rates associated with a sharp nose would cause the nose region to melt and that the subsequent ablation would produce a blunted profile.

The reason that the effect of the nose blunting is much larger in hypersonic flow than in supersonic flow is principally associated with the large pressure gradients in the nose region in hypersonic flow. At high Mach numbers the pressure must fall from a high stagnation pressure ($\sim \gamma/2 \, M_1^2 p_1$) near the stagnation point to a value which is, at the most, a few times the free stream pressure aft of the shoulder. The resulting expansion fan interacts strongly with the bow shock some way downstream of the nose causing a high shock curvature, and hence strong entropy gradients; this in turn results in a strong reflected second family back on to the surface so that the fall in pressure from the stagnation value to the free stream value, instead of being concentrated over the immediate nose region, occurs over a distance which is comparable with the distance between the shock and the afterbody rather than with the nose dimension. In supersonic flow, the change of pressure involved from the stagnation point to the shoulder is much smaller, so that the entropy gradients resulting from interaction with the shock are smaller and in addition most of the expansion fan from the nose is absorbed by the shock and by vorticity interactions with the result that the reflected second family fan reaching the surface is fairly weak. (Also, because the shock is further from the body, the pressure change is spread out over a greater axial distance.)

Associated with the blunt nose, too, is the appearance of a low density entropy layer next to the surface of the body. This arises, as discussed in Chapter 2, because the streamlines crossing the nearly normal part of the shock wave near the nose experience a much larger entropy change than those streamlines crossing the more oblique parts of the shock at some distance from the nose; the flow field may then be considered to be divided for convenience into an outer shock layer, in which the flow deflection is fairly small and in which the small disturbance equations are valid, and an inner entropy layer next to the surface, in which the streamlines have a relatively high value of entropy.

In addition to the entropy layer there will, in a viscous fluid, be a boundary layer growing along the surface. In the present chapter the flow is assumed to be inviscid; blunt-nosed slender body flows with a boundary layer are dealt with in Chapter 8.

Three types of blunted body which will be considered in the present chapter are:

1. Blunt-nosed flat plates and cylinders, for which the afterbody is parallel and has zero form drag.

2. Bodies having power law shocks.

3. Blunt-nosed wedges and cones.

5.2. The Blunt-nosed Flat Plate and Cylinder—Blast Wave Analogy

For a blunt-nosed flat plate or cylinder, the effect of a sudden concentrated addition of energy to the flow by the blunt nose may, by an extension of the equivalence principle, be regarded as analogous to the corresponding unsteady 'blast wave' problem of the explosive release of a finite amount of energy to a plane layer of gas moving with velocity U_1 relative to the body.

This method of treating the effects of nose blunting was first formulated by Lees (1956a).

We deal first with a blunt-nosed flat plate at zero incidence. Considering the upper half plane it is assumed that the forces acting at the nose can be replaced by a concentrated drag force $D_N/2$ per unit width and a force N per unit width normal to the flow direction.

The energy increment $\delta E/2$ imparted in the upper half plane to a slab of gas δx thick, and initially at rest, by the passage of the blunt nose through the slab (figure 5.1a), is given by

$$\frac{\delta E}{2} = \frac{D_N}{2} \cdot \delta x \quad \text{or} \quad \bar{E} = \frac{dE}{dx} = D_N$$

where $\bar{E}$ is the energy density (energy per unit area).

At the same time the normal force imparts an impulse

$$\bar{I} = \frac{N}{U_1}$$

(where $\bar{I}$ has the units of momentum/unit area) to the air above and below the surface.

For an axisymmetric flow such as that past a blunt-nosed cylinder (figure 5.1b), the concentrated drag force is D_N per 2π radians, and

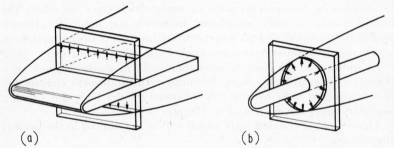

(a)   (b)

Fig. 5.1.—Blast wave analogy for blunt-nosed flat plate and cylinder.

there is a radial force of N per 2π radians. The energy density (energy per unit length) is then again $\bar{E} = D_N$, and the impulse (momentum per unit length) is $\bar{I} = N/U_1$.

The blast wave analogy then relates the motion of the gas in the slab of air to the motion caused by the explosive release of an amount of energy $\bar{E}$ together with an impulse $\bar{I}$ at a time corresponding to that at which the nose of the body passes through the slab. For a blunt-nosed flat plate or cylinder, $\bar{I}$ will normally be small (it is zero for a flat nose) and only the effect of the energy $\bar{E}$ need be considered. This then corresponds to a violent explosion occurring over an infinitely small time interval. The shock envelope generated when a flow velocity U_1, is superimposed is shown in figure 5.1.

If the amount of energy released is large compared with the energy in an appropriate volume of the gas (for instance, a volume equal to that between the shock and the body) then the shock wave will be strong and the effect of the ambient pressure (the 'counterpressure') may be neglected in comparison with the pressure behind the shock front,

Similarity methods may then be used to obtain a solution of the resulting motion of the strong blast wave. For a concentrated explosion having spherical symmetry, solutions to this problem were obtained numerically by Taylor (1950) and analytically by Sedov (1946), for cylindrical symmetry by Lin (1954), and for a plane explosion by Sakurai (1953). Only the cylindrical and plane explosions correspond to real hypersonic steady flows.

The variation of the shock radius, r_s or ordinate y_s, with time may readily be determined from dimensional arguments. Thus, if $\bar{E}$ is the energy imparted to the fluid and since, for a strong shock, the resulting motion is not dependent on the counterpressure (see for instance the strong shock relationships in Chapter 1), we have

$$y_s \text{ or } r_s = f(\bar{E}, \rho_1, t, \gamma) \tag{5.1}$$

Using the normal method of dimensional analysis, we write

$$y_s \text{ or } r_s = \bar{E}^a, \rho_1{}^b, t^c, f(\gamma) \tag{5.2}$$

and, equating the units of mass, length and time, we obtain

$$y_s = f_1(\gamma) \left(\frac{\bar{E}}{\rho_1}\right)^{\frac{1}{3}} t^{\frac{2}{3}} \qquad \text{(plane)} \tag{5.3a}$$

and

$$r_s = f_2(\gamma) \left(\frac{\bar{E}}{\rho_1}\right)^{\frac{1}{4}} t^{\frac{1}{2}} \qquad \text{(axisymmetric)} \tag{5.3b}$$

where the two functions f_1 and f_2 are of order unity.

To determine the numerical values of f_1 and f_2, the full equations must be integrated. Such an integration was made by Sedov (1959) and the resulting variation of f_1 and f_2 with γ is given in figure 5.2.

To obtain the shock shape and pressure distribution for the corresponding steady flow problem, the time coordinate is transformed to the x-coordinate (using the equivalence principle) by

$$x = U_1 t$$

(The validity of this is discussed later in this chapter) and the nose drag D_N is substituted for $\bar{E}$.

Then the expressions for the shock radii (5.3a and b) become

$$\frac{y_s}{C_{D_N} M_1{}^2 d_N} = 2^{\frac{1}{3}} f_1(\gamma) \left(\frac{1}{C_{D_N} M_1{}^3} \frac{x}{d_N}\right)^{\frac{2}{3}} \qquad \text{(plane)} \tag{5.4a}$$

and

$$\frac{r_s}{\sqrt{C_{D_N}} \cdot M_1 d_N} = 2^{\frac{1}{4}} f_2(\gamma) \left(\frac{1}{\sqrt{C_{D_N}} M_1{}^2} \frac{x}{d_N}\right)^{\frac{1}{2}} \qquad \text{(axisymmetric)} \tag{5.4b}$$

where C_{D_N} is the nose drag coefficient given by

$$C_{D_N} = \frac{D_N}{\frac{1}{2}\gamma M_1{}^2 d_N} \qquad \text{(plane)} \tag{5.5a}$$

or

$$C_{D_N} = \frac{D_N}{\frac{1}{2}\gamma M_1^2 \frac{\pi}{4} d_N^2} \quad \text{(axisymmetric)} \tag{5.5b}$$

The form of the non-dimensional groups in (5.4a and b) is chosen so that as $M_1 \to \infty$ and $d_N \to 0$ the drag remains finite, i.e. $M_1\sqrt{d_N}$

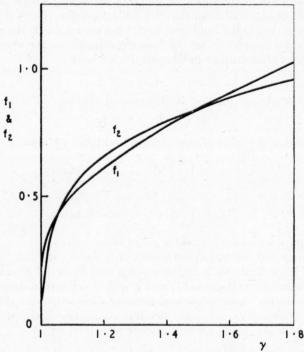

Fig. 5.2.—Variations of f_1 and f_2 with γ (Sedov, 1959).

remains constant for plane flows, and $M_1 d_N$ remains constant for axisymmetric flows. This establishes a formal analogy with the blast wave solutions which consider the instantaneous release of a finite amount of energy.

Figure 5.3a shows a schlieren photograph obtained at R.A.R.D.E. of the flow past a blunted flat plate in air at $M_1 = 13\cdot8$, and in figure 5.3b this shock shape and the shock shape measured at $M_1 = 9\cdot8$ are compared with the shape predicted by equation (5.4a) using a value of $1\cdot26$ for the constant. The form of the shock is predicted very well by the blast wave expression, although even for $M = 13\cdot8$ much of the oblique part of the shock is far from being sufficiently strong for the strong shock relationships to be valid.

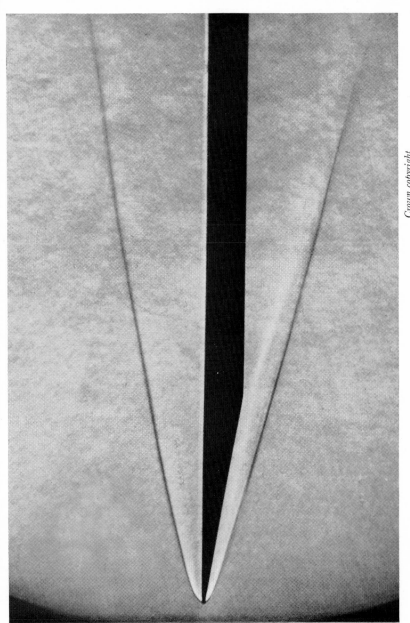

Crown copyright

Fɪɢ. 5.3a.—Flow past a blunted flat plate in air at $M_1 = 13\cdot8$
($d = 0\cdot0142$ in.)

Knowing the shock shape, the distribution of pressure and other quantities behind the shock may be determined from the strong shock relationships. Thus for the pressure distribution, we obtain

$$\frac{p_b}{p_1} = \frac{4}{9} g_1(0) f_1^2(\gamma) \left(\frac{1}{C_{D_N} M_1^3} \cdot \frac{x}{d_N}\right)^{-\frac{2}{3}} \quad \text{(plane)} \quad (5.6a)$$

and

$$\frac{p_b}{p_1} = \frac{1}{4} g_2(0) f_2^2(\gamma) \left(\frac{1}{\sqrt{C_{D_N}} M_1^2} \frac{x}{d_N}\right)^{-\frac{1}{2}} \quad \text{(axisymmetric)} \quad (5.6b)$$

where $g_1(0)$ and $g_2(0)$ are the non-dimensional pressure functions relating the ratio of the pressure at the body surface to that at the shock (Equation 4.35(b)).

$$\times \quad M_1 = 13 \cdot 8 \qquad \circ \quad M_1 = 9 \cdot 8$$
$$R_{e_{d_N}} = 3150 \qquad R_{e_{d_N}} = 8170$$

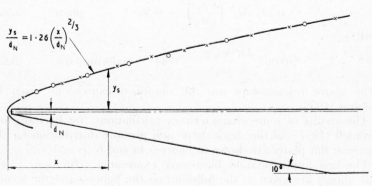

$$\frac{y_s}{d_N} = 1 \cdot 26 \left(\frac{x}{d_N}\right)^{2/3}$$

FIG. 5.3b.—Measured shock shape for flow past blunted flat plate (d = 0·0142 in.).

The above expressions are often referred to as the first approximations to blast wave formulae; they are valid for strong shocks only.

For shocks of finite strength the ambient pressure (or counter-pressure) must be added to the list of variables. Dimensional analysis then shows that the shock shape has the form

$$\frac{y_s}{C_{D_N} M_1^2 d_N} = F_1 \left(\gamma, \frac{1}{C_{D_N} M_1^3} \frac{x}{d_N}\right) \quad \text{(plane)} \quad (5.7a)$$

or

$$\frac{r_s}{\sqrt{C_{D_N}} M_1 d_N} = F_2 \left(\gamma, \frac{1}{\sqrt{C_{D_N}} M_1^2} \frac{x}{d_N}\right) \quad \text{(axisymmetric)} \quad (5.7b)$$

and similar non-dimensional relationships may be obtained for the pressure distributions.

Second approximation blast-wave theories, taking into account the finite Mach number, have been developed by Kubota (1957b) and Sakurai (1953 and 1954).

The expressions for shock shape are given for $\gamma = 1\cdot4$ by

$$\frac{y_s}{M_1{}^2 C_{D_N} d_N} = \frac{0\cdot774}{M_1{}^2 \left[\dfrac{C_{D_N}}{(x/d_N)}\right]^{\frac{2}{3}} - 1\cdot09} \qquad \text{(plane)} \qquad (5.8a)$$

and

$$\frac{r_s}{M_1 \sqrt{C_{D_N}} d_N}$$
$$= 0\cdot795 \left(\frac{x/d_N}{M_1{}^2 \sqrt{C_{D_N}}}\right)^{\frac{1}{2}} \left(1 + \frac{3\cdot15 x/d_N}{M_1{}^2 \sqrt{C_{D_N}}}\right)^{\frac{1}{2}} \quad \text{(axisymmetric)} \quad (5.8b)$$

and for the pressure distributions on the body

$$\frac{p_b}{p_1} = 0\cdot121\, M_1{}^2 \left(\frac{C_{D_N}}{x/d_N}\right)^{\frac{2}{3}} + 0\cdot56 \qquad \text{(plane)} \qquad (5.9a)$$

and

$$\frac{p_b}{p_1} = 0\cdot067\, \frac{M_1{}^2 \sqrt{C_{D_N}}}{(x/d_N)} + 0\cdot44 \qquad \text{(axisymmetric)} \qquad (5.9b)$$

(The above relationships are the simplified expressions given by Sakurai (1953).)

The results of some characteristics calculations (by Bertram and Baradell (1957)) of the shock shape and pressure distribution for the flow past flat plates are shown in figure 5.4a and b ($\gamma = 1\cdot4$).

The first approximation blast-wave expressions (equations (5.4a) and (5.6a)) are given as the full-lines on the figures, and the second approximations (equations (5.8a) and (5.9a)) as the chain-dotted lines. Figure 5.4a (which is given in a paper by Cheng (1957)) shows that the shock slope is predicted fairly well by the first approximation for the whole range of values of the parameter $x/C_{D_N} M_1{}^3 d_N$, although the shock actually lies further from the body than the blast-wave prediction. The second approximation gives a shock lying somewhat closer to that calculated by the characteristics method, but the slope is too large.

For the pressure distribution, except for the points near the nose, Figure 5.4b shows that the first approximation (equation (5.6a)) agrees with the computed pressures for $x/C_{D_N} M_1{}^3 d_N < 10^{-3}$ but that the effect of counterpressure becomes large for larger values of this parameter, and better agreement is obtained using the second approximation (equation (5.9a)).

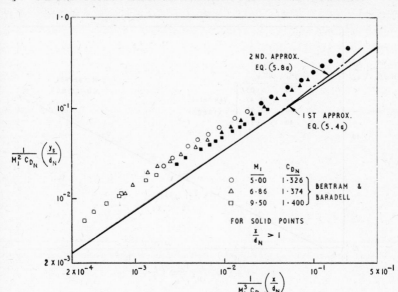

FIG. 5.4a.—Correlation of theoretical shock shapes for blunted flat plates ($\gamma = 1\cdot 4$) (Cheng, 1957).

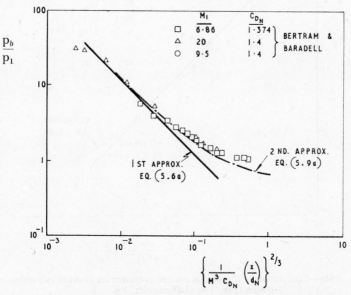

FIG. 5.4b.—Correlation of theoretical surface pressures for flow past blunted flat plate ($\gamma = 1\cdot 4$) (Lukasiewicz, 1961).

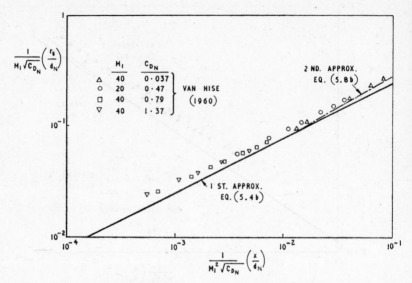

Fig. 5.5a.—Correlation of theoretical shock shapes on blunted cylindrical bodies ($\gamma = 1\cdot4$) (Lukasiewicz, 1961).

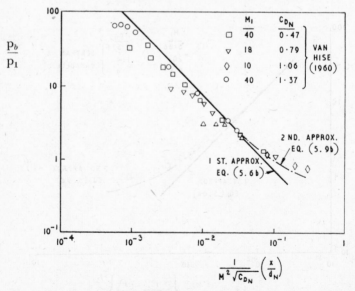

Fig. 5.5b.—Correlation of theoretical surface pressures on blunted cylindrical bodies ($\gamma = 1\cdot4$) (Lukasiewicz, 1961).

Some results of characteristics calculations by van Hise (1960) of the shock shape and pressure distribution for the flow past long cylinders with various blunt nose shapes are shown in figure 5.5a and b.

The results are similar to those for the flat plate flows, i.e. that the shock slope (but not position) is reasonably predicted by the first

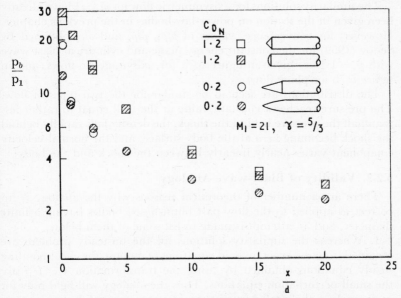

FIG. 5.6.—Nose shape independence concept (Henderson, 1960).

approximation, but that the pressure distribution is best predicted by the second approximation.

Comprehensive surveys of existing data on the blast-wave analogy appear in papers by Lukasiewicz (1961), on which figures 5.4b and 5.5a and b are based, and by Vaglio-Laurin and Trella (1960).

It is implied in the blast wave analogy that the pressure distribution is independent of the actual nose shape, and depends only on the value of the nose drag coefficient. To test this, experiments were made in the NASA Langley Helium Hypersonic tunnel using pairs of models, each pair consisting of two cylindrical rods with different nose shapes but having the same nose drag coefficient. Results for bodies with $C_{D_N} = 0.2$ and $C_{D_N} = 1.2$ are given in figure 5.6 (Henderson, 1960).

It appears from the figure that as predicted the induced pressure distribution is independent of the nose shape for points not too near the nose and for $x/d < 20$.

5.2.1. Distribution of p, ρ and v

To determine the variation of the flow quantities between the shock and the body, the numerical similarity solutions obtained for the unsteady blast wave solutions may be used to obtain the corresponding steady flow variables on the equivalence plane moving with the fluid with velocity U_1.

The similarity solutions for axisymmetric flow for $m = \frac{1}{2}$ have already been given in the section on power-law bodies in the previous chapter. However, for convenience, values of p/p_2, ρ/ρ_2 and v/v_2 obtained by Sedov (1959) for the constant energy plane and cylindrical blast wave with $\gamma = 1 \cdot 4$ are given in figure 5.7a for axisymmetric flows, and in figure 5.7b for plane flows.

The distributions are seen to be similar for the two types of flow. The pressure reaches a constant value at the wall equal to rather less than half the pressure behind the shock, the density falls rapidly behind the shock becoming zero at the body surface, and the normal velocity component varies nearly linearly between the shock and the body.

5.2.2. Validity of Blast-wave Analogy

There are a number of theoretical reasons why the analogy is incorrect as applied to the flow past blunt-nosed bodies having a finite diameter, and an attempt is made to list some of them below.

1. Whereas the similarity solutions for the unsteady problem are obtained from the exact inviscid equations of motion, the corresponding steady equations obtained by using the transformation $x = U_1 t$ are the small perturbation equations. Thus the analogy will hold only for regions where the small perturbation equations are valid, that is to say away from the nose and outside the entropy layer next to the surface (this has been discussed already in Chapter 2, Section 4.2).

2. Whereas only the v perturbation velocities are present in the unsteady problem, there are also u perturbation velocities normal to the equivalence plane in the steady problem.

The magnitude of these u perturbations may be determined using the Bernoulli equation and it is shown in the next section that u and v may be of the same order near the body. Freeman (1962) showed that this must be taken into account when establishing a correspondence between the energy integral in the unsteady flow, and the momentum integral across the equivalence plane in the steady flow. Thornhill (1962) suggested that the equivalence plane normal to the flow direction should be replaced by a curved equivalence surface such that at any point the velocity vector which represents the perturbation from the undisturbed velocity, U_1, is tangential to the surface. This surface is initially normal to the oblique shock and curves downstream as the body is approached.

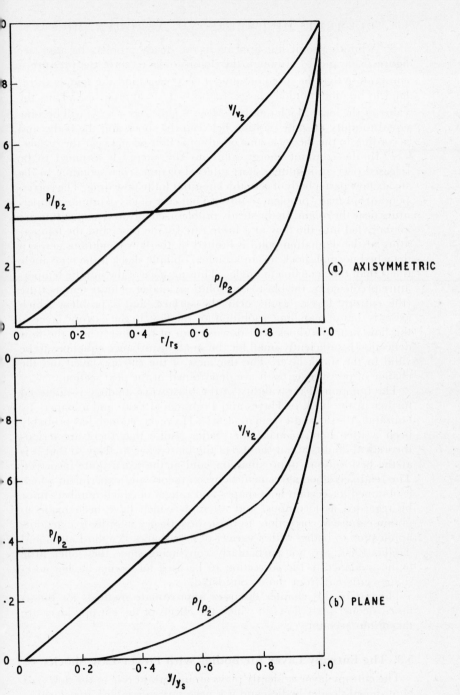

Fɪɢ. 5.7.—Pressure, density and velocity distributions for constant energy solutions (Sedov, 1959).

3. A limiting sonic line appears in the steady problem because (see figures 5.7a and b) although the density falls to zero, the pressure is constant, so that the speed of sound $a = \sqrt{\gamma p / \rho}$ (and the temperature) tend to become infinitely large as the body is approached. Thus the value of the local Mach number $M = \sqrt{U_1{}^2 + u^2 + v^2} / a$ will become equal to unity at some position between the shock and the body, and according to the theory a zone of subsonic flow occurs near the surface.

4. In the constant energy solutions the energy is assumed to be released over an infinitely short interval of time, corresponding to the steady flow past a body of zero thickness but finite nose drag. The corresponding unsteady problem results in a hot core of gas of infinite temperature near the origin. In the steady problem, energy and momentum are actually fed into the flow at a finite rate by the nose, and the temperature at the stagnation point is limited by the flow conditions across a detached normal shock (or an attached oblique shock if the nose angle is less than the detachment angle). Thus in place of the infinite temperature predicted by the blast wave solution, a layer of finite temperature (the entropy layer) occurs near the surface, and a problem which arises is that of matching a solution for the flow in the entropy layer to the flow near the shock well downstream of the nose where the flow deflection is sufficiently small for the small disturbance equations to be valid in the shock layer. The thickness of the entropy layer and the change of pressure across it are determined in the next section.

The question of the validity of the blast-wave analogy is discussed further in the book by Hayes and Probstein (1959b) and in papers by Guiraud (1961a) and Freeman (1962). However, enough has probably been written here to make the reader realise that there are serious theoretical doubts about the use of the blast-wave analogy so that it is at the best only an approximation, and at the worst quite incorrect. The relatively good agreement between theory and experiment which is obtained for certain nose shapes and ranges of Mach numbers must be regarded as fortuitous, and attempts which have been made to obtain empirical corrections to blast wave theory in order to extend its application to bodies with a variety of nose shapes (Vaglio-Laurin and Trella, 1960) are not particularly convincing since they offer little or no guidance to the correction to be used for bodies having nose-shapes different from those considered.

The rest of this chapter discusses approximate methods for blunt-nosed slender-body flows in which the effects of the entropy layer are taken into account.

5.3. The Entropy Layer for Bodies with Power-Law Shocks

The entropy layer evidently plays an important role in the flow past blunt-nosed slender bodies, and it is necessary to establish the extent of the layer, and the magnitude of the pressure change across it. The approximate analysis given here is similar to the methods used by Cheng (1957) and Sychev (1960a), and is carried out for a body supporting a shock of the form $y_s \sim x^m$.

The pressure, p_e, and the density, ρ_e, along a typical streamline in the entropy layer which is assumed to have crossed a part of the shock which is nearly normal are related to the pressure p_{2_n} and density ρ_{2_n} behind the shock by

$$\frac{p_e}{\rho_e^{\gamma}} = \frac{p_{2_n}}{\rho_{2_n}^{\gamma}} \tag{5.10}$$

whence

$$\rho_e = \left(\frac{p_e}{p_{2_n}}\right)^{1/\gamma} \cdot \rho_{2_n} \tag{5.11}$$

Now, for a strong shock

$$\frac{\rho_{2_n}}{\rho_{1_n}} = \frac{\rho_2}{\rho_1} = \frac{\gamma + 1}{\gamma - 1} \tag{5.12}$$

and, for a normal shock,

$$p_2 \simeq \frac{2\gamma}{\gamma + 1} M_1^2 p_1 \tag{5.13}$$

If we assume that, as a conservative estimate, the pressure in the entropy layer is equal to or less than that at the shock, we may write

$$p_e = \frac{2\gamma}{\gamma + 1} M_1^2 \beta^2 p_1 \tag{5.14}$$

where β is the local shock inclination (assumed small) or, from (5.11)

$$\frac{\rho_e}{\rho_1} = \frac{\gamma + 1}{\gamma - 1} \beta^{2/\gamma} \tag{5.15}$$

The Bernoulli equation is

$$(U_1 + u_e)^2 + v_e^2 + \frac{2\gamma}{\gamma - 1} \frac{p_e}{\rho_e} \simeq U_1^2 \tag{5.16}$$

Since v_e/U_1 is $\lesssim \beta$ (except near the nose), this may be approximated (ignoring second order terms) by

$$\frac{u_e}{U_1} = \frac{\gamma}{\gamma - 1} \frac{p_e}{\rho_e U_1^2} \tag{5.17}$$

and substituting for p_e and ρ_e from (5.14) and (5.15) we find that

$$\frac{u_e}{U_1} \simeq \frac{2\gamma}{(\gamma + 1)^2} \beta^{2 - 2/\gamma} \tag{5.18}$$

Sufficiently far downstream although u_e and v_e may be of the same order, u_e can become small compared with U_e. However, for finite hypersonic Mach numbers this may not occur before the shock becomes too weak for the strong shock condition to hold. Evidently only if $u_e \ll U_1$, has the subsequent analysis any validity. (See also Section 5.42 and figure 5.11.)

To estimate the thickness of the layer we define the edge of the entropy layer as the streamline for which $dy/dx \sim 1$ at the shock.

Referring to figure 5.8 for the notation to be used, we consider here the case of a plane flow, although the arguments may easily be extended to axisymmetric flows.

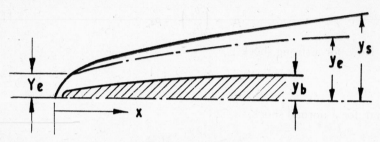

FIG. 5.8.—Flow past blunt-nosed slender body with entropy layer.

The mass flow in the entropy layer is

$$\psi_e = \rho_1 U_1 Y_e = \int_{y_b}^{y_e} \rho(U_1 + u)dy \simeq \bar{\rho}_e \bar{U}_e \delta_e \qquad (5.19)$$

where the average density $\bar{\rho}_e$ in the entropy layer is assumed to be given by equation (5.15), and the average velocity $\bar{U}_e = U_1 + u_e \simeq U_1$.

Thus the thickness of the layer, δ_e, is given by

$$\frac{\delta_e}{y_s} = \frac{\rho_1}{\rho_e} \frac{Y_e}{y_s} = \frac{(\gamma - 1)}{(\gamma + 1)} \left(\frac{y_s}{x}\right)^{-2/\gamma} \left(\frac{Y_e}{y_s}\right) \qquad (5.20)$$

where we have replaced β by y_s/x

Now, for a power law shock

$$y_s = Cx^m$$

we have

$$\left(\frac{dy}{dx}\right)_{y=Y_e} = \frac{mC}{x_e^{1-m}} \simeq 1 \qquad (5.21)$$

Since

$$Y_e = Cx_e^m \simeq C^{1/1-m}$$

and

$$\frac{Y_e}{y_s} \simeq \frac{C^{1/1-m}}{y_s} = \left(\frac{y_s}{x}\right)^{m/1-m}$$

we obtain

$$\frac{\delta_e}{y_s} \simeq \frac{\gamma - 1}{\gamma + 1} \left(\frac{y_s}{x}\right)^{\frac{m}{1-m} - \frac{2}{\gamma}} \tag{5.22}$$

If we require δ_e/y_s to be small, say of order $\beta^2 \simeq (y_s/x)^2$, then the entropy layer is of negligible thickness only for $m > m^\star$ where $m^\star$ is given by

$$\frac{m^\star}{1 - m^\star} - \frac{2}{\gamma} = 2$$

i.e.

$$m^\star = \frac{2 + 2/\gamma}{3 + 2/\gamma} \tag{5.23}$$

For axisymmetric flows the corresponding result is

$$m^\star = \frac{1 + 1/\gamma}{2 + 1/\gamma} \tag{5.24}$$

Values of $m^\star$ obtained from equations (5.23) and (5.24) for different values of γ are given in the table below (these same values of $m^\star$ have also been determined by Freeman (1962));

| | Plane | Axisymmetric |
γ	$m^\star$	$m^\star$
1	0·800	0·667
1·2	0·786	0·647
1·4	0·774	0·632
1·67	0·762	0·615

We have thus established the values of $m(1 > m > m^\star)$ for which the effects of the blunt nose may be neglected for the flow over slender power law bodies. For values of $m < m^\star$, the thickness of the entropy layer is no longer negligible and must be taken into account, for instance, in order to calculate the effective body shape corresponding to a given shock shape.

To estimate the change of pressure across the entropy layer, following Cheng (1957), we consider the y-momentum equation which gives

$$\Delta p = - \int_{y_b}^{y_e} \left[(U_1 + u)\frac{\partial}{\partial x} + v\frac{\partial}{\partial y}\right] \rho v \cdot dy \tag{5.25}$$

Since we consider $v \ll U_1 + u$, and in view of equation (5.19) this may be approximated by

$$\Delta p \simeq \overline{\rho_e} U_1^2 \left(\frac{\overline{v_e}}{U_1}\right) \cdot \frac{\delta_e}{x} \tag{5.26}$$

where $\overline{v}_e$ is the mean value of v across the layer.

Taking $\overline{ev}/U_1 \sim \beta$ as above, and substituting for p_e from (5.14) we obtain for the variation of pressure across the layer

$$\frac{\Delta p}{p_e} \lesssim \frac{\gamma + 1}{2} \cdot \frac{\rho_e}{\rho_1} \cdot \frac{\delta_e}{y_s} \tag{5.27}$$

or, from (5.15) and (5.22)

$$\frac{\Delta p}{p_e} \lesssim \frac{\gamma + 1}{2} \cdot \beta^{m/(1-m)} \tag{5.28}$$

Thus for $1 > m \geqslant \frac{2}{3}$, the change of pressure across the layer is small ($\sim \beta^2$ or less) even though as $m \to \frac{2}{3}$ the layer occupies a relatively large part of the region between the shock and the body.

Similar results apply for axisymmetric flows with $1 > m \geqslant \frac{1}{2}$.

5.4. Flow Past Blunt-nosed Wedges and Cones

5.4.1. Method of Chernyi

For blunted wedges (and inclined flat plates) and cones, the simple form of the flow similarity which led to the blast wave analogy no longer holds and other approximate methods of determining the flow field are used.

The first method which will be discussed here is an integral technique due to Chernyi (1957a and b).

Again it is assumed that as for the blunted flat plate or cylinder the effect of the nose blunting on the flow field may be replaced by a concentrated drag force, $D/2$ per unit depth for plane flow, or D per 2π radians for axisymmetric flow, which imparts an energy E to the flow, and a normal force N which imparts an impulse $I = N/U_1$.

At the same time it is assumed that a plane piston starts to move from the nose with a velocity $V \simeq U_1\theta$ normal to the flow direction so as to generate the surface of a wedge or cone of semi-angle θ.

Chernyi makes use of two integrals expressing conservation of energy and momentum in the equivalent unsteady flow problem.

The energy equation states that the sum of the excess kinetic and internal energy of the gas at any instant must be equal to the sum of the energy, E, initially given to the flow at $t = 0$, and the work done on the gas by the piston. This may be written

$$\int_{v_s - v_0} \left\{ \frac{\rho}{2} \left(\frac{\partial r}{\partial t} \right)^2 + \frac{p}{\gamma - 1} \right\} dv = E + \int_v \frac{p_0}{\gamma - 1} \, dv + \int_0^t p_0 dv_0(t) \tag{5.29}$$

Here $v_s - v_0$ is the volume occupied by the moving gas, v_s is the volume displaced by the shock, v_0 is the volume displaced by the piston, p_0 is the pressure on the piston, and r is the distance from the origin.

The second equation used equates the momentum of the gas to the impulse imparted to the gas initially together with that imparted by the piston. This equation is

$$\int_{v-v_0} \rho \, \frac{\partial r}{\partial t} \, dv = I + \int_0^t (p_0 - p_1)s \, dt \qquad (5.30)$$

where s is the surface area of the piston.

To simplify the model, Chernyi notes that for γ not too different from unity and for a strong shock most of the mass of the gas will be concentrated near the shock (this takes account, in a crude way, of the entropy layer) and that the counterpressure can be neglected.

The above two equations then become, for a wedge flow in which $v_0 = V_1 t$ ($V_1 = U_1 \tan \theta_w$), $v = y_s$ and $s = 1$

$$\tfrac{1}{2}\rho_1 y_s \left(\frac{\partial y}{\partial t}\right)^2 + \frac{p}{\gamma - 1} (y_s - V_1 t) = E + V_1 \int_0^t p_0 \cdot dt \qquad (5.31)$$

and

$$\rho_1 y_s \left(\frac{\partial y}{\partial t}\right) = I + \int_0^t p_0 \cdot dt \qquad (5.32)$$

The integral containing the body pressure may then be eliminated, and taking the velocity of the particles in the shock layer to be equal to

$$\frac{\partial y}{\partial t} = \frac{2}{\gamma + 1} \, \dot{y}_s \qquad (5.33)$$

where the dot stands for the time-derivative, and from (5.32) for the pressure (assumed to be constant across the shock layer, and with the body pressure equal to that behind the shock)

$$p = \frac{d}{dt} \rho_1 y_s \left(\frac{2}{\gamma + 1} \dot{y}_s\right) \qquad (5.34)$$

there results the single equation

$$\tfrac{1}{2}\rho_1 y \left(\frac{2}{\gamma + 1} y_s\right)^2 + \frac{y_s - V_1 t}{\gamma - 1} \frac{d}{dt} \left\{\rho_1 y_s \left(\frac{2}{\gamma + 1}\right) \dot{y}_s\right\}$$

$$= E - V_1 I + \rho_1 V_1 y_s \left(\frac{2}{\gamma + 1}\right) \dot{y}_s \qquad (5.35)$$

This may be non-dimensionalised by using variables

$$\bar{y}_s = y_s \frac{\rho_1 V_1^2}{E - IV_1} \quad \text{and} \quad \bar{t} = \frac{t \rho_1 V_1^3}{E - IV_1}$$

to give

$$\frac{\bar{y}_s - \bar{t}}{\gamma - 1} \cdot \frac{d}{d\bar{t}}(\bar{y}_s \dot{\bar{y}}_s) = \frac{\gamma + 1}{2} + \bar{y}_s \dot{\bar{y}}_s - \frac{1}{\gamma + 1} \bar{y}_s \dot{\bar{y}}_s{}^2 \qquad (5.36)$$

For small values of $\bar{t}$ the solution to this is

$$\bar{y}_s = \left[\frac{9}{4} \frac{(\gamma + 1)^2 (\gamma - 1)}{3\gamma - 1} \right]^{1/3} \bar{t}^{2/3} \qquad (5.37)$$

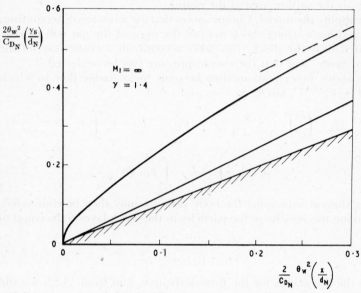

FIG. 5.9.—Shock shape for flow past blunted wedge (Chernyi, 1957a).

and for large $\bar{t}$ the solution tends to the asymptotic value

$$\bar{y}_s = \frac{\gamma + 1}{2} \bar{t} + \gamma - 1 \qquad (5.38)$$

For a blunt-nosed slender body IV_1/E will normally be small (since $V_1 \simeq U_1\theta_w$) and the solution obtained from equation (5.36), after transforming to the steady problem for the flow past a wedge of semi-angle θ_w reduces to

$$\frac{y_s}{d_N} = \frac{C_{D_N}}{4\theta_w{}^2} \bar{y}_s \left(\frac{4\theta_w{}^3}{C_{D_N}} \frac{x}{d_N}, \gamma \right) \qquad (5.39)$$

This relationship is plotted in non-dimensional form in figure 5.9 which also shows the shock shape for a sharp wedge for comparison.

It is seen how the effect of blunting is to displace the shock from the body. The magnitude, Δy_s, of this displacement may be determined from equation (5.38) and is given by

$$\frac{\Delta y_s}{d_N} = \frac{\gamma - 1}{4} \frac{C_{D_N}}{\theta_w^2} \tag{5.40}$$

and the asymptotic value of the displacement is shown as a dashed line in the figure.

For $\theta_w = 0$, expression (5.37) gives the solution for the flow past a blunted flat plate $(E \to 0)$

$$\frac{y_s}{d_N} = \left\{ \frac{9}{16} \frac{(\gamma + 1)^2 (\gamma - 1)}{3\gamma - 1} \right\}^{\frac{1}{3}} C_{D_N}^{\frac{1}{3}} \left(\frac{x}{d_N} \right)^{\frac{2}{3}} \tag{5.41}$$

For $\gamma = 1\cdot4$ the constant outside the equation is $0\cdot740$ and this may be compared with the more exact value (obtained from figure 5.2) of $0\cdot774$.

The pressure distribution for the blunted wedge, may be obtained by transforming equation (5.34), and is given by

$$C_{p_w} = \frac{p_w}{\frac{1}{2}\rho_1 U_1^2} = \frac{2}{\gamma + 1} \bar{y}_s \cdot \dot{\bar{y}}_s \tag{5.42}$$

where, again, $\bar{y}_s = \bar{y}_s \left(\dfrac{4\theta_w^3}{C_{D_N}} \cdot \dfrac{x}{d_N}, \gamma \right)$

This is plotted in figure 5.13a where it is compared with the results of the method of Cheng given in the next section. The slender sharp wedge pressure coefficient is also shown.

The drag of a blunted slender wedge is given by

$$D = D_N + 2 \int_0^l p_w \tan \theta_w \, dx \tag{5.43}$$

and the drag coefficient obtained from this expression has been evaluated by Chernyi and is shown in figure 5.10a. The drag coefficient of a sharp wedge is also shown in the figure and it is evident that the effect of nose blunting is to cause a considerable increase in the drag coefficient.

The solution for a wedge of semi-angle θ_w also applies for obtaining the shock shape and pressure distribution over a blunt flat plate at an angle of incidence θ_w. (For the leeward surface the sign of the last term of equation (5.43) is negative.)

For the cone, too, an analogous method may be employed. For details the reader is referred to Chernyi (1957b).

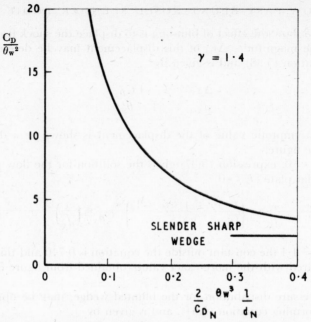

FIG. 5.10a.—Drag coefficient for flow past blunted wedge
(Chernyi, 1957b).

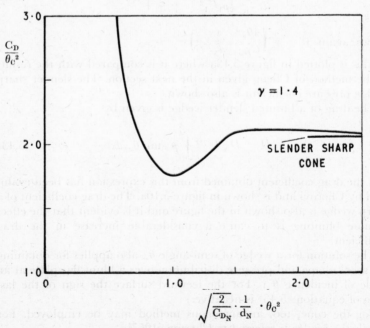

FIG. 5.10b.—Drag coefficient for flow past blunted cone
(Chernyi, 1957b).

The drag coefficient for a blunted cone predicted by this method is shown in figure (5.10b), and the pressure distribution in figure (5.13b).

The asymptotic sharp slender cone value is also shown in figure 5.10b and there is seen to be an overexpansion followed by a recompression, and a recompression overshoot. Experiments made by Bertram (1956) at $M = 6.85$ show a similar trend. The drag coefficient (figure 5.10b) has a minimum at $\sqrt{2/C_{D_N}}\, l/d_N\, \theta_c{}^2 = 0.96$. It appears also that, because of the large region of low pressure following the nose, the drag coefficient of a blunted cone can actually be less than that of a sharp cone, a result which could be of considerable importance for missile designers. It must, however, be remembered that the theory is an approximate one and the full theoretical drag reduction may not be realised in practice.

5.4.2. Method of Cheng

An approximate method of calculating the flow past a blunted flat plate or cylinder which is similar to that of Chernyi and which includes more specifically the effect of the entropy layer is that of Cheng (1960b). (See also Cheng, Hall, Golian and Hertzberg (1960).) The model assumed is that already given in figure 5.8—that is to say the flow is divided into a shock layer and an entropy layer, and the method makes use of some of the results derived in section 5.2. The assumptions which are necessary are:

1. The shock must be strong ($\frac{1}{2}(\gamma - 1)M_1{}^2\beta^2 \gg 1$). This is unlikely to be true except for very high Mach numbers.

2. The shock inclination is small throughout the flow field. (This condition excludes the nose region.)

3. The disturbance velocity, u_e, must be small compared with the free stream velocity U_1.

(Equation (5.18) gives the value of u_e/U_1 in the entropy layer, and if the first order blast wave relationship is used to obtain an approximation to the shock slope, β_s, u_e/U_1 may be determined in terms of $(x/C_{D_N}d_N)$.

The values of u_e/U_1 thus obtained are given, for $\gamma = 1.2$, 1.4 and 1.66, in figure 5.11 ($M_1 = \infty$).

Evidently, so long as γ is not too close to 1, u_e/U_1 will be small for values of $x/C_{D_N}d_N \gtrsim 10$.)

4. The variation of the pressure across the entropy layer must be small. (That this is the case has been shown from equation (5.28).)

The solution then depends on using the Newtonian–Busemann formula to obtain the pressure p_e at the inner edge of the shock layer (assumed to be of negligible thickness, which implies that $\gamma \to 1$)

i.e.

$$p_e = \rho_1 U_1{}^2(y'_e + y_e y''_e)$$
$$= \rho_1 U_1{}^2(y_e y'_e)' \qquad (5.44)$$

(The primes denote d/dx.)

This pressure is assumed constant across the entropy layer, and as an approximation (which is justified in the paper cited), we may write

$$\frac{D_N}{2} = \int_{y_b}^{y_s}\left\{\left(\frac{p - p_1}{\gamma - 1}\right) + \frac{\rho v^2}{2}\right\} dy \simeq \frac{p_e}{\gamma - 1}(y_e - y_e) \qquad (5.45)$$

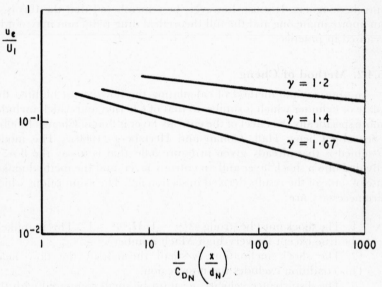

Fig. 5.11.—Perturbation velocity u_e/U_1 for flow over blunted flat plate (Cheng, 1960b).

(The $D_N/2$ appears because drag is defined as D_N for the total drag of a symmetrical nose.)

Hence, using (5.44)

$$D_N = \frac{1}{\gamma - 1}(y_e - y_b)(y_e y'_e)' = \frac{\gamma - 1}{2} C_{D_N} \cdot \frac{d_N}{2} \qquad (5.46)$$

This is the fundamental equation from which, since it is assumed that $y_e = y_s$, the shock shape may be determined.

A solution of equation (5.46), valid for a blunted flat plate with $y_b = 0$ is

$$y_s \sim x^{2/3}$$

i.e. the normal blast-wave solution is obtained.

The extension of this method to include boundary layer displacement effects is given in Chapter 8.

The method may readily be extended to include the flow past blunted wedges and cones. Thus, in equation (5.46), the body ordinate, y_b, may be taken as the surface of a wedge (or inclined flat plate). The

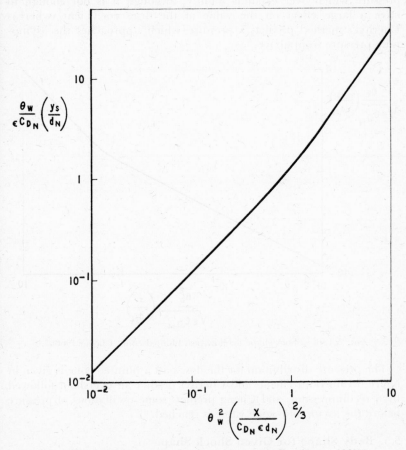

FIG. 5.12a.—Shock shape for flow over blunted wedge (Cheng, 1960b).

results obtained using this method for the shock shape for the flow past blunted wedges is given in figure 5.12a, and for blunted cones in figure 5.12b. A marked change of shock slope occurs where a nose solution changes over to an afterbody solution. The change of slope may be seen clearly in the photograph of the flow past a blunted cone given in the frontispiece. It is interesting to note that the entropy layer appears clearly on the photograph as a white region next to the body

6

on the upper surface. (This is because the density in the layer is less than the free stream value.)

The pressure distribution for blunted wedges is given in figure 5.13a for comparison with Chernyi's results, and the asymptotic slender wedge pressure is also shown on the figure. Cheng predicts a surface pressure which over expands slightly, although it is not enough to have a large effect on the value of the drag coefficient, whereas Chernyi's method predicts a pressure which approaches the asymptotic pressure from above.

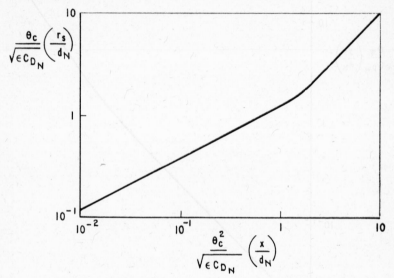

Fig. 5.12b.—Shock shape for flow past blunted cone (Cheng, 1960b).

The pressure distribution for the flow past a blunted cone is given in figure 5.13b. Both Cheng and Chernyi predict an overshoot followed by a recompression, and Cheng predicts some oscillations of pressure before the asymptotic cone value is reached.

5.5. Body Shape for Given Shock Shape

Having established some approximate relationships for the entropy layer in section 5.2, it is of interest to determine the actual body shape which is obtained for a given power law shock shape if the entropy change at the shock is taken into account. The method follows a calculation made by Sychev (1960a). Taking the case of an axisymmetric shock, he proceeds from the definition of the stream function

$$\frac{dr}{d\psi} = \frac{1}{\rho U r} \tag{5.47}$$

Using the Bernoulli equation, U may be approximated by

$$U \simeq \sqrt{U_1^2 - \frac{2\gamma}{\gamma - 1}\frac{p}{\rho}}$$

and it is then assumed that the flow variables may be expressed in the form $\psi = \psi_s(x)\Psi(\eta)$, $p = p(x)G(\eta)$, $\rho = \rho_s(x)H(\eta)$ where $\eta = r/r_s$ and ψ_s, p_s and ρ_s are the values at the shock. The non-dimensional

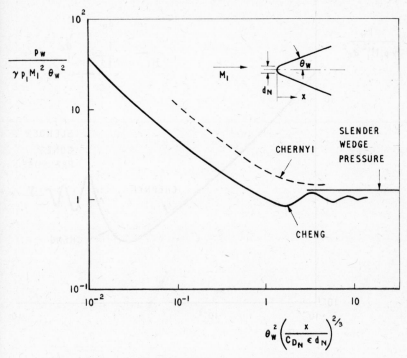

FIG. 5.13a.—Pressure distribution for flow past blunted wedge.

functions Ψ, G and H are obtained from the zero-order similarity solutions (G and H are, of course, simply related to g and h of equations (4.35)).

The body radius, r_b, may then be obtained by integrating equation (5.47) for fixed values of x to give the continuity integral

$$\frac{r_s^2 - r_b^2}{2} = \int_0^1 \frac{\psi_s(x)\, d\Psi(\eta)}{\rho_s(x)\, H(\eta)\sqrt{U_1^2 - \frac{2\gamma}{\gamma - 1}\frac{p_s(x)}{\rho_s(x)}\frac{G(\eta)}{H(\eta)}}} \quad (5.48)$$

Sychev evaluated this numerically for a shock given by $r_s = \sqrt{2x}$, and the resulting body shape is shown in figure 5.14. (The co-ordinates have been made dimensionless by dividing by the radius of curvature of the shock at the apex.)

In effect the finite entropy change at the shock is taken into account because Ψ_s, p_s and ρ_s are calculated from the given shock shape. As a result the density as one proceeds from the shock to the body is higher

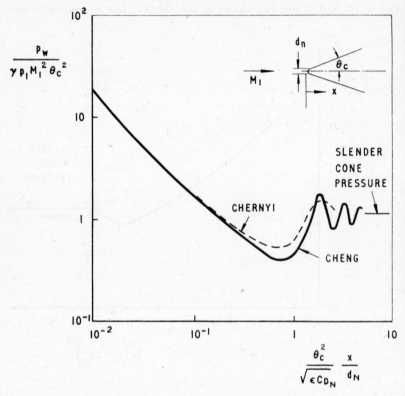

FIG. 5.13b.—Pressure distribution for flow past blunted cone.

than that of the zero order similarity solution, and the body ($\Psi = 0$) is displaced away from the axis towards the shock.

The body surface obtained in this way for $M_1 = \infty$ and $\gamma = 1\cdot4$ is quite different from the zero thickness body of the blast wave analogy. It is only very far back—of the order of a 1000 nose diameters or more —that the thickness of the body becomes small compared with the distance between the shock and the body.

The use of the continuity integral in problems of this type is discussed further in a review article by Mirels (1963).

Another method of solution of the problem of the body shape for a given shock shape is that of Yakura (1961). He uses the 'method of inner and outer solutions' of Kaplun (1957) and Lagerstrom and obtains results for the axisymmetric body shape which are close to those of Sychev.

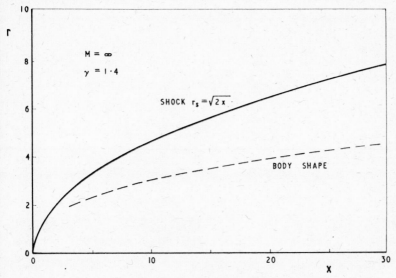

Fig. 5.14.—Body shape for paraboloidal shock of form $r_s = \sqrt{2x}$ (Sychev, 1960).

PART 2

REAL GAS, VISCOUS AND LOW DENSITY EFFECTS IN HYPERSONIC FLOW

CHAPTER 6

REAL GAS EFFECTS IN INVISCID FLOWS

6.1. Introduction

As pointed out in the main Introduction, at the high temperatures associated with hypersonic flight it is necessary to consider the effects caused by the difference in the behaviour of a real gas compared with that of an ideal or perfect gas. This is defined as a gas which obeys the equation of state

$$P = \rho R T$$

(thermally perfect) where R is the gas constant for air, and has constant specific heats (calorically perfect). According to the kinetic theory of gases the ratio of specific heats is given by

$$\gamma = (f + 2)/f$$

where f is the number of active degrees of freedom. Thus for a monatomic gas with only 3 translational degrees of freedom $\gamma = 5/3$. A diatomic gas has two modes of rotation as well so that $\gamma = 7/5$ at room temperature, and at higher temperatures the vibrational modes become excited and γ decreases with increasing temperature. The effects of vibrational excitation can be calculated by using the Berthelot equation of state as in the Tables and Charts prepared by the Ames Research Staff (1953). As the temperature rises above about 2500°K however dissociation and finally ionisation occur so that the number of active degrees of freedom becomes very large and hence $\gamma \to 1$. The variation of γ with temperature at a pressure of 1 atmosphere is shown in figure 6.1.

To get a preliminary idea of real gas effects we will consider the variation of stagnation temperature with flight speed, assuming conditions of chemical equilibrium. Figure 6.2 shows the stagnation temperature plotted against flight speed at an altitude of 200,000 ft. The top curve is for isentropic compression of air considered as a perfect gas with constant specific heats (whose ratio is $\gamma = 1\cdot4$). This shows a stagnation temperature of over 10,000°K for example at a flight speed of 15,000 ft/sec. For a real gas, curve (b), the temperature falls away from the ideal gas values at speeds above 3,000 ft/sec because of the increase in specific heat arising from excitation of the vibrational modes of the molecules. Oxygen dissociation begins at about 6,000 ft/sec, nitrogen dissociation occurs at velocities above 15,000 ft/sec and ionisation of atoms becomes of major importance at speeds of about

35,000 ft/sec corresponding to the velocity of escape from the earth's atmosphere. Since dissociation and ionisation reactions produce two particles from each original one they are inhibited by high pressure with the result that greater amounts of dissociation are found at higher altitudes, or alternatively, higher temperatures and therefore velocities are required to produce the reactions at lower altitudes. Thus it is necessary to define the type of compression and several cases are

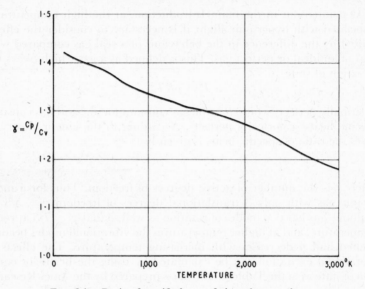

Fig. 6.1.—Ratio of specific heats of air at 1 atmosphere.

indicated in figure 6.2. Isentropic compression is the most efficient from the point of view of pressure recovery and the corresponding curve shows an isentropic stagnation temperature of about 6,500°K at 15,000 ft/sec rising to 10,000°K at 20,000 ft/sec. The stagnation pressures under these conditions are of interest in the design of experimental facilities. For an ambient pressure of 3.7×10^{-4} atmospheres (200,000 ft altitude) the ideal gas stagnation pressure is about 60 atmospheres for a flight velocity of 15,000 ft/sec, whereas for the real gas it is 500 atmospheres. This marked increase is an indication of the scale of the changes resulting from real gas effects.

The next curve shows the temperature at the stagnation point of an insulated body neglecting radiation. Because of the loss in total head across the bow shock wave the pressure recovery is much less, in fact at 15,000 ft/sec and 200,000 ft altitude the pressure at the stagnation point is only 0.075 atmospheres. A lower pressure means more dissociation as explained above, and hence lower temperature for a given enthalpy. For this case it is 4,750°K. Finally the lowest curve shows the temperature corresponding to the ambient pressure of $3\cdot7 \times 10^{-4}$ atmospheres. This corresponds to the zero heat transfer temperature on an ideal flat plate with a recovery factor of unity. For 15,000 ft/sec the temperature has fallen to about 4,000°K.

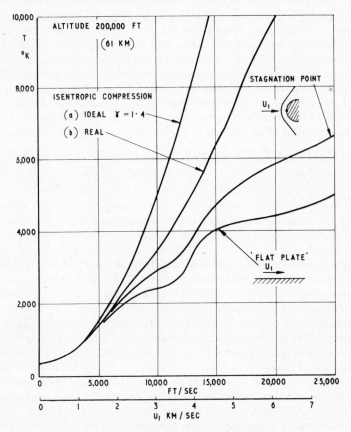

FIG. 6.2.—Real gas effects on stagnation temperature.

Thus we see how stagnation temperature is modified by pressure when dissociation is present. The altitude will of course affect the temperatures shown in figure 6.2, for example at 100,000 ft they would be increased by roughly 1,000°K at the upper end of the speed range covered in the figure.

It is clear that many of the properties of air will be affected by the reactions of vibrational excitation, dissociation and ionisation. In the next section we will discuss the effects on the thermodynamic and transport properties. Some other properties which are not considered may have important aerodynamic effects such as the electrical conductivity which is greatly increased by ionisation. The possibility of interactions with magnetic fields has led to an intensive study of magneto-hydrodynamics, but this subject will not be treated in this book. The interested reader may be referred to introductory and survey papers by Resler and Sears (1958) and by Shercliff (1959).

Under equilibrium conditions the flow field can be determined uniquely using the thermodynamic and transport properties discussed in Section 2. However the chemical reactions mentioned above proceed at finite rates, and when the time required for approach to equilibrium becomes comparable with the time taken by a particle to traverse a particular part of the flow field then these reaction rates become another set of independent parameters on which the flow depends. The non-equilibrium effects which result are discussed in later sections.

6.2. Thermodynamic and Transport Properties of High Temperature Air

Accurate calculations of the equilibrium thermodynamic properties of air such as energy, enthalpy, entropy, specific heats and speed of sound are available up to very high temperatures. They are based on molecular and atomic energy levels obtained from precise spectroscopic data; Hilsenrath and Beckett (1956) for instance have prepared tables of such thermodynamic functions which have been used by Feldman (1957) and Ziemer (1960) among others to prepare hypersonic gas-dynamic charts giving the equilibrium properties of air across normal and oblique shocks and at a stagnation point.

An important quantity which enters into these considerations is the compressibility factor Z which is the ratio of the molecular weight of air under normal conditions to the mean molecular weight of the equilibrium gas. It may be defined, alternatively, as the number of moles arising from one mole of air at normal conditions. The compressibility thus represents the correction factor to the perfect gas equation of state, $Z = p/\rho RT$, and is shown in figure 6.3 (Hansen and Heims (1958)) as a function of temperature for pressures of 1·0, 0·01, and 0·0001 atmospheres. Since it is often convenient to relate the chemical reactions in air to Z, the important reactions are also indicated in figure 6.3. One interesting feature of the curves is that the slope of Z is almost zero at transition from one reaction to another, so that one reaction is essentially complete before the next one starts. According to the above definition, Z also includes the effect of van der Waal forces on the specific volume at high pressures. However this effect does not arise at the pressures represented in figure 6.3.

Confidence in our knowledge of the transport properties of air at high temperature such as viscosity and thermal conductivity is much less than in the case of the thermodynamic properties. Even at low temperature it is difficult to obtain direct measurements and we must rely on theoretical estimates. These are obtained from approximations to the solution of the Maxwell–Bolzmann equation and depend on rather uncertain values of collision cross-sections of atoms and molecules. An outline of the present situation may be found in the survey by Goulard (1961) and further details and references have been given by Hansen (1958), and by Mason (1959).

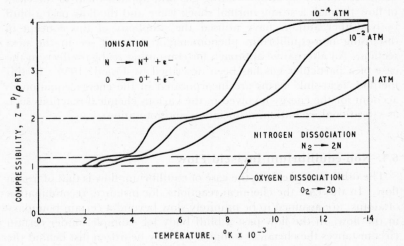

FIG. 6.3.—Compressibility factor for air in equilibrium
(Hansen and Heims, 1958).

6.3. Equilibrium Flow Calculations

In principle there is little difficulty in incorporating real gas properties into flow field calculations for the case of chemical equilibrium, that is when the reaction rates can be assumed infinitely fast in comparison with flow rates. Mathematically the problem is similar to that of a perfect gas except for the need to use the tabulated thermodynamic properties described in Section 2.

The effects of chemical reactions on the equilibrium conditions behind normal and oblique shock waves or in Prandtl–Meyer expansions for example are well known.

Feldman (1957) has given shock wave solutions in the form of graphs, and Heims (1959) has studied the problem of an equilibrium expansion process in chemically reacting gases.

For the calculation of flow fields around practical shapes however the inclusion of real gas effects often requires the use of large computing machines.

It was mainly to avoid this that the concept of an 'ideal dissociating gas' was introduced by Lighthill (1957). The gas is assumed to have its rotational and vibrational modes fully excited on passage through a shock wave of infinitesimal thickness behind which the gas begins to dissociate. When undissociated however this ideal gas behaves like a perfect diatomic gas with constant specific heats but with only half the vibrational energy that would be given by the principle of equipartition of energy. Lighthill deduced the laws governing the equilibrium behaviour of the ideal dissociating gas and applied them to the cases of flow through a strong normal shock wave and the flow past a bluff body. Other authors have utilised the simplicity of this concept in discussing non-equilibrium phenomena, as we will see in the next section. An alternative approach for computing real gas effects in the case of a particular gas has been described by Frood (1959). In this method 'heat-sink' terms are incorporated in the energy equation to account for the energy involved in the various chemical reactions such as vibrational excitation, dissociation and ionisation.

6.4. Non-equilibrium Inviscid Flow

The other extreme from the case of equilibrium flow is that of frozen flow. In this case the chemical reactions (for instance, recombination of atoms) are assumed to be infinitely slow beyond a certain boundary in the flow. In the flow past a bluff body for example, under certain circumstances the chemical composition may be frozen just behind the bow shock, or along some other specified line in the flow field such as the sonic line. However this frozen composition does not necessarily represent the equilibrium state along such a line; in the above example for instance, dissociation may not have reached equilibrium at the point where recombination freezes.

In general we may say that the n mass conservation equations for a reacting mixture of n chemical species reduce to a single equation for the mixture under the assumption of equilibrium conditions, whereas for frozen flow the n mass conservation equations must still be solved together with the rest of the system but at least the chemical generation terms vanish since the reaction rates are assumed to be infinitely slow.

There are two excellent reviews of non-equilibrium phenomena in hypersonic aerodynamics available by Ting-Yi Li (1961) and by Goulard (1961) and it is impossible to do justice to this wide field in the present book, especially in view of the enormous amount of work which is currently in progress. Therefore we shall be content with a summary of the more important results to date.

Non-equilibrium effects in boundary layers are dealt with in Chapter 7 and here we are concerned solely with inviscid flow. To begin with there are several interesting investigations into the linear theory of the

inviscid flow of a dissociating gas such as sound propagation, Prandtl–
Meyer flow, the flow generated by a thin wedge and so on. However
we shall not dwell on these studies since non-linearity is such a basic
feature of hypersonic flows. A discussion of the linear theory may be
found in Li's article referred to above.

There are four principal types of flow for which non-equilibrium
effects have been studied, the flow behind a strong normal shock, that

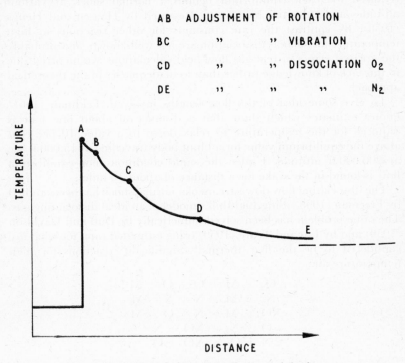

FIG. 6.4.—Relaxation effects behind a normal shock wave.

in a Prandtl–Meyer expansion, the flow in a nozzle (with applications
to propulsion and wind-tunnel design), and the more general problem
of flow around bodies of more-or-less practical shape.

The effects of relaxation on the flow behind a strong normal shock
wave in air are illustrated in figure 6.4, where the variation of temperature with distance is given. The translational degrees of freedom can
be assumed to adjust instantaneously to the new equilibrium state
behind the shock since only one molecular collision is required.
Several collisions are required for the rotational modes to come to
equilibrium and this process occurs from A to B on the curve. Relaxation of the vibrational modes occupies about one hundred collisions,

shown as B to C. From C to D the process of dissociation of oxygen is occurring, and dissociation of nitrogen is shown to be approaching equilibrium at E. If the shock is strong enough to cause ionisation there will of course be a further period of relaxation until the equilibrium electron density is attained.

The rates for vibrational excitation of oxygen and nitrogen are relatively well known, and calculated examples of the flow lengths required to reach equilibrium behind a normal shock at various altitudes and velocities have been presented by Hansen and Heims (1958). By contrast the rate constants for other reactions in high temperature air such as dissociation are less well-known, and probably the greatest errors in real gas flow field calculations are incurred due to this lack of knowledge rather than to inadequacies in the theoretical approach.

To give some idea of the flow lengths involved, Feldman (1961) quotes estimates which show that a distance of about one foot is required for the temperature to relax down to a value 10 per cent above the equilibrium value for a blunt body travelling at 15,000 ft/sec at 200,000 ft altitude. Under the same conditions non-equilibrium flow is found in the wake for a distance of about 10 miles.

The dissociating flow downstream of a normal shock has been studied by Freeman (1958) using Lighthill's model of an ideal dissociating gas. The same problem has been solved numerically by Duff and Davidson (1959) and by Lin and Teare (1959) using estimated rates for what are considered to be the five 'thermally significant' reactions for high temperature air:

$$O_2 + M \rightleftharpoons O + O + M$$
$$N_2 + M \rightleftharpoons N + N + M$$
$$NO + M \rightleftharpoons N + O + M$$
$$O + N_2 \rightleftharpoons NO + N$$
$$N + O_2 \rightleftharpoons NO + O$$

M is any other molecule involved in the reaction and serves to absorb any excess energy in the collision process. The reaction $N_2 + O_2 \rightleftharpoons 2NO$ is introduced by some authors in place of the last one, and also the reaction $NO + O \rightleftharpoons N + O_2$ is sometimes introduced (see for instance the detailed description by Ellington and Winterbon (1961)).

Prandtl–Meyer expansions with non-equilibrium effects have been treated by several authors (see Li (1961) for details) but the study of nozzle flows is perhaps more interesting from a practical point of view. Bray (1959) used the Lighthill ideal dissociating gas and found that the transition from equilibrium flow to frozen flow was usually rapid enough in a nozzle for him to postulate a criterion for the "point" at which the flow suddenly freezes. Some experimental support for this idea has been provided by Wegener (1960) who studied the flow of nitrogen tetroxide in a nozzle.

The results of Bray's analysis in a typical case are shown in figure 6.5 where the variation of the dissociation fraction α along the nozzle is

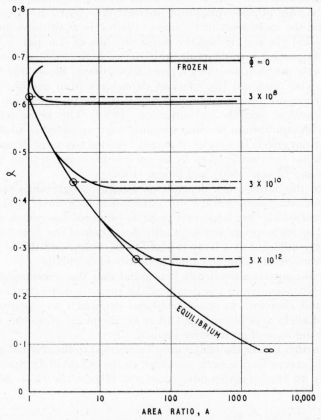

FIG. 6.5.—The dissociation fraction α during expansion through a hypersonic nozzle (Bray, 1959).

plotted for various values of a dimensionless dissociation rate parameter, Φ. The particular nozzle chosen has a hyperbolic area distribution and stagnation conditions are $T_0 = 0.1\,T_d$, $p_0 = 5 \times 10^{-6} p_d$ where T_d and p_d are the characteristic dissociation quantities introduced by Lighthill for the ideal dissociating gas. Full lines represent an exact calculation, and for values of Φ intermediate between the frozen case ($\Phi = 0$) and equilibrium ($\Phi = \infty$) it is seen that the dissociation fraction rapidly approaches a constant value during the expansion and thereafter remains constant no matter how large the area ratio,

A, becomes. This of course is a direct consequence of the three-body collision process which is required for recombination, such collisions becoming rarer as the density falls in the expansion. The broken lines in figure 6.5 are calculated by assuming that the flow freezes suddenly at a particular point, the analysis being greatly simplified thereby.

In the case of non-equilibrium inviscid flow past blunt bodies we may cite the early work of Freeman (1958). He again used the ideal dissociating gas and studied the direct problem of flow past a sphere. Other important investigations are those of Lick (1958) who studied the inverse problem assuming a given shock shape, Bloom and Steiger (1960) who discussed the effect of departures from equilibrium on typical pressure distributions of practical shapes in hypersonic flight, and Gravalos, Edelfelt and Emmons (1958). The latter reference dealt with equilibrium flow but has since been extended to cover non-equilibrium effects in a series of papers. A similarly large programme of work has been undertaken by Bloom and his associates (see Vaglio-Laurin and Bloom (1961) and Bloom (1962)).

All of this latter work depends on lengthy programmes on large electronic computers, and it is often difficult to pick out general trends from the results. One important point to be noted however is that in general at high speeds and high altitudes much of the flow field immediately adjacent to a body is likely to be frozen and this of course allows considerable simplification in flow field calculations.

Also in many practical cases it is found that the reaction rates are relatively insensitive to the details of the pressure distribution on the body and therefore a one-dimensional approach as suggested by Vaglio-Laurin and Bloom (1961) may be adequate, or at least can be used as the basis of an iterative method.

For further details the reader must be referred to the original papers, the most recent having been presented at the A.G.A.R.D. Specialists' Meeting on High Temperature Aspects of Hypersonic Flow, Brussels, April, 1962.

CHAPTER 7

BOUNDARY LAYERS IN HYPERSONIC FLOW

7.1. Introduction

In the high Reynolds number flow around a body, provided the flow remains attached, the effects of viscosity and heat conduction can be considered to be confined to a thin layer adjacent to the body surface. Within this thin viscous region, which is generally referred to as the boundary layer, there exist significant gradients of velocity, temperature and density normal to the surface. In low speed flow (with low stagnation temperature) only the velocity gradients are large but temperature gradients become of increasing importance as the speed rises into the supersonic regime and beyond.

The influence of the boundary layer at high supersonic and hypersonic speeds is three-fold. First, it gives rise to skin friction drag, second to aerodynamic heating effects, and third to displacement effects. For some applications the heat transfer coefficient may be related to the skin friction coefficient by means of the extended Reynolds analogy, as shown in Section 2, so our discussions will often concentrate on heat transfer. The general study of boundary layers growing under supersonic and hypersonic external flow fields will be discussed in this and the following chapters. For much of this work we will use the original boundary layer concept introduced by Prandtl, namely that the external inviscid flow which governs the boundary layer growth is not influenced by the boundary layer and may be calculated as if it did not exist. It will be assumed that the reader is familiar with the various aspects of classical boundary layer theory as dealt with in Goldstein (1938), Schlichting (1960) or Rosenhead (1963).

However, the third influence of the boundary layer is concerned with just those displacement effects which are ignored in the studies referred to above. The extent of the viscous region (or boundary layer) around a body grows markedly as the Mach number is increased due to the high temperatures produced at high speeds, either by shock wave compression or viscous dissipation in the boundary layer itself. In fact it may be shown that the boundary layer thickness is proportional to $\frac{\gamma - 1}{2} \cdot M_1{}^2/\sqrt{\text{Re}_1}$ at high Mach number (see Chapter 8). Thus interactions between the boundary layer and the external flow become more and more important as the Mach number increases. For a slender body at high Mach number the transverse curvature effects also become important. A second type of interaction occurs due to the vorticity generated in the external flow by a highly curved bow shock. The boundary layer will be affected by this vorticity distribution to an important degree when the external vorticity is of the same order as the average vorticity in the boundary layer due to the shear stress. A third and completely different type of process is the interaction of a shock wave with a boundary layer which has already developed before the point of impingement of the shock. In many cases such an interaction causes a shock-induced separation of the boundary layer which may have important consequences for the control and stability of practical vehicles for hypersonic flight.

As we have seen, hypersonic speeds lead to very high temperatures in the flow, of which one result is the increased boundary layer thickness over that found at the same Reynolds number at lower speeds. Another result is the appearance of phenomena in the field of high temperature gas-dynamics such as dissociation and ionisation. Since these chemical processes and the corresponding recombination processes occur at finite rates thermodynamic equilibrium may not always be achieved in a boundary layer at hypersonic speeds. This is particularly important at high altitudes, where equilibrium is less likely to be attained. In fact the whole flow field may be in a state of non-equilibrium, but as the Mach number is increased deviations from equilibrium are likely to be felt first in the boundary layer. (See Wong *et al.* (1960).) These questions are discussed in Section 6.

Since boundary layer interactions of the first two types described above also become much more important at higher altitudes (lower Reynolds numbers), they will be dealt with in more detail in the chapter on low density effects (Chapter 9).

7.2. Compressible Boundary Layers

The inclusion of compressibility effects in boundary layer theory introduces two additional variables, the density, ρ, and the absolute temperature T, in addition to the pressure and the velocity components. We must also include the possibility that the viscosity, μ, the thermal conductivity, k, and the specific heat c_p of air are all functions of the absolute temperature. In addition to the non-dimensional parameters of Mach number and Reynolds number we have to consider a parameter characterising heat transfer. Such a parameter can be formed as the ratio of rates of diffusion of vorticity and of heat, and is called the Prandtl number. Thus

$$\mathrm{Pr} = \left(\frac{\mu}{\rho}\right) \bigg/ \left(\frac{k}{\rho c_p}\right) = \frac{\mu c_p}{k} \qquad (7.1)$$

The Péclet number, occasionally used in place of the Prandtl number, is given by

$$\mathrm{Pé} = \frac{\rho c_p l}{k} \qquad (7.2)$$

l being a characteristic length in the flow. Thus, since the Reynolds number is given by $Re = \rho U_1 l / \mu$ it follows that $P\acute{e} = Pr \times Re$.

For two dimensional steady laminar flow, with no dissociation, the boundary layer approximations reduce the equation of motion in the x-direction to the following form

$$\rho \left(u \frac{\partial u}{\partial x} + v \frac{\partial u}{\partial y} \right) = - \frac{\partial p}{\partial x} + \frac{\partial}{\partial y} \left(\mu \frac{\partial u}{\partial y} \right) \tag{7.3}$$

Similarly the equation expressing conservation of energy becomes

$$\rho \left\{ u \frac{\partial}{\partial x} (c_p T) + v \frac{\partial}{\partial y} (c_p T) \right\} - u \frac{\partial p}{\partial x}$$
$$= \frac{\partial}{\partial y} \left(k \frac{\partial T}{\partial y} \right) + \mu \left(\frac{\partial u}{\partial y} \right)^2 \tag{7.4}$$

after making the boundary layer assumptions in the dissipation function and assuming for the time being a constant specific heat, c_p, but allowing for variable thermal conductivity k.

The continuity equation is

$$\frac{\partial}{\partial x} (\rho u) + \frac{\partial}{\partial y} (\rho v) = 0 \tag{7.5}$$

If we now assume boundary layer flow on a flat plate with zero pressure gradient, $\partial p / \partial x = 0$, and neglect the frictional heating term $\mu (\partial u / \partial y)^2$, equations (7.3) and (7.4) become, for constant specific heat,

$$\rho \left\{ u \frac{\partial u}{\partial x} + v \frac{\partial u}{\partial y} \right\} = \frac{\partial}{\partial y} \left(\mu \frac{\partial u}{\partial y} \right) \tag{7.6}$$

$$\rho \left\{ u \frac{\partial T}{\partial x} + v \frac{\partial T}{\partial y} \right\} = \frac{1}{c_p} \cdot \frac{\partial}{\partial y} \left(k \frac{\partial T}{\partial y} \right) \tag{7.7}$$

Thus if $\mu = k/c_p$ i.e. $Pr = \mu c_p / k = 1$, then $u/U_1 = T/T_1 = f(y)$ and the temperature profile of the boundary layer is the same function of y, the distance normal to the surface, as is the velocity profile. The thickness of the thermal and velocity boundary layers are then identical. This result is a form of Reynolds analogy for laminar flow, which postulates that heat and momentum are transferred by the same mechanism. The analogy has not found much application in laminar boundary layer problems since the equations can often be solved directly, but it has proved useful in semi-empirical methods for very high speeds where marked variations of transport properties (viscosity, thermal conductivity, specific heat) occur across the boundary layer (see Section 3).

Reynolds originally proposed the analogy for turbulent layers where of course it could be much more useful in view of the extra difficulties involved in solving such problems. In the turbulent case, a statement of the analogy requires that velocity fluctuations parallel to the mean flow be proportional to the temperature fluctuations. Analytically we write

$$\frac{\overline{vT'}}{(U_1 - U_0)(T_1 - T_0)} = \frac{\overline{uv}}{(U_1 - U_0)^2} \tag{7.8}$$

where U_0, U_1, and T_0, T_1 are the velocities and temperatures at a pair of corresponding reference planes. The rate of heat transfer in the y direction, $q = \rho c_p \overline{vT'}$, across unit area, is correlated with the Reynolds shear stress, $\tau = -\rho \overline{uv}$ in such a way that

$$\frac{q}{\rho c_p (U_1 - U_0)(T_1 - T_0)} = \frac{-\tau}{\rho(U_1 - U_0)^2} \tag{7.9}$$

Thus for heat transfer from a fixed wall at temperature T_1 for which $U_1 = 0$, the relation with skin friction at this wall is

$$\text{St} = \tfrac{1}{2}C_f \tag{7.10}$$

where the Stanton number

$$\text{St} = \frac{q_w}{\rho c_p U_0 (T_1 - T_0)}$$

and the skin friction coefficient

$$c_f = \frac{\tau_w}{\tfrac{1}{2}\rho U_0^2}$$

Returning to the laminar compressible boundary layer, a general relation between temperature and velocity may be obtained from equations (7.3) and (7.4) as follows. Multiply equation (7.3) by u and add to equation (7.4) to give

$$\rho \left(u \frac{\partial H}{\partial x} + v \frac{\partial H}{\partial y} \right) = \frac{\partial}{\partial y} \left(k \frac{\partial T}{\partial y} + \mu \frac{\partial}{\partial y} \frac{u^2}{2} \right) \tag{7.11}$$

where for a constant specific heat c_p the total enthalpy is

$$H = c_p T + \tfrac{1}{2}u^2 \tag{7.12}$$

If the specific heat is assumed to vary with absolute temperature then

$$H = \int c_p dT + \tfrac{1}{2}u^2 \tag{7.13}$$

However if we assume a unit Prandtl number $\text{Pr} = \mu c_p/k = 1$ in addition to a constant specific heat, equation (7.11) may be written

$$\rho \frac{DH}{Dt} = \frac{\partial}{\partial y}\left(\mu \frac{\partial H}{\partial y}\right) \tag{7.14}$$

which is a conduction equation for H analogous to that for vorticity, ζ, and has been generalised to include non-steady flow.

$$\frac{D\zeta}{Dt} = \nu . \Delta^2 \zeta$$

Equation (7.14) is satisfied by $H = $ constant, and by $H = u$ provided $\partial p/\partial x = 0$ as in the case of a flat plate boundary layer, since equation (7.14) then reduces to the momentum equation (7.3).

Thus we put

$$H = c_p T + \tfrac{1}{2}u^2 = A + \text{B}u \tag{7.15}$$

with boundary conditions at the surface $y = 0$; $u = 0$; $T = T_w$ and in the free stream $y = \infty$; $u = U_1$; $T = T_\delta$ where the subscript δ refers to conditions at the edge of the boundary layer.

Substitution of these conditions into equation (7.15) yields the desired relation between temperature and velocity in the boundary layer,

$$c_p T + \tfrac{1}{2}u^2 = c_p T_w + [c_p(T_\delta - T_w) + \tfrac{1}{2}U_1^2] . \frac{u}{U_1} \tag{7.16}$$

If $c_p(T_\delta - T_w) + \tfrac{1}{2}U_1^2 = 0$ as for a thermally insulated wall (see equation (7.20)) then equation (7.16) is the same as the energy equation for isentropic flow. Thus the rise in temperature from the free stream to the wall is the same as that resulting from an isentropic compression from the free stream velocity U_1, although the pressure remains constant through the boundary layer. This increase of temperature is of course due to frictional heating.

Now the heat transfer at the wall is given by

$$q_w = k_w \left(\frac{\partial T}{\partial y}\right)_w \tag{7.17}$$

and the skin friction is

$$\tau_w = \mu_w \left(\frac{\partial u}{\partial y}\right)_w \tag{7.18}$$

Thus equation (7.16) yields the result

$$\frac{q_w}{\tau_w} = \frac{k_w}{\mu_w} . \frac{T_\delta}{U_1}\left\{1 - \frac{T_w}{T_\delta} + \frac{\gamma - 1}{2} . M_\delta^2\right\} \tag{7.19}$$

where M_δ is the free stream Mach number at the edge of the boundary layer. This is the extension to high speeds of Reynolds' analogy.

It shows for example that at low speeds when $M_\delta \to 0$, the ratio of heat transfer to skin friction varies inversely as the speed of the stream relative to the surface. Therefore the cooling of a surface by a moving fluid is more efficient at low speeds than at high.

Again, the heat transfer is zero if

$$T_w = T_\delta \left(1 + \frac{\gamma - 1}{2} M_\delta^2 \right) \tag{7.20}$$

so that if, in cooling a surface at a temperature T_w by a stream at temperature T_δ, where $T_\delta < T_w$, the speed of the stream equals that given by equation (7.20), the cooling stops, and at higher values of M_δ turns to heating. The increase of heat transfer relative to skin friction at very high speeds is a result of the transfer to the wall of heat generated in the boundary layer rather than heat transferred across the boundary layer from the free stream to the wall. It should be emphasized that equation (7.20) includes the assumption $\mathrm{Pr} = 1$. For $\mathrm{Pr} \neq 1$ the R.H.S. reads $T_\delta \left(1 + r \cdot \frac{\gamma - 1}{2} M_\delta^2 \right)$ where r is the temperature recovery factor.

We will now discuss the essential features of the temperature distribution through the boundary layer on a surface moving at high speed. We have to distinguish two different temperatures: first the static temperature T as measured by an instrument at rest relative to the flow at each point, and secondly the total or stagnation temperature, T_0, measured by an instrument which decelerates the flow adiabatically to zero velocity. Representative temperature profiles are shown schematically in figure 7.1, and the full lines represent the zero heat transfer case in which no heat is conducted into the interior structure from the surface or radiated away to the atmosphere. The static temperature increases through the boundary layer towards the surface due to heat generated by the internal friction. Since no heat flows from the surface to the fluid, the temperature gradient $\partial T/\partial y$ at the surface is zero. However the wall temperature is higher than the free stream static temperature due to the effect of aerodynamic heating, at least in the case of an insulated wall.

The profiles in figure 7.1 are more representative of the idealized flat plate flow than of an actual blunt-nosed hypersonic vehicle. In the latter case, for relatively short flight times, the wall temperature can be very much less than the free-stream static value at the edge of the boundary layer. The temperature there is relatively high since the flow has passed through a strong shock wave at the nose.

The variation of the total or local stagnation temperature across the boundary layer is quite different from that of the static temperature. The total temperature is a measure of the total energy content of the fluid, internal and kinetic, and therefore is invariant in a steady flow from which no energy is extracted either as heat or mechanical energy. These conditions are fulfilled by the boundary layer as a whole under zero heat transfer conditions, so that the average value of total temperature is the same in the boundary layer as in the free stream. Therefore

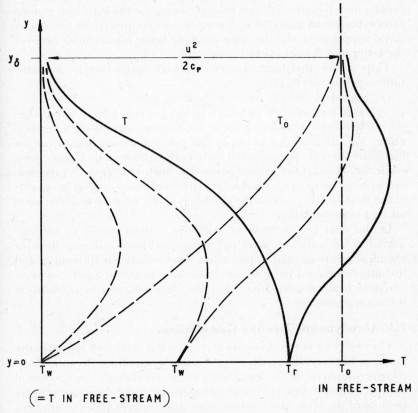

FIG. 7.1.—Temperature profiles through a high speed boundary layer.

when T_0 is found to be smaller near the wall than in the free stream (which is the case for Pr < 1) the defect must be compensated by an excess of this temperature in the outer part of the boundary layer.

The difference between total and static temperatures at any point is determined by the local velocity u. For a fluid with constant specific heat this difference is equal to $u^2/2c_p$. For variable specific heat we must consider enthalpy, h, instead of temperature, and then $H - h = \frac{1}{2}u^2$, the kinetic energy of the fluid, where H is the total stagnation enthalpy (equation 7.13).

For zero heat transfer the wall temperature, called the recovery temperature T_r, is almost equal to the free stream stagnation temperature. At high supersonic speeds this leads to very high wall temperatures. But conditions are usually more favourable because heat is radiated away from the surface of the aircraft or conducted into the interior structure. The temperature profiles in such cases are shown by broken lines in figure 7.1, one example being for the high heat transfer rates experienced when the wall temperature is equal to the free stream static temperature and the other example being intermediate between the latter and the zero heat transfer case.

Thus we see that heat transfer in a high speed flow is essentially influenced by two factors

(1) a marked effect of frictional heating, and

(2) large temperature variations in the boundary layer, even when the surface itself is cooled down to the external stream static temperature. For $M = 10$ for example the maximum temperature in the boundary layer is approximately 5 times the stream static temperature, while for $M = 20$ the ratio is about 18. Such temperature variations are so large as to cause marked variations of the transport properties of the fluid (μ, k, c_p) across the boundary layer, to cause dissociation of air and even ionisation.

In the next two sections we will give a short survey of methods available for boundary layer calculations without real gas effects or chemical reactions (and in particular, heat transfer, both laminar and turbulent) followed by a discussion of some practical aspects of aerodynamic heating calculations and the determination of equilibrium surface temperature.

7.3. Aerodynamic Heating Calculations

The ideal case of the boundary layer on a flat plate with zero pressure gradient has received much attention in the literature because of the relative simplicity of the equations. Such calculations are also useful for application to practical cases of supersonic and hypersonic vehicles because of the large areas of flow with small or zero pressure gradient that are often involved. The classical problem of incompressible heat transfer in the laminar boundary layer and the 'thermometer' problem are treated in most books on boundary layers and heat transfer so that we will not go into details here. This work has been extended to take into account the temperature variation of all the physical properties of air involved and has resulted in the reference temperature or intermediate enthalpy methods of Eckert (1954) and of Monaghan (1955) which are available for both laminar and turbulent boundary layers. Briefly the methods rely on the empirical observation that incompressible formulae for heat transfer and skin friction may be used provided that all physical properties involved are evaluated at a temperature (or enthalpy) intermediate between the values at the wall and outer edge of the boundary layer.

Application of the Mangler transformation for laminar boundary layers provides numerical factors which enable the flat plate results to be used for conical surfaces. Similar factors have been deduced for turbulent boundary layers. The method gives results to within 15 per cent accuracy in practical cases for Mach numbers up to about 10, that is, where dissociation effects begin.

An isothermal surface is assumed throughout, but the case of a surface temperature varying with axial distance has been treated by Lighthill (1950), Spalding (1958), Eckert *et al.* (1956) and Liepmann (1958) among others.

Various investigators have examined the effect of pressure gradients; in particular Cohen and Reshotko (1955) solved the equations for a compressible laminar boundary layer on a wedge and obtained a series of similar solutions for different pressure gradients and ratios of wall to free stream temperatures. They then used these results to construct an approximate method of solution of the momentum equation analogous to that of Thwaites for incompressible flow. Many similar methods have been suggested and Monaghan (1960) has given a critical survey.

Calculation methods for turbulent boundary layer growth under a pressure gradient rest on a much more empirical basis and most methods rely on a local similarity assumption to support the use of flat plate methods (see Section 5, and Phillips (1957)). Reference may also be made to the work of Reshotko and Tucker (1957) and Persh (1955).

A good deal of work has been published on general three-dimensional flow and bodies at incidence. For swept cylinders for instance we might refer to Reshotko and Beckwith (1957) and Cohen and Beckwith (1961). (See also N. B. Cohen (1961).) At large free stream Mach Numbers the effect of an angle of yaw Λ is given approximately by $(\cos \Lambda)^{1.1}$. Papers by Beckwith and Gallagher (1959) and Wisniewski (1959) should be consulted for details of the application of these results.

Vaglio-Laurin (1959) has made a study of the highly-cooled wall approximation to general three-dimensional boundary layers with emphasis on bodies of revolution at incidence. He found that cross-flow in the boundary layer is negligible even for large transverse pressure gradients and thus was able to develop expressions similar to equations (7.45) and (7.49) evaluated along the inviscid streamlines at the outer edge of the boundary layer with the radius replaced by a general length element.

We will return to the problem of laminar heating in a stagnation region in Section 6, where the effects of dissociation will be discussed. Meanwhile it is necessary to show how the methods described above can be used to calculate equilibrium surface temperatures before going on to develop a solution of the compressible laminar boundary layer equations under the same assumptions as are used in hypersonic small disturbance theory.

7.4. Equilibrium Surface Temperature

Assuming that a method is available for calculating the convective heat transfer rate (given the surface temperature) in any particular flow situation it is often important to find the equilibrium temperature reached by the surface. Now there are three other sources of heat transfer in addition to that produced by convection:

(i) The surface will be losing heat by radiation to its surroundings at a rate

$$q_r = k\varepsilon(T_w)^4$$

where k is the Stefan–Boltzmann constant,

$$k = 2 \cdot 78 \times 10^{-12} \frac{CHU}{\text{ft}^2 \text{ sec } (^\circ K)^4}$$

and ε is the surface emissivity factor. Typical values of ε are quoted in Fishenden and Saunders (1932) for instance and range from about 0·1 (for some polished metals) to more than 0·95 for certain black pigments. The value of ε depends on the surface temperature T_w as well.

(ii) The surface will be receiving back heat by radiation from the surrounding air of amount

$$k\varepsilon\varepsilon_G(T)^4$$

where ε_G is the gas emissivity and T is the temperature of the radiating gas. This source may be important in cases of re-entry at supersatellite speeds (for example, on return from a planetary voyage) and is further discussed in Section 8.

(iii) Heat will also be received by solar radiation to surfaces exposed to the sun's rays (and also by reflection from the earth or clouds). This amount of heat transfer is given by

$$L_s Q_s \cos \phi$$

where Q_s is the solar constant. At the outer limits of the atmosphere

$$Q_s = 6 \cdot 82 \times 10^{-2}$$

It is reduced to about one half this value by the time the radiation reaches ground level.

L_s is the absorption factor for solar radiation, which differs from the emissivity ε. Again some typical values of L_s are quoted in Fishenden and Saunders (1932). ϕ is the angle between the normal to the surface and the incident rays.

The proportion of incoming radiation reflected by earth or clouds is given approximately by Angstrom's formula

$$A_s = 0 \cdot 70c + 0 \cdot 17(1 - c)$$

where c is the cloud amount.

A complete heat balance equation should include, in addition to the above sources of heat transfer, the effects of longitudinal conduction through the skin if it is not isothermal and also loss of heat to the interior by conduction through joints and structural members (especially if some form of internal cooling is applied) and loss of heat by radiation to, and convection in, any interior air space.

For many purposes it is sufficient to balance the aerodynamic heating of the surface and the radiative cooling effect of (i) above, and thus obtain an upper limit to the equilibrium temperature. An iteration procedure is necessary to determine the equilibrium temperature by first estimating T_w and calculating corresponding values of q_w and q_r. The assumed value of T_w is then adjusted and the calculations repeated until $q_w = q_r$. The wall temperature for which this is achieved is then the equilibrium temperature under the above assumptions.

Transient surface temperatures may be calculated by the method of Hill (1957) for instance.

7.5. The Laminar Boundary Layer at Hypersonic Speeds

A solution of the compressible laminar boundary layer equations using the same approximations as are made in hypersonic small disturbance theory is helpful in any study involving interactions between boundary layers and shock waves or hypersonic external flows in general (see Chapter 8).

Following Lees (1956), Hayes and Probstein (1959a) and Cheng (1960b) we first transform the variables (x, y) in the boundary layer by a modification of the Howarth–Stewartson–Dorodnitsyn method as follows:

$$\xi = \int_0^x C \cdot \rho/\rho_\delta \cdot dx \tag{7.21}$$

$$\eta = \sqrt{\mathrm{Re}} \left(\int_0^y \rho/\rho_\delta \cdot dy \right)(\xi)^{-\frac{1}{2}} \tag{7.22}$$

where $\mathrm{Re} = \rho_\delta u_\delta l/\mu_\delta$ and x, y have both been non-dimensionalised with respect to the characteristic length, l. The subscript δ refers to conditions at the edge of the boundary layer, and the subscript 1 to conditions in the undisturbed free stream.

A linear relation between viscosity and temperature is assumed

$$\frac{\mu}{\mu_1} = C \frac{T}{T_1} \tag{7.23}$$

together with a Prandtl number of unity, so that the momentum and energy equations reduce to

$$2f_{\eta\eta\eta} + ff_{\eta\eta} - 2\xi(f_\eta f_{\xi\eta} - f_\xi f_{\eta\eta})$$
$$= \varepsilon\left[\left(2\frac{\partial\rho}{\partial x}\int_0^x p\,dx\right)\bigg/\rho^2\right]\left[\frac{H_w}{H_\delta} + \left(1 + \frac{H_w}{H_\delta}\right)g - f_\eta^2\right] \tag{7.24}$$

and

$$2g_{\eta\eta} + fg_\eta - 2\xi\left[f_\eta g_\xi - f_\xi g_\eta + f_\eta g\frac{d}{d_\xi}\ln\left(1 - \frac{H_w}{H_\delta}\right)\right] = 0 \tag{7.25}$$

with $\varepsilon = \dfrac{\gamma - 1}{\gamma + 1}$ and where f is the reduced stream function such that

$$\frac{\partial f}{\partial \eta} \equiv f_\eta = \frac{u}{u_\delta} \tag{7.26}$$

and g is a reduced total enthalpy,

$$g = \frac{H - H_w}{H_\delta - H_w} \tag{7.27}$$

and the subscript w refers to wall values.

The boundary conditions are

$$\left.\begin{array}{l} f = f_\eta = g = 0 \text{ at } \eta = 0 \\[2mm] f_\eta = g = 1 \qquad \text{at } \eta = \infty \end{array}\right\} \tag{7.28}$$

and

Thus for small ε a solution of the momentum equation (7.24) exists which is independent of ξ and is unique since it also satisfies the boundary conditions. Therefore the leading term in the approximate solution for small ε is governed by the Blasius equation

$$2f_{\eta\eta\eta} + f_\eta f_{\eta\eta} = 0$$

with

$$g = f_\eta$$

This result shows that the direct effect of the pressure gradient for flow over a slender body is negligible in the shock layer approximation, $\varepsilon \ll 1$. This is the local flat plate similarity postulated by Lees on the basis of his observation that the thermal boundary layer is insensitive to pressure gradient, particularly for a cold wall. The local similarity concept was used for blunt body heat transfer calculations (Lees (1956b)), and also to simplify the problem of strong shock-boundary layer interaction (Lees (1953)). However the analysis above shows the theoretical grounds for neglecting the pressure gradient on the basis of shock layer theory, and the assumption of a cold wall is not necessary (see also F. K. Moore (1960)). We will return to this question in Section 6.

Equations similar to (7.24) and (7.25) have been developed by Hayes and Probstein (1959a) in discussing viscous hypersonic similitude (see Section 8.3). In particular the results show that in the hypersonic limit $M_1 \to \infty$, the flow field depends not upon M_1 and Re separately but only upon a combination of the two,

$$\beta = \frac{M_1{}^{\omega}}{\sqrt{\text{Re}}}$$

where ω is the exponent in the assumed viscosity-temperature relation.

Returning to our solution of the laminar boundary layer equations for small ε however, we see that the heat transfer rate, skin friction and displacement thickness for example may be written explicitly in terms of the pressure distribution.

Defining the local Stanton number as the non-dimensional heat transfer rate,

$$\text{St} = \frac{q_w}{\rho_\delta u_\delta (H_\delta - H_w)} = \frac{\left(k \frac{\delta T}{\delta y} \right)_w}{\rho_\delta u_\delta (H_\delta - H_w)} \tag{7.29}$$

(Note that St may also be defined in terms of recovery enthalpy H_r rather than H_δ, see for example equation (7.51) of Section 7), and the local skin friction coefficient as

$$c_f = \left(\mu \frac{\partial u}{\partial y} \right)_w \bigg/ \tfrac{1}{2} \rho_\delta u_\delta{}^2 \tag{7.30}$$

and the displacement thickness as

$$\delta^\star = \int_0^\infty \left(1 - \frac{\rho u}{\rho_\delta u_\delta} \right) dy \tag{7.31}$$

we obtain the following results:

$$M_1{}^3 \, \text{St} \simeq 0\cdot332 \, \chi \left(\frac{p}{p_\delta} \right) \left(\int_0^x \frac{p}{p_\delta} \frac{dx}{l} \right)^{-\frac{1}{2}} \tag{7.32}$$

$$c_f \simeq 2\text{St} \tag{7.33}$$

$$M_1 \cdot \frac{\delta^\star}{l} \simeq \varepsilon \left(0\cdot664 + 1\cdot73 \, \frac{T_w}{T_0} \right) \chi \cdot \left(\int_0^x p/p_\delta \frac{dx}{l} \right)^{\frac{1}{2}} \left(\frac{p}{p_\delta} \right)^{-1} \tag{7.34}$$

assuming an ideal gas with constant specific heats. In deriving these results we have used the Blasius solutions

$$g_\eta(0) = 0\cdot664 = \int_0^\infty f_\eta(1 - f_\eta) d\eta$$

and

$$\int_0^\infty (1 - f_\eta)d\eta = 1\cdot73$$

The hypersonic viscous interaction parameter is given by

$$\chi = M_1{}^3 \sqrt{\frac{C}{\mathrm{Re}_l}} \tag{7.35}$$

where

$$\mathrm{Re}_l = \frac{\rho_1 U_1 l}{\mu_1}.$$

Note that equation (7.34) is derived on the assumption that $\delta^\star \simeq \delta$. In equation (7.31) for $\delta^\star$, the integrand may be written $\left(1 - \dfrac{T_\delta}{T} \cdot \dfrac{u}{u_\delta}\right)$ assuming p to be constant across the boundary layer. Now $\dfrac{T}{T_\delta} = 1 + \dfrac{\gamma - 1}{2} M_\delta{}^2 \left(1 - \dfrac{u^2}{u_\delta{}^2}\right)$ for an insulated wall and $\mathrm{Pr} = 1$, so that if $\dfrac{\gamma - 1}{2} M_\delta{}^2 \gg 1$ then $\displaystyle\int_0^\delta \dfrac{T_\delta}{T} \cdot \dfrac{u}{u_\delta} \cdot dy \ll 1$, and hence $\delta^\star \simeq \delta$. Of course the approximation $\delta^\star \simeq \delta$ is rather less accurate in the case of a cold wall.

7.6. Chemical Reactions in Boundary Layers

It has already been pointed out that hypersonic speeds lead to high temperatures in the boundary layer which may cause chemical reactions such as dissociation and ionisation. Chemical reactions may also occur as a result of mass addition at the surface either due to ablation of the surface material (sublimation or vaporisation) or because a foreign gas is deliberately injected through the surface for cooling purposes. In all of these processes more than one chemical species are present and concentration gradients occur in the boundary layer. Heat energy is then transported not only by heat conduction, as in the examples previously considered, but also by diffusion currents which carry chemical enthalpy.

Two non-dimensional ratios which it is convenient to introduce to describe this diffusion process are the Lewis number, Le, or relative rate of diffusion of mass and heat, and the Schmidt number Sc which represents the relative rate of diffusion of vorticity and mass.

Thus

$$\mathrm{Le} = D_{12} / \frac{k}{\rho c_p} = \rho \frac{D_{12} c_p}{k} \tag{7.36}$$

and

$$\mathrm{Sc} = \frac{\nu}{D_{12}} \tag{7.37}$$

for the special case of a binary mixture, and D_{12} is then the binary diffusion coefficient. Note that from our earlier definition of the Prandtl number have Le . Sc $= 1/Pr$.

We will follow the treatment given by Lees (1958) for the general case of chemical reactions and mass addition in a laminar boundary layer, and a particularly important case of chemical reaction is that of dissociation in a boundary layer.

There are two extreme cases which are of importance,

(a) chemical equilibrium, where the atoms recombine to the equilibrium value instantaneously, or, in general, infinitely fast reaction rates,

(b) frozen flow, where the gas phase chemical reactions are extremely slow, and recombination takes place only at the wall. In between these extremes the reaction rates are finite, the atoms recombining into molecules with a consequent heat release.

In a boundary layer flow, the rate of energy transport across streamlines is

$$q = - k \frac{\partial T}{\partial y} + \Sigma \rho k_i V_i h_i \qquad (7.38)$$

where

$$h_i = \int_0^T c_{p_i} dT + h_i^\circ \qquad (7.39)$$

and h_i° is the heat of formation of the ith species.

The mass diffusion coefficient for the special case of a binary mixture (e.g. 'atoms' and 'molecules' of air) is defined by Fick's law,

$$\rho k_i V_i = - \rho D_{12} \frac{\partial k_i}{\partial y} \qquad (7.40)$$

where $k_i =$ mass fraction of ith species
      $V_i =$ diffusion velocity of ith species in the y-direction.

$$q = - \left\{ k \frac{\partial T}{\partial y} + \rho D_{12} \Sigma h_i \frac{\partial k_i}{\partial y} \right\} \qquad (7.41)$$

The complete static enthalpy including both thermal and chemical contributions is defined by

$$h = \Sigma k_i h_i$$

so that

$$dh = c_p dT + \Sigma h_i dk_i \qquad (7.42)$$

where

$$c_p = \Sigma k_i c_{p_i}$$

Thus $\qquad q = - \frac{k}{c_p} \left\{ \underbrace{\left(\frac{\partial h}{\partial y} - \Sigma h_i \frac{\partial k_i}{\partial y} \right)}_{\text{(conduction)}} + \rho \underbrace{\frac{D_{12} c_p}{k} \Sigma h_i \frac{\partial k_i}{\partial y}}_{\text{(diffusion)}} \right\} \qquad (7.43)$

and we see that the relative magnitude of the heat energy transported by the two processes depends on the ratio of chemical to thermal enthalpy and on the Lewis number,

$$\text{Le} = \rho \, \frac{D_{12} c_p}{k}$$

When $\text{Le} = 1$,

$$q = - \frac{k}{c_p} \frac{\partial h}{\partial y} \tag{7.44}$$

and is independent of the mechanism of heat transfer (diffusion or conduction) or of the magnitude of the chemical reaction rates in the mixture. Thus the surface heat transfer rate depends principally on the total enthalpy difference across the boundary layer.

Lees (1956) has utilised the assumption that $\text{Le} = 1$ in considering the problem of laminar heat transfer to a blunt body including the effects of dissociation. He introduced the 'local similarity' concept, later to be used by many other investigators, in which it is assumed that at every station along the body the 'similar' solution corresponding to the true local value of pressure gradient parameter may be applied. Effectively this represents a patching together of local solutions. In addition Lees observed that the gas near the surface tends to be much cooler and denser than in the rest of the boundary layer, provided the surface is very much colder than the free stream stagnation temperature. He then showed that the effect of any streamwise pressure gradient is quite small, by reference to the similar solutions of Cohen and Reshotko (1959), so that the hypersonic boundary layer over a cold wall may be described quite well by the classical Blasius solution applied to compressible viscous flow over a flat plate. The pressure gradient is thus taken into account only in the effect of local pressure on local Reynolds number. Subsequently, Moore (1960) has shown that this practical hypothesis can be derived theoretically from the boundary layer equations under the set of assumptions commonly used in inviscid hypersonic flow theory and especially hypersonic small disturbance theory and shock layer calculations. This is borne out by the solution given in Section 5, and is especially important in studies of combined bluntness and boundary layer interaction phenomena (Chapter 8).

The formula for heat transfer rate at a distance x along the surface from the stagnation point of a blunt body, as given by Lees (1956) is

$$q(x) = 0 \cdot 47 (Pr)^{-\frac{2}{3}} \sqrt{(\rho_\delta \mu_\delta)_0} \, \sqrt{U_1} H_\delta F(x) \tag{7.45}$$

where the total enthalpy $H_\delta = h_\delta + \frac{1}{2} u_\delta^2 (\simeq \frac{1}{2} U_1^2$ for hypersonic speeds), $F(x)$ is a function of body shape and local external conditions which are referred to by the suffix δ (or edge of boundary layer), and subscript 0 refers to conditions at the stagnation point. Subscript 1 refers to conditions in the free stream ahead of the bow shock, so that U_1 is the flight velocity.

In particular, at the stagnation point (subscript 0)

$$q_0 = 0\cdot47\sqrt{k+1}\,(\bar{P}r)^{-\frac{2}{3}}\sqrt{(\rho_\delta\mu_\delta)_0}\,\sqrt{U_1}\,.\,H_\delta\sqrt{\frac{1}{U_1}\left(\frac{du_\delta}{dx}\right)_0} \qquad (7.46)$$

where $k = 0$ for a 2-dimensional body and $k = 1$ for an axisymmetrical body. $\bar{P}r$ is some average value of Prandtl number across the boundary layer.

Assuming the Newtonian formula for pressure distribution around the surface then

$$\left(\frac{du_\delta}{dx}\right)_0 = \frac{1}{r_b}\sqrt{2(p_0 - p_1)/\rho_1} \qquad (7.47)$$

where r_b is the nose radius, and we see immediately the effect of blunting in decreasing the stagnation point heating.

A more detailed investigation of laminar stagnation point heating with dissociation effects has been reported by Fay and Riddell (1958). They carried out a numerical solution of the differential equations of the stagnation point boundary layer using tabulated values of the properties of high temperature air in dissociation equilibrium. Their results are correlated by the expression

$$q_0 = 0\cdot54\sqrt{k+1}\,(Pr)^{-0\cdot6}(H_\delta - h_w)(\rho_w\mu_w)^{0\cdot1}(\rho_\delta\mu_\delta)^{0\cdot4}$$

$$\times\sqrt{\left(\frac{du_\delta}{dx}\right)_0}\left\{1 + (\text{Le}^\alpha - 1)\frac{h_D}{H_\delta}\right\} \qquad (7.48)$$

where h_D is the energy involved in dissociation

and
$$\begin{cases} \alpha = 0\cdot52 \text{ for equilibrium flow} \\ \\ \alpha = 0\cdot63 \text{ for frozen flow.} \end{cases}$$

This formula illustrates Lees' result that for a Lewis number of unity the heat transfer to the surface is independent of the mechanism. Fay and Riddell pointed out however that if the wall is non-catalytic to atom recombination then the heat transfer rate can be reduced by a factor of two or more. This question is discussed further in Section 7. Typical equilibrium heat transfer rates calculated by equation (7.48) are shown in figure 7.2.

A comparison of the Fay and Riddell formula with that of Lees shows a factor $[\rho_w\mu_w/(\rho_\delta\mu_\delta)_0]^{0\cdot1}$ for Le $= 1$, and this ratio may reach a value of 4 or 5 for a highly cooled surface. Thus it is claimed that equation (7.48) may give an improvement of up to 20 per cent in accuracy over equation (7.46).

This work has been extended by Kemp, Rose and Detra (1959) to cover regions away from the stagnation point. Their result is

$$\frac{q(x)}{q_0} = r_0^k \frac{\rho_w \mu_w}{\sqrt{2\xi}} u_\delta \left\{ 2(\rho_w \mu_w)_0 \left(\frac{du_\delta}{dx} \right)_0 \right\}^{-\frac{1}{2}} G(x) \qquad (7.49)$$

where ξ is a transformed x-coordinate,

$$\xi(x) = \int_0^x \rho_w \mu_w u_\delta r_0^{2k} dx \qquad (7.50)$$

and r_0 is the radius of cross-section or ordinate of the body. $G(x)$ is a factor which depends on the pressure distribution. It was found that an

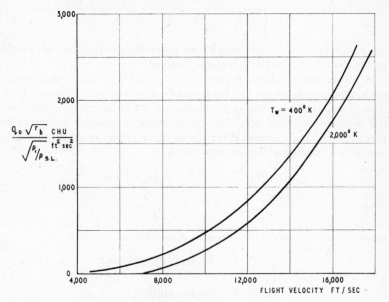

FIG. 7.2.—Stagnation point heat transfer in laminar equilibrium dissociated flow.

earlier corresponding formula due to Lees was quite accurate provided the pressure distribution did not show rapid variations with x, and the surface was highly cooled ($M > 8$ say).

The effect of a pressure gradient on the characteristics of a turbulent boundary layer, especially on the heat transfer distribution, as measured by the deviation of the actual value from that of a zero pressure gradient boundary layer having the same external conditions, is much less than that on laminar boundary layer characteristics, particularly for a cold wall. As a result predictions of heat transfer rates using zero pressure gradient formulae evaluated at a reference enthalpy and at the true local conditions have often proved quite accurate. The reason is simply that the displacement thickness is small because of the presence of a dense layer of air near the surface, and since this is a multiplying factor in the pressure gradient term of the momentum equation then pressure gradient effects tend to be small. Typical formulae are those due to Dorrance (1961) and Detra and Hidalgo (1961).

To conclude this section we might add that N. B. Cohen (1961) has calculated laminar boundary layer similar solutions in equilibrium air at velocities up to 41,100 ft/sec, in which the region where ionisation is important is also considered. In this respect Fay (1961) has analysed plasma boundary layers.

Some relevant aspects of non-equilibrium flow are contained in the work of Whalen (1961) and of Chung (1961). The latter considers the hypersonic viscous shock layer under high altitude conditions and this is discussed in Section 7.

Riddell and Winkler (1961) have recently considered the heat transfer problem in the re-entry to the earth's atmosphere of space vehicles at supersatellite speeds. (See also Scala and Warren (1962), and Adams (1960).)

The general subject of chemical reactions in boundary layers is fully treated in the book by W. H. Dorrance (1962).

7.7. Catalytic Wall Effects

As we have pointed out in Section 7.6 for a blunt body in hypersonic flight a considerable part of the energy of the gas behind the bow shock wave may be associated with the dissociation of molecules into atoms. In the case of equilibrium (extremely fast chemical reaction rates) the heat transfer to the wall is independent of the particular mode of heat transfer, diffusion or conduction, if the Lewis number is unity. For a frozen flow however (extremely slow gas phase chemical reactions) the efficiency of the wall in catalysing the recombination of atoms into molecules has a very strong effect on the heat transfer. Now the Stanton number may be defined by

$$q = \rho_\delta u_\delta \, \text{St} \, (H_r - h_w) \tag{7.51}$$

where the recovery enthalpy

$$H_r = h_\delta + \frac{rU_\delta^2}{2} + h_\delta^\circ \tag{7.52}$$

(r being the enthalpy recovery factor), and h_w is the enthalpy at the wall. In general the total enthalpy,

$$H = \int c_{p_i} \alpha T + \frac{U^2}{2} + \Sigma c_i h_i^\circ \tag{7.53}$$

and h_i° is the heat of formation of species i. However the value of h_w will be determined by the rate with which atoms diffuse to the wall, i.e. on the chemical state of the boundary layer, and on the degree of wall catalysis. Thus

$$q = \rho_\delta u_\delta \, \mathrm{St}(H_\delta - h_w + \frac{rU_\delta^2}{2} + h_\delta^\circ - h_w^\circ) \qquad (7.54)$$

where as before

$$h^\circ = \Sigma c_i h_i^\circ$$

For a completely frozen flow in the boundary layer there is a big effect of the degree of wall catalysis on the value of h_w°, but no effect if the gas is in chemical equilibrium at all points in the boundary layer.

In the frozen case, if the surface is inert, $h_w^\circ = h_\delta^\circ$, and the heat transfer may, depending on the degree of free stream dissociation (h_δ°), be considerably less than if the surface were a perfect catalyst for which $h_w^\circ = 0$.

If the catalytic efficiency of the wall is defined by

$$\eta = \frac{\text{number of atoms recombining on impact with the wall}}{\text{total number of atoms impinging on the wall}}$$

then the value of h_w° may be expressed in terms of η, h_δ°, and the transport properties of the boundary layer. Then the heat transfer rate is given by

$$q = \rho_\delta u_\delta \, \mathrm{St} \left[h_\delta - h_w + \frac{rU_\delta^2}{2} + h_\delta^\circ \, \mathrm{Le}^{2/3} \right] \bigg/ \left\{ 1 + \frac{\mathrm{St} \, \mathrm{Le}^{2/3}}{\eta \rho_w} \left(\frac{2\pi M_a}{RT_w} \right)^{1/2} \right\}$$
$$(7.55)$$

in which M_a is the atomic weight of the atomic species. Goulard (1958) has illustrated the effect of wall catalysis on frozen boundary layer heat transfer at a stagnation point as in figure 7.3 (adapted from Goulard's paper). Also indicated on the figure are materials that correspond to the catalytic efficiency scale and it is seen that large reductions in heating are possible with the use of suitable materials. However at this particular altitude the only ones which provide sufficiently low values of η are the glasses. At lower altitudes the curves of figure 7.3 move rapidly to the left and the situation is soon reached (approximately 150,000 ft) that extremely low catalytic efficiencies have to be achieved to get any appreciable reduction in heat transfer. However at these lower altitudes the boundary layer is probably in an equilibrium state so that reductions in heat transfer are not obtained anyway.

For turbulent boundary layers, utilising the formula of Dorrance (1961) for q, it can be shown that reductions of up to 20 per cent can be obtained with low values of η.

Chung and Anderson (1961) have used an integral method to analyze the laminar heat transfer to two-dimensional and axisymmetric bodies with finite catalytic activities. They point out that at high flight altitudes the dissociation energy in the external flow is not recovered completely even with highly catalytic surfaces, so that the total heat transfer may be much less than the equilibrium value for most engineering materials.

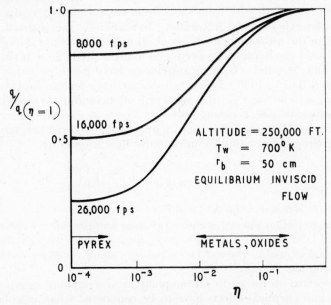

FIG. 7.3.—The effect of wall catalysis on stagnation point heat transfer to a blunt body.

More detailed discussions of the chemical kinetics of catalytic surface reactions have been given by Rosner (1958) and Scala (1958).

Chung (1961) has considered the hypersonic viscous shock layer of a non-equilibrium dissociating gas. He shows that the controlling chemical reaction for heat transfer is the dissociative shock-layer reaction at higher altitudes ($>$210,000 ft), whereas at lower altitudes it is the boundary layer recombination process described above.

7.8. Radiative Heat Transfer

At very high speeds the energy carried to the body by radiation from the high temperature air outside the boundary layer must be considered (the hot gas cap). Typically, the radiative heat transfer to the stagnation point of a blunt body of 1 foot nose radius from the air between the body and the bow shock is 10 per cent of the aerodynamic heating at a velocity of 10,000 ft/sec at sea level, and at 20,000 ft/sec at an altitude of 100,000 ft. Recent studies of equilibrium radiation from high temperature air have been discussed in detail by Kivel (1961) and Treanor (1961). An earlier and still valuable review of the subject was given by Meyerott (1958).

The data on radiation levels has been obtained in the region of temperatures from 3,000 to 8,000°K and density ratios from 10^{-2} to 10 times normal density from shock tube measurements. Within this region the experimental uncertainty indicated by the internal consistency of the measurements is about 30 per cent. Scaling laws based on statistical mechanics have been used to make predictions at temperatures and densities where measurements have not been made (see Kivel and Bailey, 1958). However for some wave-lengths and certain radiating systems there is still a good deal of uncertainty in the absorption coefficients (see Treanor, 1961).

Detra and Hidalgo (1961) give an approximate correlation formula for stagnation point equilibrium radiative heat transfer as

$$q_r = 187,200 \, r_b \left(\frac{U_1}{26,000}\right)^{8\cdot5} \left(\frac{\rho_1}{\rho_{S.L.}}\right) \frac{CHU}{\text{ft}^2 \, \text{sec}} \qquad (7.56)$$

where S.L. refers to sea-level conditions.

If the radiation energy transfer becomes comparable to the aerodynamic heat transfer, some allowance must be made for self-absorption processes within the gas layer, possibly along the lines suggested by Kennet and Strack (1961).

For re-entry to the earth's atmosphere at supersatellite speeds non-equilibrium chemical effects have to be considered when calculating not only the convective (Section 6) but also the radiative heating. At altitudes greater than about 150,000 ft the non-equilibrium radiation may in fact be the dominant effect. This is because chemical equilibrium is not attained by the gas in the nose region of a body so that high overshoot non-equilibrium temperatures can appear, leading to a considerably increased total radiation intensity. Further details of this problem may be found in the paper of Teare, Georgiev and Allen (1961).

7.9. Mass Transfer Cooling

We have already seen that one solution to the problem of aerodynamic heating, particularly for re-entry to the earth's atmosphere, is to provide sufficient nose-blunting. The heat transfer rate is then reduced, and if sufficient material is provided at the nose to absorb the total heat input the well-known heat-sink re-entry head is obtained. The surface of the body then remains below the melting point of the material, and furthermore it is impervious. Another class of problems is introduced if the surface is allowed to melt, burn or sublime (generally referred to as 'ablation'), or if a coolant is injected through it (transpiration cooling). These expedients may permit the design of slender low drag re-entry heads with consequent shortening of re-entry time. In the case of ballistic missiles this clearly creates even greater difficulties in providing defensive measures.

In the case of a hypersonic aircraft such extreme measures may not be required. The surface temperature may be kept sufficiently low by circulating a coolant under the skin. Alternatively an external layer of insulation may be effective in maintaining the internal structure at a relatively low temperature. These solutions do not impose any new problems for the aerodynamicist.

Transpiration cooling provides protection against aerodynamic heating in two ways:

(1) By absorbing heat from the hot gas in the boundary layer. In this respect the coolant should have a heat capacity that is large relative to air. On the basis of weight therefore, hydrogen or helium would be more effective than air.

(2) By altering the structure of the boundary-layer so that skin friction and heat transfer are reduced. The diffusion coefficients (and therefore the Lewis and Schmidt numbers) are important in this process, in the same way as described in Section 6.

The simplest case for theoretical treatment is when air is used as the coolant since this means altering only the boundary conditions in the ordinary boundary layer equations and it has received considerable attention (see for instance Dorrance and Dore, 1954). Other (lighter) gases are of greater interest, but extra terms have to be added to the momentum and energy equations of the boundary layer; there are separate continuity equations for the individual species, and physical properties (density, viscosity, etc.) depend on concentrations as well as on temperature. However the basic analysis is similar to that introduced in Section 6, and full details are given in the original paper of Lees (1958).

The calculations of Smith (1953) on the effects of helium diffusing through a boundary layer and the experiments of Leadon and Scott (1956) in a turbulent boundary layer show that a considerable reduction in heat transfer can be obtained with only modest amounts of fluid blown through the wall, and some typical results are shown in figure 7.4. However Baron (1961) has recently shown that such large reductions in heat transfer are not in fact achieved in practice by the injection of a light gas such as helium. This is due to the pronounced diffusion present in light-gas injection which tends to offset the favourable insulating effect of a light gas.

Ablation is the process of absorbing heat energy by removal of surface material either by melting and possible subsequent vaporisation, or by sublimation. Again the analysis follows the same lines as that for chemical reaction in boundary layers (Section 6), but for a melting surface the molten material may flow back along the surface in waves and the problem of the protection it affords is very complex.

An ablating material possesses higher heat absorptive capacity than a heat-shield in a similar fashion to transpiration cooling but in addition the heat of fusion and possibly of vaporisation is effective. Also since the surface material is maintained at a higher temperature its internal heat capacity is higher.

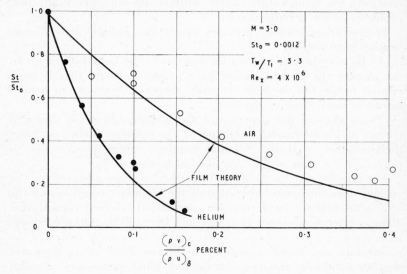

FIG. 7.4.—Transpiration cooling in a turbulent boundary layer (Smith (1953)).

However the greatest increase in heat capacity is realised (as with transpiration) when vaporisation or sublimation occur, because the countercurrent of relatively cool gas away from the surface absorbs heat energy in the boundary layer near the surface, distorts the enthalpy profile and thickens the boundary layer. Thus mass addition at the surface produces a 'blockage' of heat transfer.

A simple example first given by Lees (1959) serves to illustrate the main points made above. For simplicity we will assume that combustion of the vaporising or sublimating material is oxygen-limited so that all the oxygen near the surface is consumed. Then the heat transfer rate to the molten liquid film (or solid interior) is

$$q_w = \rho_\delta u_\delta \, \mathrm{St} \, \Delta h - (\rho v)_w L \tag{7.57}$$

where u, v are gas velocities along and normal to the surface, subscripts δ and w refer to conditions at the edge of the boundary layer and the surface respectively, and L is either the heat of sublimation (L_s) or heat of vaporisation (L_{vap}).

The "effective" enthalpy ΔL is given by

$$\Delta h = \Sigma(K_i)_\delta(h_{i_\delta} - h_{i_w}) + \frac{ru_\delta^2}{2} + (K_0)_\delta . \Delta Q_{E_0} \qquad (7.58)$$

in which ΔQ_{E_0} is the heat of reaction of the surface material per unit mass of oxygen, and K_0 is the mass fraction of oxygen.

Thus the term $\rho_\delta u_\delta$ St $(K_0)_\delta$ ΔQ_{E_0} is the rate of energy transfer that occurs if all the oxygen atoms at the outer edge of the boundary layer that could possibly diffuse to the surface were to combine with the surface material. The first two terms in Δh, of course, correspond to the case of a non-reacting surface.

For a melting-vaporising substance with a temperature at the gas-liquid interface close to the boiling temperature, practically all the molten liquid vaporises and

$$q_w = mH_0$$

where H_0 is the heat-capacity of the liquid-solid system up to the boiling temperature, and m is the rate of mass addition.

For a subliming material,

$$q_w = mL_T$$

where L_T is the thermal capacity of the solid material up to the surface temperature.

Now define

$$B = \frac{m}{\rho_\delta u_\delta \text{St}_0} = \frac{(\rho v)_w}{(\rho u)_s \text{St}_0} \qquad (7.59)$$

where St_0 is the value of the Stanton number St for zero mass transfer, and

$$B' = (\rho v)_w/(\rho u)_\delta . \text{St} \qquad (7.60)$$

so that $\text{St}/\text{St}_0 = B/B'$

Now

$$\Delta h = \frac{1}{(\rho u)_\delta . \text{St}} \left\{ mH_0 + mL_{vap} \right\} \qquad (7.61)$$

$$\therefore \quad B' = \Delta h/(H_0 + L_{vap}) \qquad (7.62)$$

or $\Delta h/(L_E + L_T)$ for a subliming material.

Thus every value of B' defines a linear relation between St/St_0 and B and these may be plotted on a graph. Figure 7.5 for example shows the effect of mass addition on heat transfer for the injection of air into air. We have plotted two sets of results on this figure, the theoretical laminar stagnation point flow calculated by Reshotko and Cohen (1955) and the turbulent flat plate experimental results of Leadon and Scott (1956).

For gaseous ablation, similar curves illustrate the self-regulating character of the phenomenon. As Δh increases, so q_w increases. This increased mass transfer acts to 'block' or prevent the heat transfer from reaching the solid interior. In other words, B increases much more slowly than B'; in fact for large B', B is nearly independent of B'.

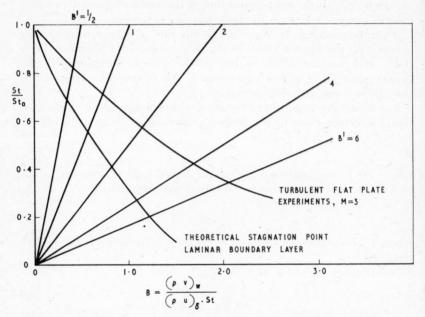

FIG. 7.5.—Effect of mass transfer on heat transfer (air to air) (Lees (1959)).

The reduction in heat transfer coefficient due to mass transfer amounts to a substantial increase in effective heat capacity. For example if $(L_E + L_T)$ or $(L_{vap} + H_0)$ is 500 CHU/lb, and using for the moment the particular curves of figure 7.5, we see that $B = 1\cdot2$ for $B' = 6$ in the laminar stagnation point flow. Thus $St/St_0 = 0\cdot2$, and the effective heat capacity is 2,500 CHU/lb. For the turbulent flat plate flow with the same rate of mass addition, we get about 1,000 CHU/lb, since B' is about 2·5.

We cannot leave the subject of ablation in a laminar boundary layer without referring to the work of Roberts (1959) and of Spalding (1961). In particular, the latter has given a rather simple physical explanation of ablation in terms of a driving enthalpy, and has described a graphical method which is most useful for design purposes.

By comparison, theories of ablation in turbulent flow are very inadequate. Adams (1959) has given a useful survey of the subject and further details may be found in papers by Georgiev, Hidalgo and Adams (1959) and Warren and Diaconis (1960).

7.10. Boundary Layer Stability and Transition to Turbulence

The connection between transition in the boundary layer and the stability of the laminar flow in response to infinitesimal disturbances is qualitatively well established. The most comprehensive treatment of the stability of the compressible laminar boundary layer is that of Lees and Reshotko (1960). They have included the effect of temperature fluctuations on the 'viscous' (rapidly varying) disturbances which were either ignored in earlier work or else accounted for incompletely. The main conclusion drawn by Lees and Reshotko is that the minimum critical Reynolds number for insulated flat plate boundary layers decreases in the range $0 \leqslant M \leqslant 3$, and then rises very sharply for hypersonic Mach numbers. A certain amount of experimental work has been reported by Laufer and Vrebalovich (1960) at $M = 2 \cdot 2$ and by Demetriades (1960) at $M = 5 \cdot 8$, but experimental verification is in general very difficult to achieve. In hypersonic wind-tunnels, for example, the thick turbulent boundary layer on the walls produces in the working section an intense sound field disturbance which leads to early transition on a model. It is almost impossible to allow for this effect as yet without actually sucking off the wall boundary layer.

The effect of heat transfer on the stability of the compressible laminar boundary layer is qualitatively well established. Thus cooling of the surface increases stability and heating produces the opposite effect. However a transition reversal has been observed with strong surface cooling; this may be a surface roughness effect which is introduced due to the thinning of the layer with extreme cooling. However, there is a very good chance of achieving large regions of laminar flow on a full-scale hypersonic vehicle operation at high altitudes and therefore relatively low values of Reynolds number. This has been observed in flight tests of rocket vehicles, and Reynolds numbers at transition of the order of 20 millions, and even higher, have been measured. These test vehicles are nearly always of conical or nearly-cylindrical shape however. For swept wings it is possible to get turbulent flow right at the leading-edge either because the spanwise flow velocity component is so high or because of the secondary flow instability which was first observed on sweptback wings at low speed.

The value of the Reynolds number at transition based on momentum thickness is often used as a criterion. For highly cooled blunt bodies experimental values of this Reynolds number lower than 300 have occasionally been found, and values as high as 1,000 have been reported.

In design work the lower figure is usually taken to calculate the location of transition.

The most recent surveys of transition in supersonic flow have been given by Wisniewski (1960) and by Potter and Whitfield (1960).

A method of calculating heat transfer actually in the transition region from laminar to turbulent flow has been suggested by Persh (1957).

CHAPTER 8

BOUNDARY LAYER INTERACTION
WITH THE EXTERNAL FLOW

8.1. Introduction

Tsien noted soon after his paper (1946) on hypersonic similarity of slender bodies with attached shock waves (see Chapter 4) that the results would probably be invalidated by interaction effects between the shock and the boundary layer because the shock lies close to the body and the boundary layer occupies a considerable proportion of the flow field between shock and body. We make a distinction here between high Mach number effects and low density effects, both of which thicken the boundary layer. The latter case more properly belongs to the realm of rarefied gas-dynamics as treated in Chapter 9.

Along the forward facing surface of a blunt body, at high Reynolds numbers, the boundary layer is thin relative to the shock stand-off distance so that the inviscid solutions of Chapter 3 predict the flow field quite well, and for high Reynolds numbers the boundary layer charac-teristics (thickness, etc.) can be calculated by means of the classical (first order) theory. At the lower Reynolds numbers appropriate to high altitude flight however a number of second-order boundary layer effects may become important—these are all neglected in classical boundary layer theory, and may be described as interaction effects. The resulting modifications of boundary layer theory apply to displace-ment effects, the effect of vorticity in the external flow, and curvature as well as slip effects.

For fairly sharp-nosed slender shapes we can recognise three im-portant interaction regions as illustrated in figure 8.1.

First is the leading-edge region where the shock is probably always detached (in practice the nose will have some finite thickness, t) and where slip flow effects for example may be important. We will deal with this region in Chapter 9. Then there are two regions in which the displacement effect of the boundary layer is particularly felt, a zone of "strong interaction" where the external flow is influenced by the boundary layer and a "weak interaction" region further back from the leading-edge, where the boundary layer growth influences the external flow but the resulting induced pressure distribution is con-sidered to have a negligible effect on the boundary layer.

We can best explain the principle of this displacement type of boundary layer interaction with the external flow by first considering the low speed case. At low speeds and for high Reynolds numbers the idea of a thin boundary layer as conceived by Prandtl implies that the flow over a body may be calculated as if the fluid were inviscid. The development of the boundary layer is then calculated on the basis of this external inviscid flow. All of the fluid entering the boundary layer has the same total head (and total enthalpy), and Bernoulli's equation can be used to relate the pressure and velocity along the outer edge of the layer. The boundary layer thickness, δ, is proportional to $x/\sqrt{\mathrm{Re}_x}$ so that the local streamline deflection induced by the boundary layer

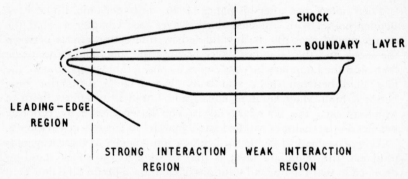

FIG. 8.1.—Regions of boundary layer interaction on a slender body.

is of order $(\mathrm{Re}_x)^{-\frac{1}{2}}$, i.e. $\theta \sim \delta/x$. Now surface pressures are roughly proportional to θ^2 so the effect of the boundary layer on the external flow field of a slender body is $0(\mathrm{Re}_x)^{-1}$. This is negligible except possibly at high angles of attack.

At supersonic and especially hypersonic speeds the situation is vastly changed. If density and viscosity in the Reynolds number in the expression for δ are evaluated at the wall temperature, then

$$\delta \sim \sqrt{\frac{\mu_w}{\rho_w ux}} = \frac{x\sqrt{\mu_\delta}}{\sqrt{\rho_\delta ux}} \sqrt{\frac{\mu_w}{\mu_\delta}} \sqrt{\frac{\rho_\delta}{\rho_w}}$$

If we assume a linear relation between viscosity and temperature then $\mu_w/\mu_\delta = T_w/T_\delta$ and also $\rho_\delta/\rho_w = T_w/T_\delta$ from the perfect gas law, since pressure is approximately constant across the boundary layer. Now $T_w/T_\delta = 1 + \dfrac{\gamma - 1}{2} M_\delta^2$ (for an insulated wall, assuming constant specific heats) so for high Mach number, δ is approximately proportional to $\dfrac{\gamma - 1}{2} M_\delta^2$. Similar arguments can be applied to the calculation of displacement thickness $\delta^\star$; in fact the hypersonic approximations of Section 7.5 led to the result that $\delta^\star \simeq \delta$.

Thus for the same Reynolds number the boundary layer can be

orders of magnitude thicker at hypersonic speeds than it is at low speeds. Such thick boundary layers alter the effective shape of a body (by an amount equal to the displacement thickness) and thus induce a significant outward deflection of the external flow streamlines. Quite small changes in flow angle are sufficient to produce large pressure gradients at high speeds, and the pressure gradient induced in this manner feeds back into the boundary layer and affects its development, at least in the strong interaction case.

As we have already pointed out, the flow behind the bow shock near the nose of a blunt body is subsonic or low supersonic even at very high speeds so that in this region the interaction between the boundary layer and external flow is negligible at high Reynolds numbers. This is the reason for dealing with slender and blunt bodies separately. The second-order boundary layer effects for low Reynolds number flow over a blunt body are considered in Section 5, but we will first consider the problem of interaction for a sharp slender body.

A more practical case is that of a slender body with a slightly blunted nose (to reduce heating rates). The inviscid treatment has been given in Chapter 5, especially that utilising similarity solutions of blast wave theory. We will deal with the boundary layer interaction problem for blunted slender bodies in Section 3.

Other second-order boundary layer phenomena such as the effects of body curvature and vorticity in the free stream are described in Sections 4 and 5.

To complete the picture of boundary-layer interactions with the external flow we deal in Section 6 with the very practical problem of shock wave—boundary layer interactions, when a shock wave impinges on an already well-developed boundary layer. The problems associated with separated flow follow on from there quite naturally.

8.2. Pointed Slender Bodies

We must first define exactly what is meant by 'pointed', since in practice it is impossible to manufacture a mathematically sharp leading-edge or pointed nose. The relative importance of viscous (interaction) and inviscid (nose bluntness) effects depends on the leading-edge Reynolds number $Re_t = \rho_1 U_1 t / \mu_1$. At hypersonic speeds the mass flux into the boundary layer is quite small and the streamlines are almost parallel to the edge of the boundary layer on a slender body. Thus the streamlines entering the boundary layer have previously crossed the shock wave far upstream near the leading-edge where the shock wave is strong and highly curved. Therefore the development of the boundary layer for a large distance downstream of the leading-edge depends to some extent on conditions around the nose region. In fact Lees (1955) has calculated the ratio of the energy imparted to the flow by the transverse field associated with a blunted nose to that of a slender afterbody. He also showed that the effects of blunting are important for hundreds of leading-edge thicknesses back from the nose (see also Chapter 5.1). Experimentally, Hammitt and Bogdonoff (1956) have shown that for flat plates the effect of the leading-edge dominates the flow for $Re_t > 10^3$ approximately. We will take this figure as our criterion for sharpness, so that for $Re_t < 10^3$ leading-edge bluntness effects may be considered negligible in comparison with the effects of interaction between the boundary layer and the external inviscid flow. The criterion for cones is $Re_d < 10^2$ where d is the nose diameter. We then expect the concepts of hypersonic similarity and the hypersonic approximations (Chapter 2) to connect the self-induced flow field with the rate of growth of the boundary layer in the strong interaction region.

In the case of a weak interaction all we have to do is to calculate the displacement thickness of the boundary layer and add this to the body shape. Available approximations such as the tangent-wedge or tangent-cone methods may then be used to calculate the pressure distribution.

Thus for the weak interaction on a flat plate the displacement thickness is given by equation (7.34) with $p = p_1$

$$\therefore \quad \delta^\star \simeq \varepsilon \left(0\cdot664 + 1\cdot73\, \frac{T_w}{T_0} \right) M_1{}^2 \sqrt{\frac{C}{u_1/\nu_1}}\, x^{\frac{1}{2}} \tag{8.1}$$

The equivalent body slope due to the displacement effect of the boundary layer is therefore

$$\theta_w = \frac{d\delta^\star}{dx} \simeq \tfrac{1}{2}\varepsilon \left(0\cdot664 + 1\cdot73\, \frac{T_w}{T_0} \right) \frac{M_1{}^2\sqrt{C}}{\sqrt{Re_x}} \tag{8.2}$$

where

$$Re_x = \frac{\rho_1 U_1 x}{\mu_1} \tag{8.3}$$

The tangent-wedge method (equation 4.7) gives, for $(M_1\theta_w)^2 \ll 1$,

$$p/p_1 = 1 + \gamma M_1 \theta_w$$

$$= 1 + \frac{\gamma}{2}\varepsilon \left(0\cdot664 + 1\cdot73\, \frac{T_w}{T_0} \right) \chi \tag{8.4}$$

where

$$\chi = M_1{}^3\sqrt{C}/\sqrt{Re_x} \tag{8.5}$$

The two extreme examples of an insulated surface and a very cold wall are represented by $T_w/T_0 \to 1$ and $T_w/T_0 \to 0$ respectively. Finally then

$$\begin{aligned} p/p_1 &= 1 + 0\cdot28\chi \ \text{(insulated wall)} \\ &\quad 1 + 0\cdot078\chi \ \text{(cold wall)} \end{aligned} \Bigg\} \tag{8.6}$$

The effect is very much larger for an insulated wall where the boundary layer is much thicker because of the higher temperatures involved. However it must be noted that $C < 1$ for an insulated wall and $C \simeq 1$ for a cold wall, which tends to reduce the difference somewhat.

A more accurate calculation giving the pressure correct to second order in χ is, for an insulated wall for example,

$$p/p_1 = 1 + 0{\cdot}31\chi + 0{\cdot}05\chi^2 \qquad (8.7)$$

(see Hayes and Probstein (1959b), p. 350).

For a bluff wedge, or the compression surface of a thin wedge at a high angle of attack, $\delta^\star$ can be calculated from the flat plate result provided free stream conditions are taken to be those behind the oblique shock. The tangent wedge formula for strong oblique shocks $(M_1\theta_w)^2 \gg 1$, gives

$$p/p_1 = \frac{\gamma(\gamma + 1)}{2} M_1{}^2 \left(\alpha + \frac{d\delta^\star}{dx}\right)^2 \qquad (8.8)$$

where α is either the wedge half-angle, the angle of attack, or the sum of both as the case may be. It can then be shown that the coefficient of χ in the pressure formula, equation (8.4), includes an extra factor of $2/(M_1\alpha)^2$. Therefore, because of the strong inviscid pressure field in this case, the viscous interaction effects are considerably smaller than those for a flat plate at zero angle of attack.

For the more complicated case of a strong interaction region on a flat plate we again use the tangent wedge formula for strong oblique shocks

$$p/p_1 = \frac{\gamma(\gamma + 1)}{2} M_1{}^2\theta_w{}^2 \qquad (8.9)$$

where $\theta_w = d\delta^\star/dx$. Now, however, the boundary layer growth is governed by the pressure distribution that the layer itself has induced. It will now be shown that for a consistent solution the displacement thickness $\delta^\star \sim x^{-\frac{3}{4}}$ and the induced pressure distribution must be of the form $p \sim x^{-\frac{1}{2}}$. We will carry out the calculation in detail for this case, using equation (7.34) to express the displacement thickness in terms of the self-induced pressure distribution.

Writing

$$p/p_1 = kx^{-\frac{1}{2}}$$

Then equation (7.34) gives

$$\delta^\star \simeq \varepsilon\left(0{\cdot}664 + 1{\cdot}73\,\frac{T_w}{T_0}\right) \frac{M_1{}^2\sqrt{C}}{\sqrt{U_1/\nu_1}} \sqrt{\frac{2}{k}} \cdot x^{3/4} \qquad (8.10)$$

hence

$$\left(\frac{d\delta^\star}{dx}\right)^2 \simeq \frac{9}{8}\frac{\varepsilon^2}{k}\left(0.664 + 1.73\,\frac{T_w}{T_0}\right)^2\frac{M_1{}^4 \cdot C}{(U_1/\nu_1)} \cdot x^{-\frac{1}{2}} \qquad (8.11)$$

so that equation (8.9) gives

$$p/p_1 = \frac{\gamma(\gamma+1)}{2}\,M_1{}^2\frac{9}{8}\frac{\varepsilon^2}{k}\left(0.664 + 1.73\,\frac{T_w}{T_0}\right)^2\frac{M_1{}^4 \cdot C}{(U_1/\nu_1)} \cdot x^{-\frac{1}{2}} = kx^{-\frac{1}{2}}$$

$$\therefore \quad k^2 = \frac{9}{16}\,\gamma(\gamma+1)\varepsilon^2\left(0.664 + 1.73\,\frac{T_w}{T_0}\right)^2 \cdot \frac{M_1{}^6 \cdot C}{(U_1/\nu_1)}$$

$$\left.\begin{aligned}\therefore \quad p/p_1 &= 0.53\% \text{ for an insulated wall}\\ &= 0.15\% \text{ for a cold wall}\end{aligned}\right\} \qquad (8.12)$$

where χ is given by equation (8.5).

For the insulated flat plate a more complete solution (again using the tangent wedge approximation) is

$$p/p_1 = 0.514\chi + 0.759 + 0(\chi)^{-1} \qquad (8.13)$$

(see Hayes and Probstein (1959), p. 360).

The same problem has been treated by Stewartson (1955) who gave numerical results from a momentum integral calculation of the boundary layer.

8.3. Blunt-nosed Slender Bodies

It is impossible to manufacture a truly sharp leading-edge, and some bluntness is usually incorporated anyway in order to reduce the heating rates in the nose region. Thus in the above analysis we have not properly taken into account the history of the flow. However the blast wave theory (with the reservations already outlined in Chapter 5) is available for calculations of the inviscid flow field generated by a blunt nose so that the initial history of the boundary layer can be incorporated into a treatment of hypersonic viscous interaction downstream of the region which is dominated by the nose. So long as $\mathrm{Re}_t > 10^3$ approximately the interaction between the boundary layer and the external flow is weak in the nose region itself. However when Re_t is much less than this value, in addition to the interaction described above, slip flow effects may occur if the free stream density is sufficiently low. The problem is altogether more involved and questions arise as to the lower limit of Reynolds number at which continuum theories remain valid. These topics will be discussed partly in Section 5 and again in Chapter 9.

For our present problem of the boundary layer interaction on a blunt-nosed slender body it would be possible to construct a perturbation of the blast wave analogy in terms of angle of attack, and then to replace α by $d\delta^\star/dx$. However a more satisfactory general analysis is that due to Cheng (1960b.) He recognised that the blast wave analogy exhibits a detached shock layer, the solution for which must be patched-on to the solution for the low-density high-entropy core consisting of particles that have come through the strong nearly normal portion of the bow shock. Cheng therefore divided up the flow field of a blunted slender body into an outer 'shock layer' and an inner 'entropy layer' as shown in figure 8.2. (See also figure 5.8.)

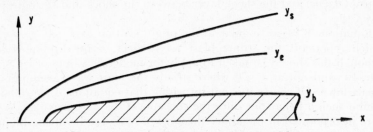

FIG. 8.2.—Flow field of a blunted slender body.

Here $y_s(x)$ is the shock shape, $\delta_e(x)$ is the entropy layer thickness $= (y_e - y_b)$, and $y_b(x)$ the effective body shape including boundary layer displacement thickness. Cheng obtains boundary layer parameters from the zero-order theory given in Chapter 7, Section 4. He then shows that the pressure variation across the entropy layer is small so that the surface pressure can be obtained from say the Busemann expression (Newtonian plus centrifugal) (see Section 4 of Chapter 5) with the effective body shape for application of this shock layer formula given by $y_e(x)$.

Thus from equation (5.44)

$$p_e \simeq \rho_1 U_1{}^2[y_e'^2 + y_e y_e''] = \rho_1 U_1{}^2(y_e y_e')'$$

The necessary relation between pressure and cross-sectional area of the entropy layer (or $y_e(x)$) is obtained from a simple momentum-integral analysis of the entropy layer. The result is (equation 5.46)

$$(y_e - y_b) \cdot p_e = \frac{\gamma - 1}{2} \cdot D_N \qquad (5.47)$$

where D_N is the nose drag, and p_e is the (constant) pressure through the entropy layer.

Since $y_b = y_w + \delta^\star$, we have finally

$$[y_e - y_w - \delta^\star](y_e y_e')' = \tfrac{1}{2}\varepsilon t C_{D_N} \qquad (8.14)$$

where

$$\delta^\star = \varepsilon \left(0{\cdot}664 + 1{\cdot}73\,\frac{T_w}{T_0}\right) \frac{\chi\sqrt{l}}{M_1{}^2} \frac{\sqrt{y_e y_e'}}{(y_e y_e')'}$$

from equations (7.34) and (5.46), t is the leading-edge thickness and C_{D_N} is a leading-edge drag coefficient

$$C_{D_N} = D_N / \tfrac{1}{2} \rho_1 U_1^2 t \tag{8.15}$$

After solving equation (8.14) for y_e, we can calculate the pressure from equation (5.44) and heat transfer and skin friction from equations (7.32) and (7.33). Thus the differential equation (8.14), accounts for the interaction of all three flow regions—the boundary layer, the entropy layer, and the shock layer between the shock and the entropy layer.

Equation (8.14) is singular at the origin, so that as $x \to 0$, $y_e \sim x^{2/3}$, which represents the strong blast wave effect of the leading-edge, although this should be taken to apply for moderate values of x/t (say 3 to 10) and not at $x = 0$ where strictly the blast wave assumptions break down. Of course it is not surprising that equation (8.14) should exhibit such a behaviour since the concepts of the blast wave analogy were incorporated in the above theory. For cases not involving bluntness equation (8.14) reveals a singular behaviour such that as $x \to 0$, $y_e \sim x^{3/4}$ which is the result obtained (for strong interaction) in Section 2. This is to be expected when displacement effects are predominant. In the original paper Cheng considered asymptotic solutions for y_e for flat plate afterbodies and treated three cases in detail;

(a) the flat plate with bluntness and displacement,
(b) the inclined flat plate with displacement, and
(c) the inclined flat plate with bluntness.

Two new variables are introduced

$$K_\varepsilon = M_1^3 \cdot \varepsilon \cdot C_{D_N} \cdot t/x \tag{8.16}$$

and

$$x_\varepsilon = \varepsilon \left(0.664 + 1.73 \frac{T_w}{T_0} \right) M_1^3 \sqrt{C} / \sqrt{\mathrm{Re}_x} \tag{8.17}$$

and the differential equation (8.14) can then be written in a simpler form. An important feature is that all parameters and spatial variables are grouped together to form a single variable $(x_\varepsilon/K_\varepsilon^{2/3})$ which therefore controls the combined effect of bluntness and displacement. The transition between the two regimes (bluntness predominant and displacement predominant) occurs in the range

$$10^{-1} < x_\varepsilon/K_\varepsilon^{2/3} < 10,$$

which is consistent with the criterion given in Section 2 that $\mathrm{Re}_t \approx 10^3$.

The actual asymptotic solutions for pressure are

(a) $$p/p_1 = \frac{\sqrt{3}}{2} \gamma \cdot x_\varepsilon \text{ for large } x_\varepsilon/K_\varepsilon^{2/3} \tag{8.18}$$

(b) $$p/p_1 = \left(\frac{1}{18}\right)^{\frac{1}{3}} . \gamma . K_\varepsilon^{\frac{2}{3}} \text{ for small } x_\varepsilon/K_\varepsilon^{\frac{2}{3}} \qquad (8.19)$$

The latter is the blast wave solution for two-dimensional flow, whereas (a) corresponds to the strong interaction solution obtained in Section 2. The difference in numerical values of the coefficient of χ may be attributed to the use of the tangent-wedge approximation in the analysis of Section 2.

Incidentally, the simple addition of the above two asymptotic solutions for p/p_1 differs from the exact solution in the transition region by less than 12 per cent. This explains the success of the empirical linear-combination laws proposed by Hammitt and Bogdonoff (1956) and by Creager (1957).

Cheng also discussed the similarity of hypersonic flows involving leading-edge bluntness and boundary layers. The treatment is based on the inviscid hypersonic similitude taking into account the effect of a slight blunting (Cheng, 1959) and a similitude involving boundary layers given by Hayes and Probstein (1959a). A full treatment of this subject is outside the scope of the present book and the reader is referred to the original papers for details.

8.4. Transverse Curvature Effects

Important effects may arise at hypersonic speeds due to the curvature of the body, and they are similar to the interaction effects already described. In axisymmetric flow, effects arise due to both longitudinal and transverse curvature whereas only the former occurs in two-dimensional flow. The parameter which determines the degree of importance of curvature effects is the boundary layer thickness times the appropriate body curvature, or alternatively, the ratio of boundary layer thickness to radius of body cross-section δ/r_b in the case of transverse curvature. On slender bodies of revolution the transverse curvature effect is by far the more important and our discussion here will be restricted accordingly. Both effects are of course covered in the second order boundary layer approximation mentioned in Section 5 with particular reference to blunt bodies.

The transverse curvature effect is particularly important on a slender cone for instance, and here also the weak interaction effect of Section 2 can be quite large. Probstein and Elliott (1953) have considered the case when the boundary layer thickness is no longer small compared with the radius of cross-section of the body, and find the two effects can be separated. This is because the transverse curvature has no effect on displacement thickness in the first approximation although there may be large increases in skin friction and heat transfer.

In the particular case of a $\frac{3}{4}$-power body of revolution a completely similar solution can be obtained even including the transverse curvature, and provided the pressure gradient is neglected similarity is possible for slender paraboloids of revolution for all values of δ/r_b, which is in fact constant over the whole body. Some numerical results have been reported by Yasuhara (1957), who found that in general the transverse curvature strongly influences skin friction and heat transfer, but has little effect on the induced pressure.

For slender cylindrical afterbodies, the transverse curvature affects the boundary layer characteristics in a marked way, and Richmond (1957) has found experimentally that the skin friction coefficient on a slender rod mounted axially in a tunnel at $M = 5\cdot8$ can reach values 4 or 5 times as high as on a flat plate with a laminar boundary layer. The ratio is reduced to about 2 with a turbulent boundary layer. This interesting problem has received much attention in the incompressible case also (see for example Glauert and Lighthill, 1955).

8.5. Vorticity Interactions

In hypersonic flow over a blunted nose the bow shock is highly curved and large entropy gradients are set up in the flow field behind the shock.

This variation of entropy leads to the presence of vorticity and indeed the flow behind the shock is strongly rotational. The connection between vorticity, $\zeta = \text{curl } u$ where u is the velocity vector, and entropy S is provided by the Crocco theorem

$$\zeta \times u = T \operatorname{grad} S \qquad (8.20)$$

and from this Lighthill (1957) has derived general expressions for the vorticity components in terms of the principal curvatures of the shock surface and the tangential velocity components, and a factor $(1 - \varepsilon)^2/\varepsilon$ where ε is the density ratio across the shock. Remembering that with dissociation, ε can approach a value as low as $0\cdot05$ it is obvious that the vorticity in the 'external' flow can be very large.

The effect of vorticity interaction is quite small on sharp-nosed slender bodies. Oguchi (1958) has demonstrated this for the strong interaction region on an insulated flat plate, and his results confirm an order of magnitude estimate made by Hayes and Probstein (1959b, p. 374).

The effects are more important however in the case of blunted slender bodies, or blunt bodies at low Reynolds number. Rott and Lenard (1959, 1962) have pointed out however that other second order boundary layer effects are of equal importance and should be considered together with the effect of external vorticity. This led van Dyke (1961) to a consideration of the second order boundary layer theory for blunt bodies in hypersonic flow mentioned below.

Historically, the first attempts to gauge the importance of this effect attempted to analyse the problem of the boundary layer on a flat plate with vorticity in the external stream, and led to a controversy as to whether the free-stream vorticity induces a pressure gradient in the flow or not. Van Dyke (1960, 1962) has critically reviewed the conflicting theories, and Stuart (1961) has carried the process one stage further. We will not repeat the arguments here but merely refer to the latter two papers for details and references. It is unfortunate that so much attention has been given to this particular problem since it is by no means clear that it has a unique solution. None of the original papers give a full discussion of whether the specified boundary conditions were sufficient to determine an exact solution, and in any case represent an unrealistic flow in that the external shear flow assumed results in an infinite streamwise velocity at infinity. Further remarks have been made by Glauert (1962).

Van Dyke (1961) investigated the physically realistic situation of the boundary layer growth over a blunt body in hypersonic flow and included all the second order effects, of which he identified seven: longitudinal curvature, transverse curvature, slip, temperature jump, entropy gradient and total enthalpy gradient (both of which lead to vorticity in the external flow), and finally (other) displacement effects.

The case of a sphere was calculated in detail for infinite Mach number, $\gamma = 1\cdot4$, $Pr = 0\cdot7$, $\mu \propto T$ and ratio $T_w/T_o = 0\cdot2$. The result for stagnation point heat transfer rate was

$$q_0/q_\infty = 1 + \frac{M}{\sqrt{Re_d}} \underset{\substack{\text{vorticity} \\ }}{(0\cdot52} - \underset{\substack{\text{slip} + \text{temperature} \\ \text{jump}}}{0\cdot14} - \underset{\substack{\text{longitudinal} \\ \text{curv.}}}{0\cdot10} + \underset{\substack{\text{transverse} \\ \text{curv.}}}{0\cdot11)} \qquad (8.21)$$

where q_∞ is the heat transfer for infinite Reynolds number.

However even this work has been criticised on the grounds that the matching condition applied to inner and outer series expansions is not necessarily correct.

Ideally one would like to deal with the full Navier–Stokes equations in this case rather than the boundary layer equations. An interesting case currently under investigation in this context is the flow of an irrotational free stream with a velocity gradient about a parabolic wedge, where it is known that far downstream the flow reverts to the Blasius solution (see Mangler (1962)).

At still lower densities the question of the limits of continuum theory arises, and we investigate this problem in Chapter 9.

8.6. Shock Wave–Boundary Layer Interactions

Much work has been done over the past decade on the behaviour of boundary layers in the presence of shock waves at moderately supersonic speeds (see for example Gadd and Holder, 1959). Much of this is experimental and has resulted in a fairly clear understanding of the phenomena of separation of a boundary layer caused by the

impingement of a shock wave. However the details of the viscous flow
in such a separated flow region are still rather vague.

The practical interest in shock wave–boundary layer interactions
and separated flow problems is clearly very strong as shown by the
following few examples.

Many hypersonic vehicles have blunt bases and there is therefore a
recurring interest in the problem of base pressure and base flows in
general including the possibility of base heating effects. Again a flared
skirt has often been suggested by vehicle designers, mainly to add
aerodynamic static stability. The flow separation resulting from interactions in such a compression corner, and the variation of the extent
of the interaction region with incidence, Reynolds number and Mach
number can have a marked effect on the stability. Also, at high
incidence the bow shock wave from the nose may impinge on the flared
skirt and have an even stronger influence on the stability of the vehicle.

Similar problems may be encountered in the flight of rocket vehicles
where a forward separation of the boundary layer may be induced due
to the pluming effect of the highly underexpanded rocket efflux at high
altitudes (see Crabtree, 1961 and Schueller (1959)).

Control surface deflections, or simply a yawning motion of the
vehicle, are likely to produce shock boundary layer interactions which
result in separation.

Again it has been suggested that reduced overall heat transfer rates
can be obtained by designing for large regions of separated flow (see
Bogdonoff and Vas, 1959).

In all these situations the corresponding drag problem (as well as
heat transfer and stability) is of great importance.

One particular model which has been utilised in many theoretical
and experimental investigations is the flow over a flat surface with a
sharp-edged cut-out; others involve the flow over forward and rear-
ward-facing steps. It is important to recognise the difference between
these cases and those in which separation occurs naturally on a smooth
surface due to an adverse pressure gradient, which may possibly be
associated with an oblique shock wave in the external flow.

Flows with separation fixed by the geometry, such as in the case of
the cut-out, are of course simpler to treat theoretically but are not met
in practice so much as flows with natural or shock-induced separation.

Now it has been pointed out by Chapman, Kuehn and Larson
(1957) and by Gadd (1953 and 1956) among others that when the
separated region is fairly large, conditions near separation are independent of the agency which induced separation, and all significant
parameters are purely functions of Mach number and Reynolds
number. Two important parameters connected with separation are
(1) the pressure rise to the separation point, and (2) the pressure rise to
the constant pressure separated region (the so-called plateau pressure

rise) and these are indicated in the schematic pressure distribution of figure 8.3 in the neighbourhood of shock-induced separation of a boundary layer.

Criteria for these pressure rises are fairly well established for both laminar and turbulent boundary layers, at least for moderately supersonic Mach numbers. In the laminar case, Chapman *et al.* (1957) gave an order of magnitude analysis yielding $C_{p_s} \sim \sqrt{c_{f_1}}/\beta$ for the pressure rise to the separation point where $C_{p_s} = (p_s - p_1)/\tfrac{1}{2}\rho_1 U_1^2$, $\beta = \sqrt{M_1^2 - 1}$ and c_f is the local skin-friction coefficient, the subscript 1 referring to conditions just upstream of the interaction. Hakkinen

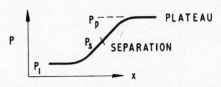

FIG. 8.3.—Schematic pressure distribution in neighbourhood of shock induced separation of a laminar boundary layer.

et al. (1959) obtained a similar relation from simple momentum considerations, and they found that $C_{p_s} = \sqrt{2c_{f_1}}/\beta$ and this correlates the data of Gadd (1956) and Chapman *et al.* quite well.

However the plateau pressure rise is more relevant for shock wave interactions since it is the total pressure rise that is important. Published data indicates that $C_{p_p} = 2C_{p_s}$ is the best correlation.

For separation of turbulent boundary layers, Mager (1955 and 1956) has given the semi-empirical formula

$$p_p/p_1 = 1 + \frac{\gamma M_1^2}{2b} \cdot (1 - K) \Big/ \left(1 + \frac{\gamma - 1}{2} \cdot M_1^2\right) \qquad (8.24)$$

with b approximately equal to 0·65. The factor K is assumed to be an empirical constant which can be adjusted to fit experimental data and Mager recommends the value $K = 0·55$.

Thus in contrast to the laminar case the model of the turbulent interaction gives a separation pressure ratio which is independent of Reynolds number. Now Kuehn (1959) has found in fact a Reynolds number dependence of separation pressure ratio at high Mach numbers and again in the lower Reynolds number range. However Kuehn's data refer more particularly to separation caused by pressure gradients more moderate than those due to shock waves.

Naturally it is not to be expected that a separation criterion is sufficient to determine the scale of the interaction and in particular the extent of the separated region since this requires the introduction of a characteristic length. Presumably this should be related to the boundary layer thickness at separation and thus to the Reynolds number at separation. The laminar separation criterion does of course depend on this Reynolds number but the dependence is too weak to be useful in determining the scale of the interaction.

Alternative methods of attacking this problem result in the reattachment criterion of Korst (1956) and Chapman (1951). These analyses are particularly aimed at the base pressure problem and in that regard have proved quite successful. It is postulated that the dividing streamline is brought to rest isentropically at reattachment, and consequently the pressure at reattachment is equal to the total pressure in the dividing streamline. If the velocity ratio u/U_1, is known along this streamline then the rest of the problem can be solved. For example, when the initial boundary layer thickness at separation is zero, $u/U_1 = 0.587$ for laminar layers, and for turbulent layers Korst (1956) has given a curve for determining u/U_1. Here again the scale of the interaction region is undetermined since the boundary layer thickness at separation is assumed to be small or zero. This thickness will of course affect the value of u/U_1 which will no longer be constant in the separated region owing to loss of similarity. Cooke (1962) has recently attempted to extend the method to deal with the case of a finite boundary layer thickness, and a specified velocity profile, at separation.

In summary then, it appears that an analysis of the complete flow is necessary, including the viscous region. An earlier attempt at this was due to Crocco and Lees (1952). They developed a mixing theory and applied it to the problem of determining base pressure for laminar and turbulent flows. Crocco (1954) later extended the method to deal with the interaction of a shock wave and a boundary layer. Still more recent developments of the original Crocco and Lees theory are due to Glick (1960) and Bray, Gadd and Woodger (1960).

Carrière and Sirieix (1961) have also extended the work of Korst and of Crocco and Lees and in particular have considered the effects of finite boundary layer thickness at separation and of fluid injection into the separated region.

An extremely important question is that of the possibility of transition to turbulence in the flow downstream of a laminar separation. As emphasised by Chapman, Kuehn and Larson (1957), the position of transition in the separated flow has a marked effect on the whole flow.

The particular problem of heat transfer in separated flow regions has received perhaps more detailed study than any other. Most of the work is experimental, and little of it was done with a hypersonic free stream. However quite often in a hypersonic flow the separated region lies below only a moderately supersonic flow so that existing theories (e.g., Chapman et al., 1957) may provide reasonable agreement. A useful survey of hypersonic separated flow problems has been given by Sprinks (1960), and further details can be found there.

CHAPTER 9

LOW DENSITY EFFECTS

9.1. Introduction

Space research has given a tremendous impetus to the study of rarefied gas-dynamics, and has shown quite clearly the large gaps in our knowledge concerning both the upper atmosphere and the phenomena involved in the passage of a body through this rarefied region. For motion through the denser parts of the atmosphere we can consider the air to be a continuous fluid and the Navier–Stokes equations are appropriate. At extremely high altitudes however the molecular structure of the air has to be taken into account, and the aerodynamic forces and heating experienced by a moving body must be related to the interactions of the individual gas molecules with the surface of the body. These interactions result in exchanges of energy and momentum and also produce such inter-molecular processes as excitation and ionisation as well as extra-molecular phenomena such as ablation and sputtering which are not yet fully understood. Except for these molecule-surface interactions the so called free molecule flow regime is fairly well understood in terms of the kinetic theory of gases, but little is known about the intermediate regime between free molecule flow and continuum flow. Recent investigations indicate however that there may be only a relatively narrow region (in terms of altitude) between the limits of applicability of continuum-type theories on the one hand and extensions to higher densities of free-molecule kinetic theories on the other.

9.2. Flow Regimes

It is worth emphasising at the outset that aerodynamic studies in the field of rarefied gas-dynamics exemplify the usual distinction between blunt bodies (a typical example being flow in the stagnation region) and slender shapes (for example, the rarefied flow near the leading-edge of a flat plate). In the rest of this chapter we shall be referring to the former geometry unless otherwise stated.

As we have pointed out, the study of rarefied gas-dynamics is concerned with those phenomena related to the molecular (as distinct from continuum) nature of a gas flow which occur at sufficiently low densities. In order to delineate the flow regimes of interest we need to define a parameter which will determine the relative importance of these effects. This is the Knudsen number, Kn, or ratio of the length of the molecular mean free path to some characteristic dimension of the flow field. In his pioneering paper Tsien suggested using either a particular body dimension (diameter for instance) or the boundary layer thickness for this characteristic length.

From kinetic theory the mean free path can be expressed as

$$\lambda_1 = 1 \cdot 26 \ \sqrt{\gamma} \cdot \frac{\nu}{a} \tag{9.1}$$

and hence Kn can be expressed in terms of the Mach and Reynolds numbers, since $M = U_1/a$ and $Re = U_1 l/\nu$ where l is a characteristic body dimension.

Hence

$$Kn = \frac{\lambda_1}{l} = 1 \cdot 26 \ \sqrt{\gamma} \frac{M_1}{Re}. \tag{9.2}$$

If we use the boundary layer thickness, δ, as a characteristic length, since $\delta/l \sim 1/\sqrt{Re}$, then $Kn \sim M_1/\sqrt{Re}$, and this relation has been used extensively in the classical literature (see for instance Schaaf and Chambré (1958), and Patterson (1956)). However we would not expect the results of ordinary boundary layer theory, for which it is assumed that the Reynolds number is high, to apply to a rarefied gas flow in which Re is usually small. Thus this particular definition of Kn is not very appropriate (see also Liepmann and Roshko (1957)). In any case it has been usual to compare the particular characteristic length chosen with the mean free path in the free stream. For hypersonic problems this is not satisfactory either, since the local density is appreciably increased across a strong shock wave so that the mean free path near the surface of a body is much smaller than in the free stream (see Adams and Probstein (1958)).

A careful discussion of the problem of choosing an appropriate definition of the mean free path has been given by Probstein (1961), and this leads to a criterion for free molecule flow as

$$\frac{\lambda_1}{r_b} \gg \frac{\sqrt{\pi\gamma}}{4} \left(\frac{T_1}{T_b}\right)^{1/2} \cdot M_1 \tag{9.3}$$

where λ_1 is the free stream mean free path, and r_b is the body nose radius.

According to Probstein the appropriate mean free path, λ_σ, is that of molecules emitted from the surface relative to the incident molecules, and is given by

$$\lambda_\sigma = \frac{4}{\sqrt{\pi\gamma}} \cdot \left(\frac{T_b}{T_1}\right)^{1/2} \frac{\lambda_1}{M_1} \tag{9.4}$$

and figure 9.1 shows that with this definition the free molecule flow limit is at a much higher altitude than if λ_1 were used in forming the Knudsen number. The criterion for free-molecule flow, that $\lambda_\sigma \gg r_b$ is here interpreted to be given by $\lambda_\sigma/r_b = 10$.

In terms of decreasing density, the next important regime is that of near-free-molecule flow. The methods which have been proposed for dealing with this regime involve corrections to the free-molecule flow theory due to certain types of intermolecular collisions, and are described in Section 4 below. The results given there may be expected to hold down to a value of λ_σ/r_b of about $\frac{1}{3}$, as illustrated in figure 9.1.

Let us now consider the other, high density extreme of the continuum flow regime which is encountered by a blunt body at lower altitudes. Here we have the familiar situation, described in earlier chapters, of a negligibly thin bow shock wave, a thin viscous boundary layer next to the surface of the body, and an inviscid region in between. The details of the flow structure within the shock wave can be ignored if the free-stream density is sufficiently high, that is it can be treated as a discontinuity and the Rankine–Hugoniot relations can be applied across the shock. The shock layer, or flow between shock and body can then be calculated by methods previously described, first assuming inviscid flow, and then modifying the solution near the body surface by an analysis of the boundary layer.

The bow shock wave ahead of a blunt body generates vorticity in the inviscid flow outside the boundary layer. Thus conventional boundary layer theory can no longer be used when the external vorticity becomes comparable with that in the boundary layer. This has been called the vorticity interaction regime although as pointed out in Chapter 8, Section 5, other second order effects should also be included in a treatment of this regime. As a rough guide to the onset of the vorticity interaction regime we have taken van Dyke's result for stagnation point heat transfer, equation 8.21, and postulated an increase in q_0 of, say, 10 per cent due to the external entropy gradient. This gives the criterion

$$M_1/\sqrt{\text{Re}} = \tfrac{1}{5} \tag{9.5}$$

and this limit is plotted in figure 9.1. (See also Section 5.)

Before proceeding further in our delineation of flow regimes it is necessary, following van Dyke (1961), to develop estimates of the thicknesses of shock wave and boundary layer. For a blunt body it is known that as the Mach number tends to infinity the thickness Δ of the full shock layer is some fraction of the nose radius,

$$\frac{\Delta}{r_b} \to 0(1) \text{ as } M_1 \to \infty$$

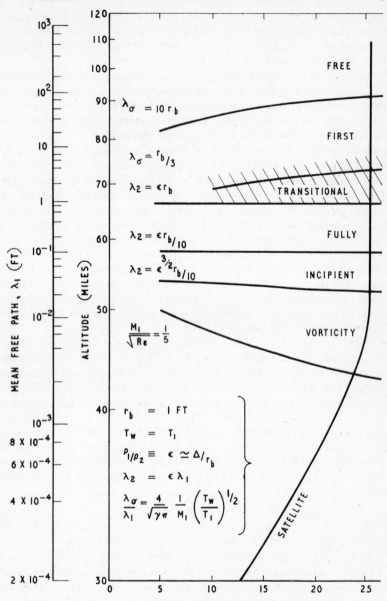

FIG. 9.1.—Flow field regimes.

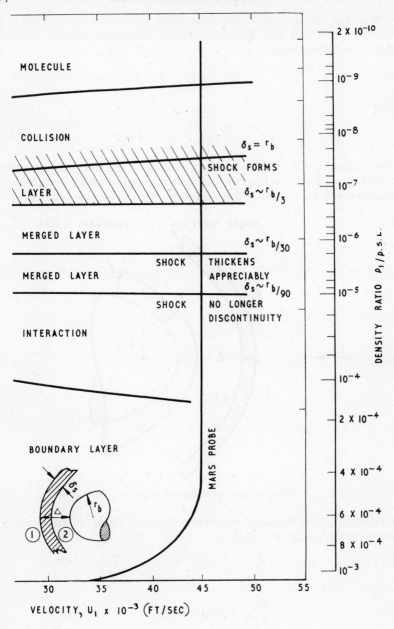

Now the thickness δ_s of the bow shock wave is of order ν^*/a^* according to Adams and Probstein (1958), where the asterisk denotes sonic conditions, hence

$$\frac{\delta_s}{r_b} = 0\left(\frac{\nu^*}{r_b a^*}\right)$$

and

$$\frac{\nu^*}{r_b \cdot a^*} = \frac{\mu^*}{\mu_1} \cdot \frac{a_1}{a^*} \cdot \frac{\rho_0}{\rho^*} \cdot \frac{\rho_1}{\rho_0} \cdot \frac{\nu_1}{U_1 r_b} \cdot \frac{U_1}{a_1} = \left(\frac{T_0}{T_1}\right)^{\omega - \frac{1}{2}} \cdot \frac{M_1}{\text{Re}} \qquad (9.6)$$

where subscripts 1 and 0 refer to conditions in the free stream ahead of the bow shock and at the inviscid stagnation point respectively (see figure 9.2), and ω is the exponent in the viscosity temperature

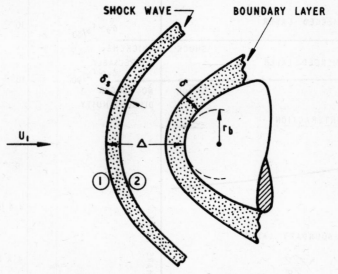

FIG. 9.2.—Flow field in the stagnation region of a blunt body.

relationship. The temperature corresponding to the latter condition is given by the energy equation as

$$\frac{T_0}{T_1} = 1 + \frac{\gamma - 1}{2} M_1{}^2$$

$$\therefore \quad \frac{T_0}{T_1} = 0(M_1{}^2) \text{ as } M_1 \to \infty$$

Thus $\quad \dfrac{\delta_s}{r_b} = 0\left(\dfrac{M_1{}^{2\omega}}{\text{Re}}\right) = 0(\beta)^2 \qquad (9.7)$

where

$$M_1 = \frac{U_1}{a_1} \quad \text{and} \quad \text{Re} = U_1 \cdot r_b/\nu_1$$

The thickness of the boundary layer can be estimated in a simple way using Stewartson's transformation which reduces the problem to that of an equivalent incompressible flow with kinematic viscosity ν_0. Thus

$$\frac{\delta}{r_b} \propto \left(\frac{U_1 r_b}{\nu_0}\right)^{-\frac{1}{2}} = \left(\frac{\mu_0}{\mu_1}\right)^{\frac{1}{2}} \left(\frac{\rho_1}{\rho_0}\right)^{\frac{1}{2}} \left(\frac{U_1 r_b}{\nu_1}\right)^{-\frac{1}{2}}$$

$$\therefore \quad \frac{\delta}{r_b} = 0\left(\frac{M_1^\omega}{\sqrt{\text{Re}}}\right) = 0(\beta) \tag{9.8}$$

where β is the viscous hypersonic similarity parameter for blunt bodies (see Section 7.5).

Thus the boundary layer thickness is of $0(\beta)$ and the shock wave thickness is of $0(\beta)$, and although both increase as the free stream density is decreased the shock wave will grow in thickness more rapidly than the boundary layer. Thus a situation is reached in which we can no longer ignore the thickness of the shock wave, although there is still an inviscid region separating it from the thick boundary layer; this has become known as the 'incipient merged layer' regime. Eventually, with a further decrease in free stream density the inviscid region disappears altogether and the whole of the shock layer must be considered viscous. This is the fully merged layer in which, as in the incipient merged layer, the methods used for the boundary layer regime described above are no longer applicable and the flow must be considered as a whole. There is a good deal of evidence, both theoretical and experimental, to indicate that a continuum flow analysis is justified for these two regimes and the Navier–Stokes equations have been employed in several investigations (see for example Probstein and Kemp (1960) or Levinsky and Yoshihara (1961)). The limits of these flow regimes are shown in figure 9.1 (following Probstein (1961)) and it can be seen that the transition from the fully merged layer to the region of applicability of first collision theories takes place over quite a narrow region—about 10 miles—of altitude.

We will now deal with each of the flow regimes described above in more detail, finally describing some recent investigations which have yielded special solutions covering the whole range from the boundary layer regime to free molecule flow.

9.3. Free-molecule Flow

Analysis by kinetic theory has given a good understanding of aerodynamic characteristics in free molecule flow where by definition the density is so low that molecules re-emitted from the surface have no effect on the incident molecules. However, calculations depend upon the particular model of surface interaction assumed and the importance of this has been emphasised by the problem of predicting the drag of artificial satellites. Expressions for heat transfer and aerodynamic forces are obtained from kinetic theory in terms of momentum and energy exchange accommodation coefficients, the limiting conditions being diffuse reflection for which such exchanges are complete and specular reflection for which there is no exchange. In many cases it appears that the actual physical interaction may be such as to give aerodynamic characteristics which are not intermediate between the above supposed limits. Schaaf (1960) quoted the case of a sphere whose drag coefficient in free molecule flow is exactly 2·00 at both limits, whereas a more realistic model for the surface interaction gives values between 2·2 to 2·6. Such alternative surface interaction models have been proposed by Schamberg (1959) and Schaaf (1959). In any case, as Hartnett (1961) has pointed out, measurements of accommodation coefficients in the past have suffered from serious deficiencies in technique so that the values cannot be used with any confidence.

Further information on free molecule flow theory may be found in texts such as Patterson (1956), Schaaf and Chambre (1958) and in the proceedings of the International Symposia on Rarefied Gas-dynamics, e.g. Devienne (1959) and Talbot (1961), and we do not propose to pursue this branch any further in this book.

9.4. Near Free-molecule Flow

There is a great deal of current interest in flows at densities which are just beginning to depart from strictly free molecular values. Molecules re-emitted from the surface of a body occasionally strike incident molecules either deflecting them from the surface which they would have struck or deflecting them into the surface when otherwise they would have passed by. It appears that the former is the dominant process producing a shielding effect which reduces heat transfer and drag as the density increases above the free molecule limit. As indicated in figure 9.1 this limit is at surprisingly low densities; for instance at $M = 20$ the mean free path in the free stream must be of the order of 50 times the nose radius to ensure pure free molecule flow.

The main approaches to the calculation of near free-molecule flows involve corrections to the free molecule theory due to interaction of the body surface and flow field by means of intermolecular collisions. They include the formal approach of Willis (1959) in which the Boltzmann integro-differential equation is transformed into a pure integral equation. The solution for the distribution function is then obtained by an iterative scheme based on the free-molecule solution as the zero-th iterate, and neglecting certain classes of collisions. Another method is the so-called 'first collision' theory of Baker and Charwat, (1958) which involves a detailed consideration of collisions between certain classes of molecules in the body flow field; in particular only those collisions between free stream molecules and molecules directly emitted from the body are considered.

Both methods give an expansion about the free molecule solution in terms of the reciprocal of the Knudsen number, and show that the net effect of such intermolecular collisions is a partial shielding of the body from direct momentum transfer from the free-stream and therefore a reduction in drag.

The case of a sphere in rarefied gas flow has been treated by both methods and give the drag as

$$C_D/C_{D_{fm}} = 1 - c/\mathrm{Kn} \qquad (9.9)$$

to first order, where $C_{D_{fm}}$ is the free-molecule drag coefficient and c is given by

$$c = 0{\cdot}15\,\frac{U_1}{\bar{c}} + 1{\cdot}06 \qquad \text{(1st iterated solution)}$$

$$c = 0{\cdot}14\,\frac{U_1}{\bar{c}} + 0{\cdot}64 \qquad \text{(1st collision method)}$$

where $\bar{c}$ is the mean random speed of a Maxwellian gas at the body surface temperature.

Charwat (1961) has also applied the technique of the 'first collision' method to study the leading-edge interaction for hypersonic rarefied flow over a sharp-edged flat plate. Such a flow in fact passes through all the regimes of aerodynamics from free-molecule to continuum as we go downstream from the leading-edge. For instance somewhat downstream of the molecular region studied by Charwat is a viscous region with a thin shock wave, and this has been investigated by Oguchi (1961) using continuum flow concepts. The results of both studies yield pressure distributions in good agreement with the measurements of Nagamatsu, Sheer and Schmid (1961).

9.5. Continuum Regimes

Starting from the high density hypersonic flow past a blunt body the various regimes encountered as density is decreased have been enumerated in Section 2. They are the boundary layer regime, the vorticity interaction regime, the incipient merged layer and the fully merged layer. The first needs no further description here and some details of the vorticity interaction regime have been given in Chapter 8. There we discussed van Dyke's second-order theory of the boundary layer. Following Guiraud (1961b), he postulates a systematic expansion scheme in which boundary layer theory is embedded. An independent treatment on similar lines has been given by Maslen (1963). Successive terms of such an expansion in terms of the viscous hypersonic similarity parameter $\beta = M_1^\omega/\sqrt{\text{Re}}$ correspond to inviscid flow, the boundary layer regime and the vorticity interaction regime. The Navier–Stokes

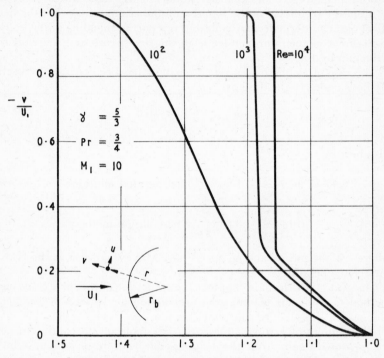

FIG. 9.3.—Effect of Reynolds number on shock thickness and velocity profiles, adiabatic wall (Levinsky and Yoshihara, 1961).

equations have been applied for still lower Reynolds numbers, but although there is evidence to suggest that these equations are indeed appropriate, the limits of continuum theory have not yet been rigorously investigated.

In the case of the vorticity interaction regime, we should point out that van Dyke's solution differs numerically from those of Hayes and Probstein (1959b) and of Ferri, Zakkay and Ting (1961) the latter being supported by their own experimental data. In fact the theories of Hayes and Probstein and of Ferri et al. differ by a factor of five or more in their predictions of the increase in heat transfer due to external vorticity, and van Dyke's numerical results are less than half the values found by Ferri et al. These discrepancies have yet to be resolved.

Proceeding to the incipient and fully merged layer regimes, a continuum approach using the Navier–Stokes equations was suggested by Adams and Probstein (1958), and their ideas were modified and extended by Hayes and Probstein (1959b), who also outline the reasons supporting this approach. Physically of course we can see the main justification as being the high density resulting from the strong compression across the bow shock wave of a hypersonic blunt body.

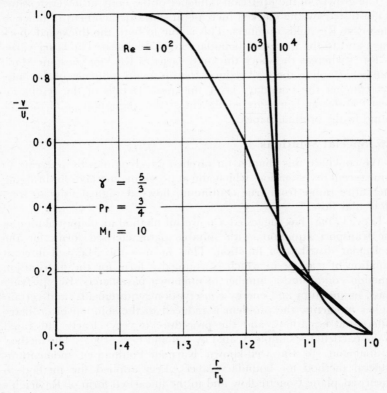

FIG. 9.4.—Effect of Reynolds number on shock thickness and velocity profiles, cold wall (Levinsky and Yoshihara, 1961).

Typical of the investigations of these regimes are the calculations of Levinsky and Yoshihara (1961) for rarefied hypersonic flow over a sphere. Several simplifying assumptions have become common in this work, including that of a monatomic gas. Some of their results are shown in figures 9.3 and 9.4 which illustrate the effect of Reynolds number (based on the adiabatic wall temperature and density) varying from 100 to 10,000 at a free-stream Mach number of 10, for the cases of a perfectly insulated (adiabatic) surface and a highly cooled wall $(T_w = T_1)$. At Re = 10,000, the shock is seen to be essentially a discontinuity for both cases. However, for Re = 1,000 the shock thickness is about 10 per cent of the detachment distance; the shock and boundary layer remain distinct and are separated by an inviscid region. At Re = 100 the shock thickness is about half the detachment distance, and there is no distinct inviscid region so that the shock layer is fully merged.

The growth of the upstream influence of the body at lower densities is illustrated by the marked increase in shock detachment distance at the lower Reynolds numbers. This is due to both the thickened shock wave and to the increased boundary layer thickness. The latter varies as $Re^{-1/2}$ whereas the shock thickness varies as Re^{-1} for constant Mach number. Cooling the wall reduces the upstream influence of the body by reducing the boundary layer thickness. Details of the results for heat transfer and pressure coefficient at the stagnation point may be found in the original paper.

9.6. Special Solutions

We conclude this chapter on rarefied gas-dynamics by referring to some recent investigations which aim at providing methods for bridging the entire range from true continuum flows at high density to free-molecular flow.

Lees (1959a) has suggested a powerful method involving solution of the transport equations with suitable parameterised forms for the molecular distribution function. Thus he uses the Maxwell integral equation of transfer in which is assumed a form for the distribution function containing a number of unknown parameters. By satisfying mass, momentum and energy conservation requirements, and certain higher moments, the problem is reduced to the solution of ordinary differential equations, and the procedure is very clearly illustrated in the particular example treated by Liu and Lees (1961). The method is analogous to the well-known Karman–Pohlhausen momentum-integral method for boundary layers. Lees applied the method to linearised plane Couette flow and to the linearised form of Rayleigh's problem. Since this does not provide a serious test of such a general method, the technique was applied by Liu and Lees (1961) to steady plane compressible Couette flow in order to study the effects of large temperature differences and dissipation in the simplest possible geometry. However even in this case the continuum approach using the Navier–Stokes equations plus the slip boundary condition gives reasonable answers for skin friction and heat transfer. Thus the problem of heat conduction between two concentric cylinders is currently under study, since here the continuum approach is known to be very inaccurate. An interesting conclusion reached by Liu and Lees is that the continuum approach is likely to provide valid answers for $\lambda_2/r_b \gtrsim 1/20$

approximately, where λ_2 is the mean free path evaluated just behind the bow shock. This is in general agreement with the estimates shown in figure 9.1.

Rott and Whittenbury (1961) have proposed a two-component fluid model of an incident molecular beam mixing with a gas-like flow near the surface, which is intended to account for both continuum fluid aspects and the microscopic structure of the fluid. The model was applied to the description of shock wave structure with great success. Also the results obtained for sphere drag were in qualitative agreement with experimental data. Incidentally the most complete set of data on high-speed sphere drag in the transitional regime is that of Wegener and Ashkenas (1961). At a Mach number of about 4 the drag coefficient increases monotonically from a value of 1·19 at a free stream Reynolds number of 1,000 to 1·73 at Re = 50, whereas in free molecule flow with an accommodation coefficient of unity, $C_D = 2$.

An entirely different approach is that of Cheng (1961) who extends the continuum approach in a shock-layer analysis of the stagnation region of a blunt body. The Rankine–Hugoniot shock conditions are modified to take into account the effects of shear and heat conduction behind the shock. Using the new shock conditions as outer boundary conditions in a thin shock-layer viscous analysis, Cheng shows that the calculated shear and heat transfer results can be extended to cover the whole range from boundary layer to free molecule flow. In fact his results go over smoothly to the free-molecule value for an accommodation coefficient of unity. A rigorous proof of the validity of using continuum equations at such low densities is still awaited however.

Liepmann (1960) has made a study of effusive flow which promises the solution to a particular problem providing a complete transition from free-molecular flow conditions to the Navier–Stokes solution. He points out that the flow of gases through orifices represents a problem in fluid mechanics for which theoretical solutions for free molecular flow, i.e. Re → 0, and inviscid compressible fluid flow, i.e. Re → ∞, are known. Furthermore the free molecular solution (and obviously the gas-dynamical solution) is independent of gas-surface interactions such as slip or accommodation effects and can thus be considered very reliable. Effusive flow then represents a problem for the study of the transition from gas-dynamics to gas-kinetics for which the end points are strictly defined independent of *ad hoc* and dubious corrections. Liepmann(1961) has followed up this idea in a later paper, and includes the results of some experiments (see also Narasimha (1961)).

LIST OF REFERENCES

Adams, M. C. (1959) "Recent advances in ablation." *A.R.S. Journal* **29**, 625–632

Adams, M. C. (1960) "A look at the heat transfer problem at supersatellite speeds." ASTIA No. AD250313 AVCO AMP53 ARS Preprint No. 2556–60

Adams, M. C., Probstein, R. F. (1958) "On the validity of continuum theory for satellite and hypersonic flight problems at high altitudes. *Jet Propulsion* **28**, 86–89

Allen, H. J., Eggers, A. J. (1953) "A study of the motion and aerodynamic heating of missiles entering the Earth's atmosphere at high supersonic speeds." NACA RM A53 D28

Ames Research Staff (1953) "Equations, Tables and Charts for Compressible Flow." NACA Report 1135

Ashley, H. Zartarian, G. (1956) "Piston theory—a new aerodynamic tool for the aeroelastician. *J. Aero. Sci.* **23**, 1109–1118

Bam-Zelikovitch, G. M., Bunimovich, A. I., Mikhailova, M. P. (1949) "The motion of bodies at hypersonic speeds." Collection of papers No. 4. *Teoretich. Gidromekhanika. Oborongiz. Moscow*

Baker, R. M. L., Charwat, A. F. (1958) "Transitional correction to the drag of a sphere in free-molecule flow." *Phys. Fluids* **1**, 73–87

Baron, J. R. (1961) "Thermodynamic coupling in boundary layers." *ARS Journal* **32**, 1053–1059

Beckwith, I. E., Gallagher, J. E. (1959) "Local heat transfer and recovery temperatures on a yawed cylinder at a Mach number of 4.15 and high Reynolds numbers." NASA Memo. 2–27–59L

Belotserkovskii, O. M. (1958) "Flow past a circular cylinder with a detached shock wave." *Vychislitel'naya Matematika* **3**, 149–185

Belotserkovskii, O. M. (1960) "On the calculation of flow past axi-symmetric bodies with detached shock waves using an electronic computing machine." *Prikl. Mat. Mekh.* **24**, 511–517. *Transl. as Journ. App. Math. Mech.*, **24**, 745–755

Bertram, M. H. (1956) "Tip bluntness effects on cone pressure at $M = 6.85$." *J. Aero. Sci.* **23**, 898–900.

Bertram, M. H., Baradell, D. L. (1957) "A note on the sonic-wedge leading-edge approximation in hypersonic flow." *J. Aero. Sci.* **24**, 627–629

Bloom, M. H., Steiger, M. H. (1960) "Inviscid flow with non-equilibrium molecular dissociation for pressure distributions encountered in hypersonic flight." *J. Aero/Space Sci.* **27**, 821–835

Bloom, M. H. (1962) "Thermal and chemical effects in wakes." AGARD Specialist Meeting on High Temp. Aspects of Hypersonic Flow, Brussels April, 1962

Bogdonoff, S. M., Vas, I. E. (1959) "Hypersonic separated flows," Proc 7th Anglo-American Aeronautical Conf. New York 1959 pp. 177–196. Inst. Aero. Sciences Inc. 1960

Bogdonoff, S. M., Vas, I. E. (1961) "Some experiments on hypersonic separated flows." *ARS Journ.* **32**, 1564–1572

Bray, K. N. C. (1959) "Atomic recombination in a hypersonic wind-tunnel nozzle." *J. Fluid Mech.* **6**, 1–32

Bray, K. N. C., Gadd, G. E., Woodger, M. (1960) "Some calculations by the Crocco-Lees and other methods of interactions between shock waves and laminar boundary layers, including effects of heat transfer and suction." ARC 21834

Briggs, B. P. (1959) "Calculation of supersonic flow past bodies shaped like elliptic cones." NASA Rep. D. 24

Busemann, A. (1933) "Flüssigkeits-und-Gasbewegung. Handwörterbuch der Naturwissenschaften." Vol. IV. 2nd Edition. 244–279. Gustav Fischer, Jena

Buseman, A. (1935) "Aerodynamic lift at supersonic speeds." *Luftfahrt-Forschung.* **12**, No. 6

Cabannes, H. (1951) "Détermination théorique de l'écoulement d'un fluide derrière une onde de choc détachée." ONERA note technique. No. 5

Carriére, P., Sirieix, M. (1960) "Facteurs d'influence du recollement d'un écoulement supersonique." Paper presented at 10th International Congress of Applied Mechanics Stresa Sept. 1960. ONERA publication No. 102 pp. 3–46 (1961)

Chapkis, R. L. (1961) "Hypersonic flow over an elliptic cone: theory and experiment." *J. Aero/Space, Sci.* **28**, 844–854

Chapman, D. R. (1951) "An analysis of base pressure at supersonic velocities and comparison with experiment." NACA Rep. 1051 (Supersedes NACA TN 2137 July 1950)

Chapman, D. R., Wimbrow, W. R., Kester, R. H. (1952) "Experimental investigation of base pressure on blunt trailing-edge wings at supersonic velocities." NACA Rep. 1109 (Supersedes NACA TN 2611)

Chapman, D. R., Kühn, D. M., Larson, H. K. (1957) "Investigation of separated flows in supersonic and subsonic streams with emphasis on the effect of transition." NACA TN 3869

Charters, A. C., Thomas, R. N. (1945) "The aerodynamic performance of small spheres from subsonic to high supersonic velocities." *J. Aero. Sci.* **12**, 468–476

Charwat, A. F. (1961) "Molecular flow study of the hypersonic sharp leading-edge interaction." Proc. 2nd Int. Symp. on Rarefied Gasdynamics. (L. Talbot Ed.) pp. 553–578 Academic Press

Cheng, H. K. (1957) "Interim report on investigations related to hypersonic flow and boundary layer phenomena." Cornell Aero. Lab. Rep. No. AF-1180. A-1

Cheng, H. K. (1959) "Similitude of hypersonic real-gas flow over slender bodies with blunted noses." *J. Aero/Space Sci.* **26**, 575–585.

Cheng, H. K. (1960a) "On the structure of vortical layers in supersonic and hypersonic flows." *J. Aero/Space Sci.* **27**, 155–156

Cheng, H. K. (1960b) "Hypersonic flow with combined leading-edge bluntness and boundary layer displacement effect." Cornell Aero. Lab. Report No. AF-1285-A-4

Cheng, H. K. (1961) "Hypersonic shock-layer theory of the stagnation region at low Reynolds number." Proc. Heat Transfer and Fluid Mech. Inst.

pp. 161–175 Stanford Univ. Press 1961. Cornell Aero. Lab. Rept. No. AF-1285-A-7

Cheng, H. K. (1962) "Hypersonic flows past a yawed circular cone and other pointed bodies." *J. Fluid. Mech.* **12**, 2 169–191

Cheng, H. K., Hall, J. G., Golian, T. C., Hertzberg, A. (1960) "Boundary layer displacement and leading edge bluntness effects in high temperature hypersonic flow." Cornell Aero. Lab. Report No. AD-1052-A-9 also *J. Aero/Space Sci.* **28**, 353–381, 410 (1961)

Chernyi, G. G. (1957a) "Hypersonic flow past an airfoil with a slightly blunted leading edge." *Dokl. Akad. Nauk. SSSR.* **114**, 721–724

Chernyi, G. G. (1957b) "The flow around a narrow blunted cone at high supersonic velocity." *Dokl. Akad. Nauk. SSSR.* **115**, 681–633

Chernyi, G. G. (1958) "The effect of slight blunting of the leading edge of a profile on flow at high supersonic speeds." *Izv. A.N. SSSR. OTN No.* 4

Chernyi, G. G. (1961) *Introduction to Hypersonic Flow.* Academic Press. New York

Chester, W. (1956) "Supersonic flow past a bluff body with a detached shock." *J. Fluid Mech.* **1**, 353–356 and **1**, 490–496

Chu, B. T. (1952) "On weak interaction of strong shock and Mach waves generated downstream of the shock." *J. Aero. Sci.* **19**, 443–446

Chung, P. M., Anderson, A. D. (1960) 'Surface recombination in the frozen compressible flow of a dissociating gas past a catalytic flat plate." *A.R.S. Journ.* **30**, 262–264

Chung, P. M. (1961) "Hypersonic viscous shock layer of non-equilibrium dissociating gas." NASA TR R-109

Chushkin, P. I., Shchennikov, V. V. (1960) "Calculation of certain conical flows without axial symmetry." *Inzhenerno—Fizicheskii. Zhurnal.* **3**, 88–94

Cohen, C. B., Reshotko, E. (1955) "Similar solutions for the compressible laminar boundary layer with heat transfer and pressure gradient." NACA TN 3325

Cohen, N. B. (1961) "Boundary layer similar solutions and correlation equations for laminar heat-transfer distribution in equilibrium air at velocities up to 41,100 feet per sec." NASA TR R-118

Cohen, N. B., Beckwith, I. E. (1961) "Boundary layer similar solutions for equilibrium dissociated air and application to the calculation of laminar heat-transfer distribution on blunt bodies in high-speed flow." International Developments in Heat Transfer Part II, Paper No. 47 pp. 406–414 A.S.M.E. 1961 Presented at the 1961 International Heat Transfer Conference

Cole, J. D. (1957) "Newtonian flow theory for slender bodies." *J. Aero. Sci.* **24**, 448–455

Crabtree, L. F. (1961) "The flow field associated with a rocket jet efflux at very high altitudes." *W.G.L. Jahrbuch* 1961, 240–243

Creager, M. O. (1957) "Effects of leading-edge blunting on the local heat transfer and pressure distributions over flat plates in supersonic flow." NACA TN 4142

Crocco, L., Lees, L. (1952) "A mixing theory for the interaction between dissipative flows and nearly isentropic streams." *J. Aero. Sci.* **19**, 649–676

Crocco, L. (1954) "Considerations on the shock-wave boundary-layer interaction." Proc. Centenary Meeting of the Brooklyn Polytechnic Institute p. 75

Demetriades, A. (1960) "An experiment on the stability of hypersonic laminar boundary layers." *J. Fluid Mech.* **7**, 385–396

Detra, R. W., Kantrowitz, A., Riddell, F. R., Rose, P. H. (1959) "The drag brake manned satellite system." Proc. of 10th Congress of the Int. Astronautical Federation, London

Detra, R. W., Hidalgo, H. (1961) "Generalized heat transfer formulae and graphs for nose-cone re-entry into the atmosphere." *ARS Journ.* **31**, 318–321

Devienne, F. M. (1960) *Rarefied Gas Dynamics.* Proc. 1st Int. Symposium on Rarefied Gas Dynamics, Nice, July 1958. Pergamon Press, London, 1960

Dorodnitsyn, A. A. (1957) "On a method of numerical solution of some non-linear problems of Aero-Hydrodynamics." Proc. 9th Int. Congr. Appl. Mech., Brussels. Vol. I. p. 435

Dorrance, W. H. (1952) "Two dimensional airfoils in hypersonic flows." *J. Aero. Sci.* **19**, 593–600

Dorrance, W. H. (1961) "Dissociation effects upon compressible turbulent boundary layer skin friction and heat transfer." *A.R.S. Journ.* **31**, 61–70

Dorrance, W. H. (1962) *Viscous Hypersonic Flow.* 1st Ed. McGraw-Hill Book Co.

Dorrance, W. H., Dore, F. J. (1954) "The effect of mass transfer on the compressible turbulent boundary layer skin friction and heat transfer." *J. Aero/Space Sci.* **21**, 404–410

Duff, R. E., Davidson, N. (1959) "Calculation of reaction profiles behind steady-state shock waves." II. The dissociation of air. *J. Chem. Phys.* **31**, p. 1018

Eckert, E. R. G. (1954) "Survey on heat transfer at high speeds." WADC Tech. Report 54–70

Eckert, E. R. G., Hartnett, J. P. (1956) "Simplified procedures for the calculation of heat transfer to surfaces with non-uniform temperatures." WADC Tech. Report No. 56–373 (AD. 110450)

✓ Eggers, A. J. (1957) 'Performance of long-range hypervelocity vehicles." *Jet Propulsion* **27**, 1147–51

Eggers, A. J. (1959) "Aircraft configurations for long-range hypersonic flight." *Hypersonic Flow* (ed. Collar & Tinkler), Butterworth's, London. 369–390

Eggers, A. J., Resknikoff, M. M., Dennis, D. H. (1957) "Bodies of revolution having minimum drag at high supersonic airspeeds." NACA Rep. 1306 (Supersedes NACA TN 3666, 1956)

Eggers, A. J., Savin, R. C., Syvertson, C. A. (1955) "The generalised shock-expansion method and its application to bodies travelling at high supersonic airspeeds." *J. Aero. Sci.* **22**, 231–238, 248

Eggers, A. J., Syvertson, C. A. (1952) "Inviscid flow about airfoils at high supersonic speeds." NACA TN 2646

Eggers, A. J., Syvertson, C. A., Kraus, S. (1953) "A study of inviscid flow about airfoils at high supersonic speeds." NACA Rep. 1123

Ellington, D., Winterbon, B. K. (1961) "On the development of a method for predicting the gaseous radiation characteristics of blunt bodies at hypersonic speeds." Part I: Chemical kinetics and gasdynamics. Can. Arm. Res. & Dev. Est. T.M. 627/61

Epstein, P. S. (1931) "On the air resistance of projectiles." *Proc. Nat. Acad. Sci. U.S.A.* **17**, 532–547

Fal'kovitch, S. V. (1947) "Two dimensional motion of a gas at large supersonic velocities." *Prikl. Mat. Mekh.* **11**, 459–464

Fay, J. A., Riddell, F. R. (1958) "Theory of stagnation point heat transfer in dissociated air." *J. Aero/Space Sci.* **25**, 73–85

Fay, J. A. (1961) "Plasma boundary layers." A.R.S. Preprint No. 2010–61. Published in "Magnetohydrodynamics: Proc. 4th Biennial Gasdynamics Symposium" Edited by Cambel, Anderson and Slawsky. Northwestern Univ. Press, 1962

Feldman, S. (1957) "Hypersonic gas dynamic charts for equilibrium air." AVCO Research Report No. 40

Feldman, S. (1961) "On trails of axisymmetric hypersonic blunt bodies flying through the atmosphere." *J. Aero/Space Sci.* **28**, 433–448

Ferri, A. (1951) "Supersonic flow around circular cones at angles of attack." NACA Rep. 1045

Ferri, A., Zakkay, V., Ting, L. (1961) "Blunt body heat transfer at hypersonic speed and low Reynolds numbers." *J. Aero/Space Sci.* **28**, 962–971 Pibal Report No. 611 and 743

Fishenden, Saunders (1932) "The calculation of heat transmission." H.M.S.O.

Fraasa, D. G., Wisenbaker, E. M. (1957) Reported in Lees (1957)

Freeman, N. C. (1956) "On the theory of hypersonic flow past plane and axially symmetric bluff bodies." *J. Fluid Mech.* **1**, 366–387

Freeman, N. C. (1958) "Non-equilibrium flow of an ideal dissociating gas." *J. Fluid Mech.* **4**, 407–425

Freeman, N. C. (1959) "On the Newtonian theory of hypersonic flow for a blunt body." Princeton Rep. 467, AFOSR TN 59–634, ARC 21,594

Freeman, N. C. (1960) "A note on the explosion solution of Sedov with application to the Newtonian theory of unsteady hypersonic flow." *J. Aero/Space Sci.* **27**, 77–78 and 995

Freeman, N. C. (1962) "Asymptotic solutions in hypersonic flow: an approach to second-order solutions of hypersonic small disturbance theory." NPL Aero Rep. 1035 ARC. 23,999

Frood, D. G. H. (1959) "Strong shock waves in real atomic and molecular gases." Ministry of Supply A.R.D.E. Report (B) 11/59

Gadd, G. E. (1953) "Interactions between wholly laminar or wholly turbulent boundary layers and shock waves strong enough to cause separation." *J. Aero. Sci.* **20**, 729–739

Gadd, G. E. (1956) "A theoretical investigation of the effects of Mach number, Reynolds number, wall temperature and surface curvature on laminar separation in supersonic flow." ARC 18494

Gadd, G. E., Holder, D. W. (1960) "The behaviour of supersonic boundary layers in the presence of shock waves." Proc. 7th Anglo-American Aeronautical Conf. New York 1959 pp. 146–174. Inst. Aero, Sciences Inc. (1960)

Garabedian, P. R., Lieberstein, H. M. (1958) "On the numerical calculation of detached bow shock waves in hypersonic flow." *J. Aero./Space Sci* **25**, 109–118

Georgiev, S., Hidalgo, H., Adams, M. C. (1959) "On ablation for the recovery of satellites." Proc. 1959 Inst, of Heat Transfer and Fluid Mech. Stanford Univ. Press 1959. AVCO Research Report No. 47

Glauert, M. B., Lighthill, M. J. (1955) "The axisymmetric boundary layer on a long thin cylinder." *Proc. Roy. Soc.* (A)**123**, 216–225

Glauert, M. B. (1962) "The pressure gradient induced by shear flow past a flat plate." *J. Aero/Space Sci.* **29**, 540–542

Glick, H. S. (1960) "Modified Crocco-Lees mixing theory for supersonic separated and reattaching flows." Galcit Hypersonic Research Project Memo. No. 53

Goldstein, S. (Ed.) (1938) *Modern Developments in Fluid Dynamics.* Oxford Univ. Press

Goldsworthy, F. A. (1952) "Two-dimensional rotational flow at high Mach number past thin aerofoils." *Quart J. Mech. Appl. Math.* **5**, 54–63

Goulard, R. (1958) "On catalytic recombination rates in hypersonic stagnation heat transfer." *Jet Propulsion*, **28**, 737–745

Goulard, R. (1961) "High temperature aerodynamics." *Applied Mech. Rev.* **14**, 257–261

Gravalos, F. G., Edelfelt, I. H., Emmons, H. W. (1958) "Supersonic flow about a blunt body of revolution for gases at chemical equilibrium." Proc. Ninth Inter. Astro. Conf. Amsterdam. Vol. 1. pp. 312–332

Grimminger, G., Williams, E. P., Young, G. B. W. (1950) "Lift on inclined bodies of revolution in hypersonic flow." *J. Aero. Sci.* **17**, 675–690

Guiraud, J. P. (1960) "Newtonian flow over a surface—theory and application." *Hypersonic Flow* (ed. Collar & Tinkler) Butterworth's London, (Colston Papers XI)

Guiraud, J. P. (1961a) "Écoulement bidimensional hypersonique d'un fluide parfait sur un obstacle mince plan óu de révolution comportant un nez émoussé." ONERA Mémo Technique No. 21

Guiraud, J. P. (1961b) *Math Rev.*, **22**, p. 219, review no. 1267

Gusev, V. N. (1957) "On unsteady self-similar motion of a gas displaced by a piston according to an exponential law." Ts. AGI Rep. B.N.I.

Hammitt, A. G., Bogdonoff, S. M. (1956) "Hypersonic studies of the leading-edge effect on the flow over a flat plate." *Jet Propulsion*, **26**, 241–246 1956

Hakkinen, R. J., Greber, I., Trilling, L., Abarbanel, S. S. (1959) "The interaction of an oblique shock wave with a laminar boundary layer." NASA Memo. 2–18–59W

Hamaker, F. M., Neice, S. E., Wong, T. J. (1953) "The similarity laws for hypersonic flow and requirements for dynamic similarity of related bodies in free flight." NACA Rep. 1147

Hansen, C. F., Heims, S. P. (1958) "Thermodynamic and transport properties and chemical reaction rates for high-temperature air." NACA TN 4359

Hansen, C. F. (1958) "Approximations for the thermodynamic and transport properties of high-temperature air." NACA TN 4150

Hartnett, J. P. (1961) "A survey of thermal accommodation coefficients." Proc. 2nd Int. Symp. on Rarefied Gas-dynamics (L. Talbot Ed.) pp. 1–28 Academic Press

Hayes, W. D. (1947) "On hypersonic similitude." *Quart. Appl. Math.* **5**, 105–106

Hayes, W. D. (1955a) "Some aspects of hypersonic flow." Ramo-Wooldridge Corpn. Rep. Los Angeles

Hayes, W. D. (1955b) "Hypersonic flow fields at small density ratios." Ramo-Wooldridge Corpn. Rep. Los Angeles. (1955)

Hayes, W. D. (1958) "Newtonian flow theory in hypersonic aerodynamics." Proc. 1st Int. Congr. of Aeronautical Sciences, Madrid

Hayes, W. D., Probstein, R. F. (1959a) "Viscous Hypersonic Similitude." *J. Aero/Space Sci.* **26**, pp. 815-824

Hayes, W. D., Probstein, R. F. (1959b) *Hypersonic Flow Theory.* Academic Press, New York

Heims, S. P. (1958) "Prandtl-Meyer expansion of chemically reacting gases in local chemical and thermodynamic equilibrium." NACA TN 4230

Henderson, A., Jr. (1960) "Investigation of the flow over simple bodies at Mach numbers of the order of 20." NASA TN D-449

Heybey, W. H. (1953) "Shock distances in front of symmetrical bodies." NAVORD Rep. 3594

Hida, K. (1953) "An approximate study on the detached shock wave in front of a circular cylinder and a sphere." *J. Phys. Soc. of Japan,* **8**, 740–745

Hill, P. R. (1957) "A method of computing the transient temperature of thick walls from arbitrary variation of adiabatic wall temperature and heat-transfer coefficient." NACA TN 4105

Hilsenrath, J., Beckett, C. W. (1956) "Tables of thermodynamic properties of argon-free air to 15000°K." AEDC-TN-56-12 (Astia No. AD-98974)

Hilsenrath, J., Klein, M., Woolley, H. W. (1959) "Tables of thermodynamic properties of air including dissociation and ionisation from 1500°K to 15000°K." AEDC-TR-59-20

Hodges, A. J. (1957) "The drag coefficient of very high velocity spheres." *J. Aero. Sci.* **24**, 755–758

Holt, M. (1958) "Calculation of pressure distribution on hypersonic bodies of revolution by Belotserkovskii's method." AVCO Mfg. Corp. RAD-2-TM-58

Holt, M. (1961) "Direct calculation of pressure distribution on blunt hypersonic nose shapes with sharp corners." *J. Aero/Space. Sci.* **28**, 872–876

Holt, M., Hoffman, G. H. (1961) "Calculation of hypersonic flow past spheres and ellipsoids." IAS/ARS Tech. Paper 61-209-1903

Il'yushin, A. A. (1956) "The law of plane sections in hypersonic aerodynamics." *Prikl. Mat. Mekh.* **20**, 733–755

Ivey, H. R., Klunker, B. E., Bowen, E. N. (1948) "A method for determining the aerodynamic characteristics of two and three dimensional shapes at hypersonic speeds." NACA TN 1613

Ivey, H. R., Cline, C. W. (1950) "Effect of heat capacity lag on the flow through oblique shock waves." NACA TN 2196

Kaplun, S., Lagerstrom, P.A. (1957) "Asymptotic expansions of Navier-Stokes solutions for small Reynolds numbers." *J. Rat. Mech. Anal.* **6** 585–93

Kawamura, T. (1950) "On the detached shock wave in front of a body moving at speeds greater than that of sound." *Univ. of Kyoto, College of Science Memoirs, Ser. A.* **26**, 207–232

Kemp, N. H., Rose, P. H., Detra, R. W. (1959) "Laminar heat transfer around blunt bodies in dissociated air." *J. Aero/Space Sci.* **26**, 421–430

Kennet, H., Strack, S. L. (1961) "Stagnation point radiative transfer." *A.R.S. Journ.* **31**, 370–372

Kivel, B. (1961) "Radiation from hot air and its effect on stagnation point heating." *J. Aero./Space Sci.* **28**, 96–102

Kivel, B., Bailey, K. (1958) "Radiation from high-temperature air." AVCO Research Report No. 21

Kopal, Z. (1947) "Tables of supersonic flow around cones." Tech. Rep. No. 1 Dept. of Elec. Eng. M.I.T. Cambridge (Mass.)

Korst, H. H. (1956) "A theory for base pressures in transonic and supersonic flow." A.S.M.E. Paper No. 56-APM-30

Kubota, T. (1957a) "Investigation of flow around simple bodies in hypersonic flow." Memo. No. 40. Hypersonic Research Project. GALCIT, Pasadena, Calif.

Kubota, T. (1957b) "Inviscid flow over blunt nosed slender bodies." Vth Heat Transfer & Fluid Mech. Inst., Pasadena

Kuehn, D. M. (1959) "Experimental investigation of the pressure rise required for the incipient separation of turbulent boundary layers in two-dimensional supersonic flow." NASA Memo. 1-21-59A

Laitone, E. V., Pardee, O. O'M. (1947) "Location of a detached shock wave in front of a body moving at supersonic speeds." NACA R.M. A7I10

Laufer, J., Vrebalovich, T. (1960) "Stability and transition of a supersonic laminar boundary layer on an insulated flat plate." J. Fluid Mech. 9, 257–299 Oct. 1960

Leadon, B. M., Scott, C. J. (1956) "Transpiration cooling experiments in a turbulent boundary layer at $M = 3$." J. Aero. Sci. 23, 798–799

Lees, L. (1951) "Note on the hypersonic similarity law for an unyawed cone." J. Aero. Sci. 18, 700–702

Lees, L. (1953) "On the boundary layer equations in hypersonic flow and their approximate solutions." J. Aero. Sci. 20 pp. 143–145

Lees, L. (1955) "Hypersonic Flow." Proc. 5th Int. Aero. Conf. Los Angeles. Inst. Aero. Soc. New York. 241–276

Lees, L. (1956a) "Inviscid hypersonic flow over blunt nosed slender bodies." GALCIT Hypersonic Research Project. Memo. No. 31

Lees, L. (1956b) "Laminar heat transfer over blunt-nosed bodies at hypersonic flight speeds." Jet Propulsion, 26, pp. 259–269

Lees, L. (1957) "Recent developments in hypersonic flow." Jet Propulsion, 27 1162–1178

Lees, L. (1958) "Convective heat transfer with mass addition and chemical reactions." Proc. 3rd AGARD Colloquium on Combustion p. 451 Palermo. Pergamon Press

Lees, L. (1959a) "A kinetic theory description of rarefied gas flows." GALCIT Hypersonic Research Project Memo. 51

Lees, L. (1959b) "Re-entry heat transfer." Astronautics, 4, p. 22

Lees, L., Kubota, T. (1957) "Inviscid hypersonic flow over blunt nosed slender bodies." J. Aero. Sci. 24, 195–202

Lees, L., Reshotko, E. (1960) "Stability of the compressible laminar boundary layer." J. Fluid Mech. 12, 555–590. AGARD Report No. 268

Levinsky, E. S., Yoshihara, H. (1961) "Rarefied hypersonic flow over a sphere." Presented at the Intern. Hypersonics Conf., M.I.T., 1961 Published in Hypersonic Flow Research (F. R. Riddell Ed.) Academic Press 1962

Li, T. Y. (1961) "Recent advances in non-equilibrium dissociating gas-dynamics." ARS Journal, 31, 170–178

Lick, W. (1958) "Inviscid flow around a blunt body of a reacting mixture of gases." AFOSR TN 58-1125 (Astia No. AD207833) *J. Fluid Mech.* **7,** 128-144

Liepmann, H. W. (1958) "A simple derivation of Lighthill's heat transfer formula." *J. Fluid Mech.* **3,** 357-360

Liepmann, H. W. (1960) "A study of effusive flow." *Aeronautics and Astronautics,* 153-160 Pergamon Press 1960

Liepmann, H. W. (1961) "Gas kinetics and gasdynamics of orifice flow." *J. Fluid Mech.* **10,** 65-79

Liepmann, H. W., Roshko, A. (1957) *Elements of Gasdynamics.* Wiley, New York

Lighthill, M. J. (1949) "The flow behind a stationary shock." *Phil. Mag.* **40,** 214-220

Lighthill, M. J. (1950) "Contributions to the theory of heat transfer through a laminar boundary layer." Proc. Roy. Soc. (A) **202,** pp. 359-377

Lighthill, M. J. (1953) "Oscillating airfoils at high Mach number." *J. Aero. Sci.* **20,** 402-406

Lighthill, M. J. (1954) "Higher approximations." In *General Theory of High Speed Aerodynamics.* (Ed. Sears) Vol. VI of *High Speed Aerodynamics and Jet Propulsion.* Princeton Univ. Press, Princeton, N.J. pp. 345-489

Lighthill, M. J. (1957) "Dynamics of a dissociating gas. Pt. I. Equilibrium Flow." *J. Fluid Mech.* **2,** 1-32

Lin, C. C., Rubinov, S. I. (1948) "On the flow behind curved shocks." *J. Math. & Phys.* **27,** 105-129

Lin, C. C., Shen, S. F. (1951) "An analytic determination of the flow behind a symmetrical curved shock in a uniform stream." NACA TN 2506

Lin, S. C. (1954) "Cylindrical shock waves produced by instantaneous energy release." *J. Appl. Phys.* **25,** 54-57

Linnell, R. D. (1949) "Two-dimensional airfoils in hypersonic flows." *J. Aero. Sci.* **16,** 22-30

Liu, C. Y., Lees, L. (1961) "Kinetic theory description of plane compressible Couette flow." Proc. 2nd Int. Symposium on Rarefield Gasdynamics pp. 391-428 (L. Talbot Ed.) Academic Press

Lukasiewicz, J. (1961) "Hypersonic flow-blast analogy." AEDC-TR-61-4 also "Blast-Hypersonic Flow Analogy—Theory and Application." *ARS Journal* **32,** 1341-6 (1962)

McClellan, C. H. (1951) "Exploratory wind-tunnel investigations of wings and bodies at $M = 6.9$." *J. Aero. Sci.* **18,** 641-48

Mager, A. (1955) "Prediction of shock-induced turbulent boundary layer separation." *J. Aero. Sci.* **22,** 201-202

Mager, A. (1956) "On the model of a free-shock-separated turbulent boundary layer." *J. Aero. Sci.* **23,** 181-184

Mangler, K. W., Evans, M. E. (1957) "The calculation of the inviscid flow between a detached bow wave and a body." RAE Tech. Note Aero 2536

Mangler, K. W. (1959) "Some special aspects of hypersonic flow fields." *J. Roy. Aero. Soc.* **63,** 508-512

Mangler, K. W. (1960) "The calculation of the flow field between a blunt body and the bow wave." In *Hypersonic Flow* (ed. Collar & Tinkler), Butterworth's, London.219-238

Mangler, K. W. (1962) "The solution of the Navier-Stokes equations for laminar incompressible flow for large Reynolds numbers." RAE Tech. Note No. Aero. 2832

Maslen, S. H. (1963) "Second order effects in laminar boundary layers." *AIAA Journ.* **1**, 33–40

Mason, E. A. (1959) "Methods for the calculation of high-temperature gas transport properties." AGARD Report No. 330

Mauger, F. E. (1960) "Steady supersonic flow past conical bodies." A.R.D.E. Rep. (B)3/60

Mauger, F. E. (1963) "The extension of shock expansion theory to flows past three-dimensional bodies." R.A.R.D.A. Report (8) 10/63

Meyerott, R. E. (1958) "Radiation heat transfer to hypersonic vehicles." Proc. 3rd AGARD Colloquium on Combustion. Palermo, Sicily. pp. 431-450 Pergamon Press

Mirels, H. (1959) "Approximate analytical solutions for hypersonic flow over slender power-law bodies." NASA TR R-15

Mirels, H. (1962) "Hypersonic flow over slender bodies associated with power law shocks." *Advances in Applied Mechanics*, VII. Academic Press N.Y. and London

Monaghan, R. J. (1955) "On the behaviour of boundary layers at supersonic speeds." Proc. 5th Anglo-American Aeronautical Conference, Los Angeles

Monaghan, R. J. (1960) "Effects of heat transfer on laminar boundary layer development under pressure gradients in compressible flow." R.A.E. Report No. Aero. 2640 R & M No. 3218

Moore, F. K. (1960) "On the local flat plate similarity in the hypersonic boundary layer." Cornell Aero. Lab. Report AF-1285-A-2

Nagamatsu, H. T. (1949) "Theoretical investigation of detached shock waves." GALCIT Publn. Reported in van Dyke (1958b)

Nagamatsu, H. T., Sheer, R. E., Schmid, J. R. (1961) "High temperature rarefied hypersonic flow over a flat plate." *ARS Journal*, **31**, 902–910

Narasimha, R. (1961) "Orifice flow at high Knudsen numbers." *J. Fluid Mech.* **10**, 371–384

Neice, S. E., Ehret, D. M. (1951) "Similarity laws for slender bodies of revolution in hypersonic flows." *J. Aero. Sci.* **18**, 527–530, 568

Oguchi, H. (1958) "First-order approach to a strong interaction problem in hypersonic flow over an insulated flat plate." Rep. No. 330, Aero. Res. Inst. Univ. of Tokyo, Japan

Oguchi, H. (1961) "The sharp leading-edge problem in hypersonic flow." Proc. 2nd Int. Symp. on Rarefield Gasdynamics (L. Talbot Ed.) pp. 501–524. Academic Press

Oliver, R. E. (1956) "An experimental investigation of flow over simple blunt bodies at a nominal Mach number of 5.8." *J. Aero. Sci.* **23**, 177–179

Oswatitsch, K. (1951) "Ähnlichkeitsgesetze für Hyperschallströmung." *Z. Angew. Math. Phys.* **2**, 249–264

Patterson, G. N. (1956) *Molecular Flow of gases.* Wiley, New York

Persh, J. (1955) "A theoretical investigation of turbulent boundary layer flow with heat transfer at supersonic and hypersonic speeds." NAVORD Report No. 3854 Proc. 4th Mid-West Conf. on Fluid Mech. p. 43

Persh, J. (1957) "A procedure for calculating the boundary-layer development in the region of transition from laminar to turbulent flow." U.S. Naval Ordnance Lab. NAVORD Report No. 4438

Phillips, R. L. (1957) "A summary of several techniques used in the analysis of high-enthalpy level, high cooling-ratio turbulent boundary layers on blunt bodies of revolution." Ramo-Wooldridge Report GM-TM-194

Potter, J. L., Whitfield, J. D. (1960) "Effects of unit Reynolds number, nose bluntness and roughness on boundary layer transition." AGARD Report No. 256

Probstein, R. F. (1961) "Shock wave and flow field development in hypersonic re-entry." *ARS Journal* 31, 185–194

Probstein, R. F., Bray, K. N. C. (1955) "Hypersonic similarity and the tangent-cone approximation for unyawed bodies of revolution." *J. Aero. Sci.* 22, 66

Probstein, R. F., Elliott, D. (1953) "The transverse curvature effect in compressible axially symmetric laminar boundary-layer flow." *J. Aero. Sci.* 20, 291–292

Probstein, R. F., Kemp, N. H. (1960) "Viscous aerodynamic characteristics in hypersonic rarefied gas flow." *J. Aero/Space. Sci.* 27, pp. 174–192, 218, 554–555

Radhakrishnan, G. (1958) "The exact flow behind a yawed conical shock." College of Aeronautics, Cranfield. Rep. 116

Reshotko, E., Cohen, C. B. (1955) "Heat transfer at the forward stagnation point of blunt bodies." NACA TN 3513

Reshotko, E., Tucker, M. (1957) "Approximate calculation of the compressible turbulent boundary layer with heat transfer and arbitrary pressure gradient." NACA TN No. 4154

Reshotko, E., Beckwith, I. E. (1957) "Compressible laminar boundary layer over a yawed infinite cylinder with heat transfer and arbitrary Prandtl number." NACA Rep. No. 1379 (formerly TN 3986)

Resler, E. L., Sears, W. R. (1958) "The prospects for magneto-aerodynamics." *J. Aero. Sci.* 25, 235–245. Correction *J. Aero/Space Sci.* 26, 318

Richmond, R. L. (1957) "Experimental investigation of thick axially symmetric boundary layers on cylinders at subsonic and hypersonic speeds." GALCIT Memo. 39

Riddell, F. R., Winkler, H. B. (1961) "From I.C.B.M. re-entry to meteorite entry." I.A.S./A.R.S. Preprint No. 61–113–1807

Roberts, L. (1959) "Stagnation point shielding by melting and vaporisation." NASA T.R. R-10

Rosenhead, L. (Editor) (1963) *Laminar Boundary Layers.* Fluid Motion Memoirs, Oxford Univ. Press

Rosner, D. E. "Recent advances in convective heat transfer with dissociation and atom recombination." *Jet Propulsion* 28, 445–451

Rossow, V. J. (1951) "Applicability of the hypersonic similarity rule to pressure distributions which include the effects of rotation for bodies of revolution at zero angle of attack." NACA TN 2399

Rott, N., Lenard, M. (1959) "Vorticity effect on the stagnation point flow of a viscous incompressible fluid." *J. Aero/Space Sci.* 26, 542–543

Rott, N., Whittenbury, C. (1961) "A flow model for hypersonic rarefied gasdynamics with applications to shock structure and sphere drag." Douglas Report SM-38524

Rott, N., Lenard, M. (1962) "The effect of slip, particularly for highly cooled walls." *J. Aero. Space Sci.* **29**, 591–595

Sakurai, A. (1953) "On the propagation and structure of the blast wave, I." *J. Phys. Soc. Japan* **8**, 662–669

Sakurai, A. (1954) "On the propagation and structure of the blast wave, II." *J. Phys. Soc. Japan* **9**, 256–266

Sänger, E. (1933) *Raketenflugtechnik.* R. Oldenbourg, Munich

Sänger, E. (1939) "Gleitkörper für sehr hohe Fluggeschwindigkeiten," German Patent 411/42. Berlin

Scala, S. M. (1958) "Hypersonic heat transfer to catalytic surfaces." *J. Aero/ Space Sci.* **25**, 273–275

Scala, S. M., Warren, W. R. (1962) "Hypervelocity stagnation point heat transfer." *A.R.S. Journ.* **32**, 101–102

Schaaf, S. A. (1959) "Aerodynamics of satellites." Rand Report 339

Schaaf, S. A. (1960) "Recent progress in rarefied gasdynamics." *ARS Journal* **30**, 443–447

Schaaf, S. A., Chambré, P. L. (1958) "Flow of rarefied gases." Div. H. of Fundamentals of Gasdynamics (ed. H. W. Emmons) Vol. III of High Speed Aerodynamics and Jet Propulsion, Princeton Univ. Press

Schamberg, R. (1959) "A new analytic representation of surface interactions for hyperthermal free-molecule flow with application to satellite drag." Proc. 1959 Heat Transfer and Fluid Mechanics Institute pp. 1–16

Schamberg, R. (1959) "A new analytic representation of surface interactions for hyperthermal free-molecule flow with application to satellite drag." Proc. 1959 Heat Transfer and Fluid Mechanics Institute pp. 1–16

Schlichting, H. (1960) *Boundary Layer Theory.* 4th Ed. Translated by J. Kestin. McGraw-Hill Book Company

Schueller, C. F. (1959) "Interactions between the external flow and rocket exhaust nozzle." Proc. 7th Anglo-American Aeronautical Conference New York 1959 pp. 269–279

Sedov, L. (1946) "Propagation of strong blast waves." *Prikl. Mat. Mekh.* **10**, 241–250

Sedov, L. (1959) *Similarity and Dimensional Methods in Mechanics.* Academic Press, New York

Seiff, A. (1962) "Secondary flow fields embedded in hypersonic shock layers." NASA TN D. 1304

Shercliff, J. A. (1959) "Magnetogasdynamics and its possible aeronautical applications." *J. Roy. Aero. Soc.* **63**, 518–521

Smith, J. W. (1953) "A note on the effect of diffusion fields on the laminar boundary layer." *J. Aero. Sci.* **20**, pp. 847–848

Spalding, D. B. (1958) "Heat transfer from surfaces of non-uniform temperature." *J. Fluid Mech.* **4**, 22–32

Spalding, D. B. (1961) "The theory of melting ablations, with vaporisation, gas phase chemical reactions, surface pyrolysis and transient effects." *Aeronaut. Quart.* **12**, 237–274

Sprinks, T. (1960) "A review of work relevant to the study of heat transfer in hypersonic separated flows." University of Southampton, U.S.A.A. Report No. 138

234 ELEMENTS OF HYPERSONIC AERODYNAMICS

Stevens, V. I. (1950) "Hypersonic research facilities at the Ames Aeronautical Laboratory." *J. Appl. Phys.* **21**, 1150–1155

Stewartson, K. (1955) "On the motion of a flat plate at high speed in a viscous compressible fluid I. Impulsive motion." Proc. Cambridge Phil. Soc. **51**, 202–219 II. Steady motion. *J. Aero. Sci.* **22**, 303–309

Stocker, P. M. (1958) "A second approximation in shock-expansion theory." A.R.D.E. Report (B) 17/58

Stocker, P. M., Mauger, F. E. (1962) "Supersonic flow past cones of general cross-section." *J. Fluid Mech.* **13**, 383–399

Stuart, J. T. (1961) "Note on the interaction of the boundary layer with an external flow containing vorticity." A.R.C. 23,231

Sychev, V. V. (1960a) "On the theory of hypersonic gas flow with a power law shockwave." *Prikl. Mat. Mekh.* **24**, 518–523. *Transl. as Journ. App. Math. Mech.* **24**, 756–764

Sychev, V. V. (1960b) "Three-dimensional hypersonic gas flow past slender bodies at high angles of attack." *Prikl. Mat. Mekh.* **24**, 205–212. *Transl. in J. Appl. Math. Mech.* **24**, 296–306

Syvertson, C. A., Dennis, D. H. (1957) "A second-order shock-expansion method applicable to bodies of revolution near zero lift." NACA Rep. 1328

Swigart, R. J. (1962) "A theory of axisymmetric hypersonic blunt body flows." Stanford Univ. Dept. of Aeronautics and Astronautics. SUDAER Rep. 120

Talbot, L. (1961) Proc. 2nd Int. Symposium on Rarefied Gas Dynamics, Berkeley, Calif. Academic Press

Taylor, G. I. (1950) "The formation of a blast wave by a very intense explosion." *Proc. Roy. Soc. (A)* **201**, 159–186

Teare, J. D., Georgiev, S., Allen, R. (1961) "Radiation from non-equilibrium shock front." Presented at Intern. Hypersonics Conf., M.I.T., 1961. Published in *Hypersonic Flow Research* (F. R. Riddell Ed.) Academic Press 1962

Telenin, G. F. (1956) "Similarity laws for hypersonic speeds." Oborongiz, Moscow

Thornhill, C. K. (1962) "The analogy between intense explosions and bodies in flight at very high speeds." Int. Cong. of Mathematicians, Stockholm

Traugott, S. (1962) "Some features of supersonic and hypersonic flows about blunted cones." *J. Aero/Space Sci.* **29**, 389–399

Treanor, C. E. (1961) "Radiation at hypersonic speeds." Presented at Intern. Hypersonics Conf., M.I.T., 1961. Published in *Hypersonic Flow Research* (F. R. Riddell Ed.). Academic Press 1962

Tsien, H. S. (1946) "Similarity laws of hypersonic flows." *J. Math. Phys.* **25**, 247–251

Tsien, H. S. (1946) "Superaerodynamics, mechanics of rarefied gases." *J. Aero. Sci.* **13**, 653–664

Vaglio-Laurin, R. (1959) "Heat transfer on blunt-nosed bodies in general three-dimensional hypersonic flow." Proc. 1959 Heat Transfer and Fluid Mech. Inst. p. 95. *ARS Journ.* **29**, p. 123. WADC TN 58–147

Vaglio-Laurin, R. (1962) "On the P.L.K. method and the supersonic blunt body problem." *J. Aero/Space Sci.* **29**, 185–206

Vaglio-Laurin, R., Bloom M. H. (1961) "Chemical effects in external hypersonic flows." AFOSR 1273 (Pibal Rept. 640) August 1961 *Hypersonic Flow Research* (F. R. Riddell Ed.) Academic Press 1962

Vaglio-Laurin, R., Ferri, A. (1958) "Theoretical investigation of the flow field around blunt-nosed bodies in supersonic flight." *J. Aero/Space Sci.* **25,** 761–770

Vaglio-Laurin, R., Trella, M. (1960) "A study of flow fields about some typical blunt-nosed slender bodies." Polytechnic Inst. of Brooklyn. PIBAL Rep. 623. AFOSR 2 (1960). See also *Aerospace Engineering* **20,** 20–21 and 80–88. (1961)

van Dyke, M. D. (1951) "The combined supersonic-hypersonic similarity rule." *J. Aero. Sci.* **18,** 499–500

van Dyke, M. D. (1954) "A study of hypersonic small-disturbance theory." NACA Rep. 1194

van Dyke, M. D. (1958a) "A model of supersonic flow past blunt axi-symmetric bodies, with application to Chester's solution." *J. Fluid Mech.* **3,** 515–522

van Dyke, M. D. (1958b) "The supersonic blunt slender body problem-review and extension." *J. Aero/Space Sci.* **25,** 485–495

van Dyke, M. (1960) "Higher approximations in boundary layer theory." Lockheed Report LMSD-703097, 1960. *J. Fluid Mech.*, **14,** 161–177 and 481–495, 1962

van Dyke, M. (1961) "Second-order boundary-layer theory for blunt bodies in hypersonic flow." Presented at Intern. Hypersonics Conf., M.I.T., 1961. Published in *Hypersonic Flow Research* (F. R. Riddell Ed.). 370-75 Academic Press 1962

van Dyke, M. (1962) "A review and extension of second-order hypersonic boundary-layer theory." Presented at 3rd Int. Symposium on Rarefied Gas Dynamics. Paris. Stanford Univ. Report No. Sudaer 127

van Dyke, M. D., Gordon, H. D. (1959) "Supersonic flow past a family of blunt axi-symmetric bodies." NASA Rep. 1

van Hise, V. (1960) "Analytic study of induced pressure on long bodies of revolution with varying nose bluntness at hypersonic speed." NASA TR R-78

Vas, I., Bogdonoff, S. M., Hammitt, A. G. (1958) "An experimental investigation of the flow over simple two-dimensional and axi-symmetric bodies at hypersonic speeds." *Jet Propulsion* **28,** 97–103

Velesko, L. G., Grodzovskii, G. L., Krashchennikova, N. L. (1956) "Table of flow parameters for power law bodies of revolution at hypersonic speeds." TsAGI Rpt.

Waldman, R., Probstein, R. F. (1961) "An analytic extension of the shock-expansion method." *J. Aero/space Sci.* **28,** 119–132

Warren, W. R., Diaconis, N. S. (1961) "Air-arc simulation of hypersonic environments." Presented at Intern. Hypersonics Conf., M.I.T., 1961 ARS Preprint No. 1986–61, August 1961 *Hypersonic Flow Research* (F. R. Riddell Ed.), 663–700. Academic Press

Wegener, P. P. (1960) "Experiments on the departure from chemical equilibrium in a supersonic flow." *ARS Journal* **30,** 322–329

Wegener, P. P., Ashkenas, H. (1961) "A simple method of sphere drag measurement in rarefied supersonic gas flows." Proc. 2nd Int. Symp. on Rarefied

Gasdynamics pp. 663–668 (L. Talbot Ed.) Academic Press. *J. Fluid Mech.* **10**, 550–560

Whalen, R. J. (1961) "Viscous and inviscid non-equilibrium gas flows." I.A.S. Preprint No. 61–23 Jan. 1961. *J. Aero/Space Sci.* **29**, 1222–1237 Dec. 1962.

Whitham, G. B. (1957) "A note on the stand-off distance of the shock in high speed flow past a circular cylinder." *Comm. on Pure & Appl. Math.* **10**, 531–535

Willis, D. R. (1959) "A study of nearly free molecule flow in Aerodynamics of Satellites." Rand Report 339

Wisniewski, R. J. (1959) "Methods of predicting laminar heat rates on hypersonic vehicles." NASA TN D-201

Wisniewski, R. J. (1960) "Note on a correlation of boundary layer transition results on highly cooled blunt bodies." NASA TM X-412

Wong, T. J., Goodwin, G., Slye, R. E. (1960) "Motion of heating during atmosphere re-entry of space vehicles." NASA TN D-334

Yakura, J. K. (1962) "A theory of entropy layers and nose bluntness in hypersonic flow." In *Hypersonic Flow Research* (ed. Riddell). *Progress in Astronautics & Rocketry*, Vol. 7, pp. 421–457. Academic Press

Yasuhara, M. (1957) "An exact approach to the hypersonic viscous flow past a slender body of revolution." Proc. 6th Japan Nat. Congress. Appl. Mech. Kyoto, Japan 291–294

Ziemer, R. W. (1960) "Extended hypervelocity gasdynamic charts for equilibrium air." Space Technology Lab. Report. STL/TR-60-0000-09093

SUBJECT INDEX

Transverse curvature effects on boundary layer, 167, 203, 205
Truncated cone, 68
Turbulent boundary layer,
  effect of wall catalysis, 186
  heat transfer, 184
  with ablation, 193
  with air injection, 189–193
Two-fluid model in rarefied gasdynamics, 221

Unified supersonic hypersonic similitude, 49

Van der Waal forces, 15, 160
Vaporisation, 180, 190
Variational calculus for minimum drag bodies, 100
Velocity of escape, 158
Vibrational excitation, 157, 162
Vibrational relaxation, 163
Viscosity, 15, 160, 168
  -temperature relation, 177
Viscous hypersonic similarity, 179, 203, 218

Viscous interaction, 12, 180
Vortical layer, 36, 62, 106
Vortical singularity, 63
Vorticity, 2, 12, 16, 27, 62, 171
  interaction, 64, 168, 204, 211
    experimental verification, 218
    variation behind parabolic shock, 27
    conical shock, 62

Wake, non-equilibrium flow in, 164
Weak interaction, 198
  on wedge, 199
Wedge in hypersonic flow, 29, 49–52
  blunt-nosed, 142–153
  Newtonian model, 59
  pressure coefficient on, 51, 98
  tangent-wedge method, 95
Wing-body interference principle, 5
Winged bodies at incidence, 47

Yawed bodies, boundary layer on, 175

Zero heat transfer temperature, 159, 172